Developments in Soil Science 11A

PEDOGENESIS AND SOIL TAXONOMY

I. CONCEPTS AND INTERACTIONS

Developments in Soil Science 11A

PEDOGENESIS AND SOIL TAXONOMY

I. CONCEPTS AND INTERACTIONS

EDITED BY

L.P. WILDING, N.E. SMECK AND G.F. HALL

ELSEVIER
Amsterdam—Oxford—New York 1983

ELSEVIER SCIENCE PUBLISHERS B.V.
1 Molenwerf
P.O. Box 211, 1000 AE Amsterdam, The Netherlands

Distributors for the United States and Canada:

ELSEVIER SCIENCE PUBLISHING COMPANY INC.
52, Vanderbilt Avenue
New York, N.Y. 10017

Library of Congress Cataloging in Publication Data
Main entry under title:

Pedogenesis and soil taxonomy.

  (Developments in soil science ; 11)
  Includes bibliographies and index.
  Contents: 1. Concepts and interactions.
  1. Soil science--Collected works. 2. Soils--Classi-
fication--Collected works. 3. Soil formation--Collected
works. I. Wilding, L. P. II. Hall, G. F. III. Smeck,
N. E. IV. Series.
S591.P39 1983   631.4'4   82-24198
ISBN 0-444-42100-9 (U.S. : v. 1)

ISBN 0-444-42100-9 (Vol. 11A)
ISBN 0-444-41882-7 (Series)

Printed in The Netherlands

We dedicate this book to the late

Dr. GUY D. SMITH,

father of Soil Taxonomy, pedologist, soil correlator, scholar, professor, administrator, public servant and world authority on soil science.

"The elements of knowledge, our understanding of nature and the classification systems we devise are, of course, inseparable from the capacities and functioning of the human mind". M.G. Cline

LIST OF CONTRIBUTORS

B.L. Allen
Department of Plant and Soil Science, Texas Tech University, P.O. Box 4169, Lubbock, TX 79409, U.S.A.

R.W. Arnold
U.S. Department of Agriculture, Soil Conservation Service, P.O. Box 2891, Washington, D.C., U.S.A.

J. Bouma
Department of Soil Physics, Netherlands Soil Survey Institute, P.O. Box 98, Wageningen, The Netherlands.

L.R. Drees
Department of Soil and Crop Sciences, Texas A&M University, College Station, TX 77843, U.S.A.

R.L. Edmonds
College of Forest Resources, University of Washington, Seattle WA 98105, U.S.A.

D.S. Fanning
Department of Agronomy, University of Maryland, College Park, MD 20742, U.S.A.

G.F. Hall
Department of Agronomy, The Ohio State University, Columbus, OH 43210, U.S.A.

E.E. Mackintosh
Department of Land Resource Science, University of Guelph, Ont. N1G 2WI, Canada.

E.C.A. Runge
Department of Soil and Crop Sciences, Texas A&M University, College Station, TX 77843, U.S.A.

N.E. Smeck
Department of Agronomy, The Ohio State University, Columbus, OH 43210, U.S.A.

G.D. Smith
U.S. Department of Agriculture, Soil Conservation Service, Washington, D.C., U.S.A. (deceased).

F.C. Ugolini
College of Forest Resources, University of Washington, Seattle, WA 98105, U.S.A.

L.P. Wilding
Department of Soil and Crop Sciences, Texas A&M University, College Station, TX 77843, U.S.A.

D.H. Yaalon
Institute of Earth Sciences, The Hebrew University, Jerusalem, Israel.

PREFACE

The need for a process-oriented text suitable as a reference for pedologists, allied earth scientists and teaching advanced-level undergraduate and graduate students is recognized, especially with the increasing worldwide use of Soil Taxonomy[1]. Soil Taxonomy is a published reference book that incorporates the series of successive stages or approximations in construction of our current comprehensive soil-classification system entitled "Soil Taxonomy. A Basic System of Soil Classification for Making and Interpreting Soil Surveys". The 7th Approximation represented one of the later stages of this effort. To avoid confusion, the term 7th Approximation is not used in this text; it is considered an obsolete term and its use is discouraged in favor of the term Soil Taxonomy. Because Soil Taxonomy is a morphogenetic system in which morphology serves as the marker of genesis, it is essential that genetic processes be emphasized in pedological instruction and application of Soil Taxonomy. Thus, the purpose of this text and a companion book entitled "Pedogenesis and Soil Taxonomy: II. The Soil Orders" is to provide a balance between morphology and genesis in understanding and utilizing this comprehensive soil-classification system.

A multi-authored text was chosen because the depth and breadth of subject matter encompassed was beyond the scope of any one individual. The authors were selected on the basis of their expertise in given geographical regions of the world and in using Soil Taxonomy. A balance was maintained between U.S. and international contributors. In most cases, professionals were chosen who would be available for updating and revising the text as the state of knowledge advances over the next 5 to 10 years.

The volume "Concepts and Interactions" and the one on "Soil Orders" should serve as a unit for instructional purposes. The subject matter in this volume serves as a prelude for the companion text on Soil Orders and is equally relevant to disciplines outside pedology. The topics covered in the nine chapters are pervasive to all soils and yet are often underemphasized in previous pedology texts. In the first two chapters, the historical development which formed a framework leading to Soil Taxonomy are explored. This is followed by chapters covering the nature of soil-forming processes, the relationship between soil-forming processes and more basic sciences, the incorporation of soil-forming processes into models, and the composition and spatial variability of soils in landscape settings. The remaining chapters

---

[1] Soil Survey Staff, 1975. Soil Taxonomy. A Basic System of Soil Classification for Making and Interpreting Soil Surveys. Soil Conservation Service, U.S. Dept. of Agriculture. Agriculture Handbook No. 436. Superintendent of Documents, U.S. Govt. Printing Office, Washington, D.C., pp. 1—754.

are devoted to soil-forming processes subdivided into the following categories: geomorphologic, climatic, biologic and hydrologic. While state factors for soil formation are included in this text, they are envisioned more as interactive effects coupled with soil dynamics rather than as discrete soil variables. Because water is such an important factor in geomorphic and pedogenic processes and serves as an energy determinant contributing to spatial variability in most soils, a chapter on hydrology with emphasis on the saturated spectrum is included.

We are grateful to many persons who helped in the preparation, typing, proofing and reviewing of this manuscript. However, without the diligence and unselfish labors of one very special secretary, Mrs. Mabel N. Haddox, Texas A&M University, this task could not have been brought to a successful fruition. We are indeed grateful for her services on our behalf.

L.P. Wilding,
N.E. Smeck and
G.F. Hall

CONTENTS

CONCEPTS OF SOILS AND PEDOLOGY*

R.W. ARNOLD

INTRODUCTION

It seems likely that throughout history most humans have had an intuitive sense of soil — what it is, how it is used and what it is not. Definitions of soils are verbal and written expressions that attempt to separate some portion of the real universe in a meaningful way within the mental limits of the beholder.

Concepts, including those about soils, can be thought of as explanations of relationships among observable phenomena of the real world. They serve to simplify and to unify the myriad of fragmented bits of information about objects or segments of the universe of interest. If we assume that the facts of nature are observable and measurable qualities, then we soon become aware that all facts are determined or conditioned by the operations through which we observe and measure. The methods of measuring sizes or distances vary depending on whether we deal with subatomic components at one end of the scale to the components of the cellestial universe at the other end. The facts we have are those obtained by the methods we use; for example, there are many facts about soil pH depending on the methods and conditions of measurement.

Sets of facts are commonly used to characterize objects of interest. Relationships among the measured facts provide a basis for classification. The ideas or concepts that permit the human mind to perceive order and causal relations are, therefore, the basis for arbitrarily defining and naming parts of the real world and for developing classifications that assist in consolidating such information into abstract models of the complex world about us.

As Strzemski (1975) noted, there are two general ways to consider soils: (1) on the basis of the nature of its properties; and (2) on the basis of specified functions or use of soil. When considering the nature of soil, it is usual to start with principal factors of soil formation or from phenomena involved in the origin and evolution of soil. When considering the function of soil, it is usual to evaluate those factors that are a function, or derivative

---

*Contribution from the Department of Agronomy, Cornell University, Ithaca, NY 14853.

function, of the properties of soil according to the role soil plays in our individual or social life.

Historically the distinction of soil as a developed and altered material involving soil genesis versus soil as a variable proportioned mixture of constituents was often not appreciated.

THE U.S. NATIONAL COOPERATIVE SOIL SURVEY DEFINITION OF SOIL

Of all the possible ways to define soils, the pedological one currently in use by the National Cooperative Soil Survey of the U.S. (Soil Survey Staff, 1975a) is of particular interest because many of the concepts and definitions discussed in this book are a direct consequence of this definition. Soil is defined as "the collection of natural bodies on the earth's surface, in places modified or even made by man of earthy materials, containing living matter and supporting or capable of supporting plants out-of-doors".

There are some interesting implications of this definition that help us understand how such a wording has developed historically, and how it reflects our model of understanding soils at this point in time.

(1) As a collection of natural bodies it focuses on subdivisions of a continuum as discrete definable parts that can be treated as members of a whole, and the whole is considered to be an organized collection of its parts.

(2) Natural soil bodies are thought of as complete units on the earth's surface that must have living matter in them and must be capable of supporting plants. It does not specifically refer to the effects of soil genesis, therefore, such bodies include those having genetically related internal features as well as those which are not pedogenically interrelated providing that they contain living matter and can support plant life. Thus, a "natural body" relates more to the presence of living matter than to the presence of pedogenically related horizons. In effect it recognizes the significance of man as a force or factor in producing natural bodies of earthy materials.

(3) Bodies of earthy materials that contain living matter implies that some deposits are not yet soil, and others which have become buried to the extent that living matter is now commonly excluded are currently considered as not soil. The application of this concept is not consistent throughout the scheme of taxonomy.

(4) The body as a complete unit is expected to support or be capable of supporting plants out-of-doors. Plants in widely spaced cracks in rocks and floating plants not rooted in sediments are not considered as sufficient biological evidence of a body of soil.

This concept of soil is qualitative in that it does not provide precise limits which separate soil from non-soil. It embraces pedogenically altered materials as well as those with a minimal degree of genetic expression, whether resulting from natural or man-made influence. As such, soil includes material bodies that once were thought of as only geological material. The concept emphasizes the role of biologic activity and its effect in distinguishing soils from non-soils and by this definition soil is limited to the earth's surface.

SOME NON-PEDOLOGIC CONCEPTS OF SOIL

Throughout much of recorded history soil has simply been considered to be a more or less loose mixture composed of comminuted solids of rock and materials of organic origin, as well as liquids and gases having different proportions of the respective constituents. Soils were related to their use in society or according to concepts derived from other disciplines. The many non-pedological classifications of soil reflect viewpoints of individual evaluations of properties of soil and land that relate to functional uses of soil.

Influence of cultural stigma

Although man has tilled soil for many thousands of years, thereby providing a base for cultural development, the status of the tiller has been lowly. In the eras of slavery, it was usually their lot to work the fields. During feudal times the peasants and serfs were often considered to comprise the lowest forms of humanity. They worked in mud and filth and their status and endeavors were not worthy of consideration by the educated. Few are the fairy tales that romanticize the hopes and aspirations of the landless peasant. The inherent and skillfull knowledge of many a so-called primitive agriculturalist is still often disregarded in the modern world.

Influence of crop husbandry

Two concepts related to crop husbandry are prevalent in the historical perception of soil. One is the suitability of soils or land for crop production, thus there are numerous use classifications depending on the locality of the classifiers. Early nomads knew the areas of wheat soils, barley soils, grazing soils, etc. The Greeks, the Romans, and even modern man often have referred to corn soils, alfalfa soils, cotton soils, rice soils, and so forth. These concepts likely developed by the trials and errors of numerous cropping seasons, and even today can result from empirically relating the successes and failures of cropping. As such these concepts do not depend on knowledge of the internal properties of soils.

The other functional concept relates to tillage of soil. Regardless of the energy source — human, animal or machine — there is a corresponding knowledge of the expenditure of energy to prepare the soil for a crop. Consequently, there are heavy soils, light soils, sticky soils, push soils and tens of local terms that distinguish among the soils.

Some historical concepts of soil

In a book titled "Ideas Underlying Soil Systematics", Strzemski (1975) has reviewed and summarized many of the early writings that can be linked to what we today call soil. A few highlights from his book are mentioned below.

In Aristotle's (384—322 B.C.) explanations of the universe there were four elementary forms that originated from the same amorphous matter and were shaped into form by a spirit endowed with reason. The four elements or states of matter were: fire, air, water and earth, and all were in opposition to ether, which was not perceived by the senses. These elements were the carriers of qualities, namely heat and cold, which were active qualities, and dryness and wetness, which were passive qualities, and from these all kinds of relative opposites could be described. Earth (terrae) was differentiated into sets of opposing qualities, such as warm and cold, dry and wet, heavy and light and hard and soft.

Theophrastos (371—286 B.C.), a student of Aristotle, gave soil the name "edaphos" to distinguish it from earth as a cosmic body. He recognized a surface stratum varying in its humus content, a subsoil as a fatty layer supplying nutrients to the roots of grasses and herbs, a substratum providing nutrient juices to tree roots, and below this was Tartarus — the realm of darkness. In addition to describing numerous properties of soil that affect plant relationships, he also recognized six groups of land suitable for different kinds of crops.

Cato (234—149 B.C.), a prominent Roman scientist, developed a classification of arable soils based on farming utility. His functional system had nine major classes that were subdivided into twenty-one classes. Numerous Roman writers were keen observers and they empirically derived relationships that guided the use and care of land for the production of food and fiber.

In summarizing the pedological heritage from Roman scientists, Strzemski (1975) noted that: "Cato emphasized the suitability of soils for farming and their quantitative productive potentials; Varro was concerned with the physical composition of soils; Columella focused mainly on the physical properties of soils; and Plenuis devoted considerable attention to rocks and minerals as soil-forming materials."

Ancient knowledge of soils was very extensive and a pedological terminology was established which influenced the agricultural literature for many centuries. With the downfall of Rome, agricultural soil science stagnated and very few contributions were made until the mid-nineteenth century when additional utilitarian classifications were proposed.

Until the end of the nineteenth century there was no recognized discipline called soil science. The earth sciences of geology, geography and geomorphology treated soil as a subset of their domain and developed classifications accordingly. The fields of botany, chemistry and climatology also superimposed their concerns and understanding on the earthy substance.

It seems that these classifications are premised on soil as being functionally related to the subject matter of the discipline, thus the properties of soils themselves were not as important as the unifying concepts offered by the discipline. Several examples illustrate these ideas.

From the botanist's sense of native vegetation it was natural that terms such as pine soils, oak soils and prairie soils would be used. The fact that many qualities of soil are well correlated with naturally occurring ecotypes is evidenced in the general model of soils that includes biota as a major soil-forming factor.

The physiography of landscapes employed in geography has been used to speak of upland soils, valley soils, coastal soils and similar terms.

From the geologists who thought of soil as a more or less straight-line function of rock weathering came terms such as granite soils, shale soils, limestone soils and other parent-rock modifiers.

According to Strzemski (1975), Fallou's work in 1862 was perhaps one of the strongest foundations from which an independent soil science developed. Fallou noted that all previous classifications had been inseparably linked with agriculture while the strictly natural sciences had not been very concerned with soil. He hoped to provide a scientific base for the study of soils and became the founder of the geological—petrographic school of pedology. Soils were either primitive or washed in, and separated according to their petrogenic character.

As geomorphologists began to study the processes of landscape evolution, soils could be related to landscape position and process. When age and location were considered it was possible to speak of old upland soils, young alluvial soils and many other combinations of interest to the geomorphologists.

Richthofen developed a geological—geographic approach to soils in which he proposed a global classification from a soil-forming process viewpoint. He classified regions as those with: autogenic soil formation, weathering equilibrium, preponderant denudation, preponderant accumulation and eroded sediments of eolian origin.

Climatologists with an interest in the geographic patterns of climate have referred to tundra soils, humid temperate soils, tropical soils and other classes related to climatological classifications.

As chemists became involved in studying the make-up of earth that supported plants it was normal that a balance of nutrient supply could be used to characterize and classify soils. Leibig's storehouse or bank-balance concept of soil fertility was employed for many years in the understanding of nutrient cycling in plants and soils.

The school of Thaer summarized in his 1821 work emphasized soil constituents and a more precise characterization of their chemical and physical aspects, differentiated variations of the chemical and physical composition, outlined fundamental principles of physiochemical classification of soils, and established a nomenclature based on soil composition.

The 19th century saw the development of many physical, chemical, and physiochemical classifications of soils which peaked in the 20th century.

In most engineering disciplines, soil refers to the regolith or any unconsolidated earthy materials regardless of depth or mode of deposition, and it is commonly characterized by its particle-size composition and manipulative behavior. The AASHTO and Unified Systems of Soil Classification exemplify the use of such a concept.

In the above examples it should be noted that many of them deal with features (plants, rocks, landscapes) that themselves have geographic distribution, which suggests that numerous relationships will exist among systems that attempt to categorize patterns on the earth's surface.

PEDOLOGICAL CONCEPTS OF SOILS

In retrospect it seems inevitable that an independent science of soil would emerge as more and more serious attention was given to the earth's outer crust and as problems of agricultural production were investigated.

Morphogenetic concepts developed in Russia

The following comments on the morphogenetic concepts developed in Russia are based on the more detailed material presented by Strzemski (1975).

In 1879, Dokuchaev stated that soil is a self-existent product of specific origin very distinct from parent rock. He indicated that soils were the product of the combined activity of the following agencies: (1) living and dead plant and animal organisms; (2) parent rock; (3) climate; and (4) relief. He extended and modified his statement in 1886, indicating that "By the name of soil one should call surface layers of rock (no matter which) that have undergone change in a natural way by the complex action of water, air, and living and dead organisms of different kind". Dokuchaev also mentioned the age that rock has been subjected to processes, but he did not use it in his classification of soil.

Silbertsev, a student of Dokuchaev and holder of the first chair of pedology, emphasized that soil included such terrestrial surface sediments or such surface layers of rocks in which ectodynamic (external) processes are associated with the activities of organisms penetrating them or with phenomena originating from factors of the biosphere.

In Glinka's writings (1927), it is evident that he considered soil to be the whole layer of the earth's crust where the soil-forming processes that most conspicuously refashion the earth's surface distinctly manifest themselves. He made an interesting statement about soil parent material, namely that if we consider soil to be the product of weathering, then if it is transferred from the place of origin and deposited again at any other place, it is not soil any more. Rather, it is simply a geological deposit from which soil is likely to develop.

These ideas about soil as a product of its own history were slow to disseminate largely because of language, however, closely related ideas expressed in other parts of the world foreshadowed the awareness and acceptance of Dokuchaev's concepts.

Evolution of pedologic concepts in the U.S.

Hilgard (1906) summarized many years of field work in his classic text on soils. He felt that in a general sense soil was the more or less loose and friable material in which plants find a foothold and nourishment, as well as other conditions of growth. As such, soils form the uppermost layer of the earth and can be considered a residual product of the physical disintegration and chemical decomposition of rocks with a small proportion of the remnants of organic life. Hilgard (1892) wrote about the interactions of parent material and climate on vegetation forms and distribution, thereby emphasizing the regional significance of climate and vegetation as agencies of change.

King (1902), regarded as the father of American soil physics, wrote about soil as a scene of life and energy. He said that agriculturally it was important as a storehouse of water and nutrients, and it was a wonderful laboratory in which a large variety of the lower microscopic forms of life were at work, and that soil was also a means for transforming sunshine and putting it into a form available for carrying on the kinds of work which are accomplished there. In a more philosophical vein he said that soil makes possible a very much greater profusion of landlife than could otherwise exist and also it has played an extremely important part in the long continued, never ending and sublime process of evolution, thus, if we want to understand soil, we must see it in action helping in the work of the whole world as well as in producing food.

Lyon et al. (1916) continued to portray soil mainly as a geologic product, indicating that soil comes from rock and returns to rock, thus it was merely a transitory stage in the change from one form of rock to another. In an agricultural context it was suggested that soil becomes purely a medium for crop production.

The concepts of Coffey (1912) that visualized soils as products of complex interactions in the landscape were generally eclipsed by Whitney (1925) who emphasized the chemical and physical nature of soils rather than their genetic relationships.

Influence of soil survey

By 1920, the Bureau of Soils had been mapping soils for twenty years, and Marbut (1921) noted that no such thing as soil science existed in such a state of development that its principles could be applied to the mapping of soils when soil mapping was first attempted in the United States. Marbut pointed out that the work of creating the ultimate soil unit, as it existed in 1921, was done by the Americans. The soil man, in his opinion, had to determine what features of soil have been acquired during their development as soils after the soil material was accumulated by geological processes, and what features had been inherited from the geological formations which furnished the soil material. The soil man had to define the soil unit in terms of soil characteristics — he had to create the soil unit.

Marbut outlined ten features of the soil profile that permit the designation and recognition of soil series and their types. He concluded that the recognition of soil horizons and the description and identification of soils on the basis of the number, character, arrangement and composition of horizons constituted probably the most significant contribution to soil science that had been made by soil survey.

Marbut (1922) discussed a number of fundamental concepts related to soil classification and formulated the concept of mature soils. He stated that soil is a natural body developed by natural forces acting through natural processes on natural materials, thus its true nature cannot be determined except through a study of the natural or virgin soil. This concern for "natural" promoted the study of genetic profiles as a basis for comparison among regions and also among local associates.

Consensus at the First International Soil Congress

The various attitudes prevalent in the U.S. in the late 1920's are recorded in the proceedings of the First International Congress of Soil Science that was convened in Washington D.C., in 1927. It is apparent that controversy was arising about classification; should soils be classed by theories of genesis, or should they be classed on soil properties? The goal was similar but the approaches differed.

As the lead speaker at the Congress, Marbut (1928) offered a definition of soil that he said had no element of theory in it and presupposed no process nor assumed any cause of the soil facts on which it was based. His definition was: "The soil consists of the outer layer of the earth's crust, usually unconsolidated, ranging in thickness from a mere film to a maximum of somewhat more than ten feet, which differs from the material beneath it, also usually unconsolidated, in color, structure, texture, physical constitution, chemical composition, biological characteristics, probably chemical processes, in reaction and in morphology".

Partly because of the previous bias toward soil as geological material and partly to emphasize the importance of biological processes in soil formation, Marbut reconfirmed that the material below the solum, regardless of how it was accumulated, whether by processes of rock decay or by the several processes of natural transportation and redeposition, was not soil. It was geological material and was the product of geological processes.

In a concise article discussing principles of classification, Weir (1928) pointed out that in the world of things soils exist as real physical objects, but in classification we deal with them as thought entities called classes. The content of each "thought unit" consists of the distinguishing characteristics that are common to a group of individuals, and recognition of these common-to-all characteristics is the process of creating a general concept in soil classification. Weir (1928) concluded that a category or a class in soil classification represents a general concept and may be *defined*, whereas an individual soil as a natural object may only be *described*.

Afanasieff (1928), a Russian, confirmed that the pedological concept was one in which the geneology and distinctive characters of the morphological and chemical properties are determined by the combination of soil-forming elements; climate, vegetation and animals, parent material, relief, ground waters and time. Lebedeff (1928) noted that with the development of the genetic school of soil science, a soil map may be considered as a reflection of this point of view and provides the distribution of this or the other "type of soil". He also believed that the most complete soil map is the one which gives the soil types and their variations. The Russian soil types he refers to are analogous to some of the suborders and great groups of the U.S. Taxonomy (Soil Survey Staff, 1975a). Lebedeff commented that some thirty years previously it had been suggested by Nefedov that it would be useful not only to map soil types and their variations (in the Russian context) but also to map specific soil characteristics, however, this suggestion was not readily accepted.

The experience of the U.S. Soil Survey at that time was eloquently summarized by Bushnell (1928) who noted that apparently the odds are greatly against the soil surveyor in his efforts to know the facts. Soil mapping is possible, he pointed out, only because men can examine a profile at one point and successfully predict its occurrence at another point where surface indications are similar. Bushnell said that soil surveyors seldom can map soil profiles, instead they separate mapping units such as slight depressions, deep depressions, low flats, convex rises, slopes of a certain degree, light and dark surfaces of soils and so forth. Each physiographic division of any surface form, he said, is likely to have its own characteristic soil profile, and conversely, a careful mapping of complete profiles will show up physiographically on the maps.

Refinements of pedological concepts

The concept of the mature profile was changed to the normal soil (Kellogg, 1936, 1937) and functionally related to soil-forming factors. Kellogg (1936) stated that the principles of geography, associated with the modern concept of the soil as a dynamic natural body in equilibrium with its environment, leads us to consider two sorts of activities during the genesis of a soil, namely: (a) destructional activities of physical and chemical weathering; and (b) constructional biologic forces. He pointed out the importance of geomorphology, saying that as the whole process of soil genesis is one of evolution together with the development of the entire landscape, of which it is a part, age (in a relative sense) is important.

The 1937 Soil Survey Manual (Kellogg, 1937) states that the mappable soil unit is a geographic body and its entity can be established only on the basis of a definite repetition of certain differentiating characteristics in the soils associated with some particular environment. The fundamental data of soil science are the descriptions of soil profiles; classification of soils is predicted on a knowledge of their morphology and unless it is precisely known, classification is impossible (Kellogg, 1937).

Textbooks on soils (Lyon and Buckman, 1938; Joffe, 1949) reflected this changing concept of soil and noted that the soil was a natural body distinct from, yet transitional to, the parent material, with characteristics both obvious and unique. The unification of concepts was becoming more apparent throughout the United States.

A new USDA Soil Survey Manual (Soil Survey Staff, 1951) accepted the general model of soil as a concept but discussed additional facets of soil such as:

(a) Soil is the natural medium for the growth of land plants whether or not it has "developed" soil horizons (p. 6) and in this sense covers land as a continuum.

(b) It is difficult to work with the whole continuum at once, thus, individual kinds of soil must be recognized (p. 6).

(c) In the sense of an individual in the continuum, a soil is a dynamic three-dimensional piece of landscape that supports plants (p. 6).

(d) Soil is the collection of natural bodies occupying portions of the earth's surface that support plants and that have properties due to the integrated effect of climate and living matter, acting upon parent material as conditioned by relief, over periods of time (p. 8).

(e) A normal soil is one having a profile in equilibrium or nearly in equilibrium with its environment . . . the typical representatives of the zonal great soil groups are normal soils (p. 126).

(f) Every soil is "normal" in the sense that it reflects its own history (p. 126).

(g) Many thousands of unique kinds of soil exist in the world — as many as there are significant combinations of the genetic factors (p. 7).

The significance of an active national cooperative soil survey in the development of working concepts of soils and in the mapping of soils is an outstanding feature of pedological thought in the United States.

The quantification of the ideas expressed above has been the sense of direction and effort since the 1950's. Soil science has consolidated and confirmed its belief in a general model of soil, however, the search for understanding and the unravelling of intricate complexities of nature are destined to destroy time and again our imperfect models of classification.

SOIL CONCEPTS IN RELATION TO CLASSIFICATION

There is almost no controversy over the simplified statements referring to soil as being functionally related to a select number of factors. As consistently presented for almost a hundred years, the factors are climate, biota, parent material, topography and age. It is also generally accepted that these factors have geographic expression and that the degree and amount of overlap and interaction throughout time provide the fundamental concept of soils as geographic bodies. It is further agreed that this basic pedological model of soil is one that emphasizes the interactions of climatic and biologic activities working on a parent material and which are modified by local topography and landscape evolution throughout time giving rise to recognizable soil horizons.

There is, however, no clear-cut agreement on what a basic or fundamental unit of soil is, although the literature is full of opinions and reasonably well argued rationale for such a unit. Two different viewpoints emerge; one is in the domain of classification, or taxonomy, with a view toward showing meaningful relationships among soils in an orderly manner, and the other is in the domain of soil geography, or soil survey, with a view toward delineating meaningful segments of the earth's surface. These two approaches are seldom mutually exclusive, consequently, there have been numerous attempts to define a basic unit acceptable to all.

Influence of soil concepts on classification

The genetic concept of soil which distinguishes soil as a developed and altered material rather than as a variable proportioned mixture of constituents is significant in terms of developing classifications because it focuses attention on what is, and how it developed. This complicates and greatly expands the possibilities for criteria useful in constructing classification systems. For example, how many categories and classes are needed, are useful, or are significant when considering each of the factors that have influenced soil development? Or if one refers to the observed properties that now exist, how does one organize the myriad of measurable properties into units of acceptable homogeneity? Should single properties or simple sets of properties be the basis of definition, and how many classes and categories are visualized as necessary? And possibly, the concepts most open to speculation are the processes that are thought to be responsible for the genetic development of soil horizons. The literature abounds in such speculations and proposals, almost to the extent that it is difficult to comprehend all of the systems that have been offered as solutions to the "determineless" processes that explain soil as a worldwide phenomenon.

Impact of pedogenic concepts on classification

The exact combination of physiochemical and biological reactions that have actually transformed materials into soil horizons of a specific soil can never be known with certainty. Many useful generalizations have, nevertheless, guided the attempts to organize the available knowledge of soils. The factors of soil formation that are generally recognized are thought of as controls on processes that result in observable and measurable features. Individual reactions that alter the state of materials have been studied by many disciplines. Simplified concepts of solution, oxidation, reduction, hydrolysis, hydration, chelation, ionic substitution, synthesis and crystallization have been applied to transformations of individual compounds and components of soils. Combinations of these elementary processes are believed to occur in the development of soils. Where a combination has been dominated by a particular process, or by the rates of a particular process, the resulting combination has often been given a name. The terms podzolization, calcification, solodization, laterization and so forth were commonly used as simplifications and each process was related to observable sets of soil properties.

In an attempt to emphasize the combinational aspects of processes, Simonson (1959) discussed the general concepts of gains, losses, translocations and transformations. Thus, by inferring the initial state of materials accumulated in a profile (Jenny, 1961) and observing the present state of a soil, the overall net changes of soil development and combinations and rates of processes could be estimated. Inherent in the generalized theory is that the rate of a process may reach zero. For example, the loss of carbonates by translocation from a horizon may stop when the last molecule of carbonate is removed, and the rate becomes zero from that time on. At another extreme, the rate of carbonate loss is zero in the absence of water.

The work of Nikiforoff and Drosdoff (1943), Haseman and Marshall (1945) and Barshad (1964) demonstrate the type of calculations and conclusions about net changes related to soil genesis. The ideas of Butler (1959) and Ruhe (1956) are representative of the interest in using geomorphology to assist in determining the unity and uniformity of soil systems in soil-genesis studies, and Arnold (1965) illustrated the use of multiple-working hypotheses in unravelling genetic pathways.

A brief summary of both the generalized processes suggested by Simonson

Some processes of soil formation that are complexes of subprocesses and reactions

Term	Fourfold categorization*	Brief definition	Term	Fourfold categorization*	Brief definition
Eluviation	3	Movement of material out of a portion of a soil profile as in an albic horizon	Laterization (desiccation, feralization, ferritization, allitization)	3,4	The chemical migration of silica out of the soil solum and thus the concentration of sesquioxides in the solum (goethite, gibbsite, etc.), with or without formation of ironstone (laterite; hardened plinthite) and concretions
Illuviation	3	Movement of material into a portion of soil profile as in an argillic or spodic horizon	Decomposition	4	The breakdown of mineral and organic materials
Leaching (depletion)	2	General term for washing out or eluviating soluble materials from the solum	Synthesis	4	The formation of new particles of mineral and organic species
Enrichment	1	General term for addition of material to a soil body	Melanization	1,3	The darkening of light-colored mineral initial unconsolidated materials by admixture of organic matter (as in a dark A1 (Ah) or mollic or umbric horizon)
Erosion, surficial	2	Removal of material from the surface layer of a soil	Leucinization	3	The paling of soil horizons by disappearance of dark organic materials either through transformation to light-colored ones or through removal from the horizons
Cumulization	1	Aeolian and hydrologic additions of mineral particles to the surface of a soil solum	Littering	1	The accumulation on the mineral soil surface of organic litter and associated humus to a depth of less than 30 cm
Decalcification	3	Reactions that remove calcium carbonate from one or more soil horizons	Humification	4	The transformation of raw organic material into humus
Calcification	3	Processes including accumulation of calcium carbonate in a Cca (Ck) and possibly other horizons of a soil	Paludization	4	Processes regarded by some workers as geogenic rather than pedogenic, including the accumulation of deep (>30 cm) deposits of organic matter as in mucks and peats (Histosols)
Salinization	3	The accumulation of soluble salts such as sulfates and chlorides of calcium, magnesium, sodium and potassium in salty (salic) horizons	Ripening	4	Chemical, biological and physical changes in organic soil after air penetrates the organic deposit, making it possible for microbial activity to flourish
Desalinization	3	The removal of soluble salts from salic soil horizons	Mineralization	4	The release of oxide solids through decomposition of organic matter
Alkalization (solonization)	3	The accumulation of sodium ions on the exchange sites in a soil	Braunification, Rubifaction, Ferrugination	3,4	Release of iron from primary minerals and the dispersion of particles of iron oxide in increasing amounts; their progressive oxidation or hydration, giving the soil mass brownish, reddish-brown and red colors, respectively
Dealkalization (solodization)	3	The leaching of sodium ions and salts from natric horizons	Gleization	3,4	The reduction of iron under anaerobic "waterlogged" soil conditions, with the production of bluish to greenish-gray matrix colors, with or without yellowish-brown, brown and black mottles, and ferric and manganiferous concretions
Lessivage	3	The mechanical migration of small mineral particles from the A to the B horizons of a soil, producing in B horizons relative enrichment in clay (argillic horizons)			
Pedoturbation	3	Biologic, physical (freeze-thaw and wet-dry cycles) churning and cycling of soil materials, thereby homogenizing the solum in varying degrees			
Podzolization (silication)	3,4	The chemical migration of aluminum and iron and/or organic matter, resulting in the concentration of silica (i.e., silication) in the layer eluviated			

*The four categories (see text) are: 1. additions to a soil body; 2. losses from a soil body; 3. translocation within a soil body; 4. transformation of material within a soil body.

(1959) and specifically named processes was given by Buol et al. (1973), and is shown in Table 1.1.

The concepts of soil development are entrenched in pedologic thought and have influenced most soil classification systems presently in use. Soil Taxonomy (Soil Survey Staff, 1975a) is a product of applying genetic concepts to the accumulated soil data of the United States. Smith (1963) discussed the objectives of Soil Taxonomy, Cline (1963) outlined the logic applied in the development of the system, and Cline and Johnson (1963) pointed out the genetic threads that permeate the system.

The Order category of Soil Taxonomy is abstractly defined as soils whose properties are the result of and reflect major soil-forming processes. Each of the ten classes have properties that are believed to result from conceptual processes that influence the development of sets of horizons. For example, the Histosols reflect the dominance of accumulation of organic materials, the Aridisols reflect the low levels and rates of modification resulting from small amounts of moisture at the present time, and the Oxisols reflect a highly altered state of soil materials which has a limited capacity for further alteration. Soils belonging to the Order classes are discussed in this book and it is possible to follow the threads of genetic processes within each Order.

The Suborder of Soil Taxonomy is abstractly conceived and defined as soils whose properties reflect a major control on the current soil-forming processes. This definition is in addition to that of the Order category, consequently, the soil properties associated with these definitions reflect both a history and a present. If the diagnostic features of the Order classes are thought to represent a significant degree, or influence, of genetic alteration, such as the presence of argillic or oxic horizons, mollic epipedons, or vertic properties, then the current control of process is the present soil climatic conditions. If the Order class properties reflect a lesser degree, or influence, of genetic alteration as evidenced by a cambic horizon or lack of diagnostic subsurface horizons, then major controls on current processes may be the nature of the materials and their ability to respond to change, or the present stage of the soil which is thought to be transitional to better expressed development in the future.

The Great Group of Soil Taxonomy can be abstractly conceived and defined as soils whose properties reflect additional controls on current soil-forming processes. Some properties are pans and other restrictive layers, some are soil climatic properties, and some are properties that represent a balance of processes that are modified at very slow rates in their present environments. The strong influence of genetic concepts of soils is evidenced in the chapters that follow, however, it should also be recognized that concepts of soil use and soil survey have influenced both the development and application of Soil Taxonomy.

The perceptions of genetic classes are many, they are varied and they express the richness of human reasoning and experience. In retrospect it is noted that the limitations of our knowledge are also limitations on our endeavors to integrate new information and different insights for structuring that knowledge.

The conflict of experience

The classes of any given taxonomy for a specified universe of soils need only satisfy the objectives of that taxonomy relative to its universe to be a valid and internally consistent scheme.

When Ollier et al. (1971) attempted to comprehend the soil knowledge of the Baruya tribe in New Guinea they noted that there were no names for soil profiles but at least twenty names for soil as material.

These people had no perceived need for a classification of soil profiles but they did find it important to have a classification of the materials as they related to their societal uses. The classes of the Baruya tribe taxonomy are valid and internally consistent for their purposes.

The experience of Ollier et al. was, in part, nicely summarized when they said: "We tend to be limited by our own concepts of the things classified, and when we encounter a new way of regarding common objects it takes an effort to accept new criteria that cut across the boundaries of our old classifications".

As the experience and knowledge of one's universe is expanded there is a desire to understand, organize, and expand existing systems, consequently, the overlap of domains of interest forces us to recognize the need to compare classification systems. To do this in soil science there must be a basic individual soil unit that cannot be divided and which permits one to evaluate taxonomic systems. Knox (1965) and Van Wambeke (1966) have discussed aspects of the dilemma and concluded that a small arbitrary unit or volume, independent of taxonomy, appears to be the only feasible solution at the present time.

Soil classification per se, as an exercise in organizing knowledge employs understanding of geographic distributions that are associated with concepts of genesis and genetic processes but is not dependent on identifiable geographic units either for construction or comparison of taxonomic systems. Current soil-classification schemes need only rely on an acceptable reference body.

A reference soil body

Some reference bodies that have been suggested include: profile (Marbut, 1922; Muir, 1962), ultimate individual (Cline, 1949), tessera (Jenny, 1958), pedon and polypedon (Simonson and Gardner, 1960; Johnson, 1963), elementary soil areal (Fridland, 1965), arbitrary individual (Knox, 1965; Van Wambeke, 1966), modal profile (Protz et al., 1968) and pedomorphic form (Dan and Yaalon, 1968).

According to Van Wambeke (1966), an ideal basic unit for classification should: (a) be an object which is observable and measurable in three dimensions and includes the whole vertical thickness of the soil; (b) be independent of all taxonomic systems; (c) have clear boundaries, although arbitrarily fixed; and (d) be of a size convenient for study, measurement and sampling.

Most practical methods used to examine soils meet these requirements whether the excavation is called a profile, pedon, arbitrary soil individual or other name. In practice, field soil scientists throughout the world do about the same things to describe and sample soils.

Thus, there is little usefulness in searching for a better word, or a more restrictive definition than is already applied by practicing field soil scientists. A variable size unit that changes according to cyclicity of horizons is more subject to taxonomic criteria and theoretically is less favorable as a reference body for comparing taxonomic systems.

In conclusion it can be stated that systems that classify knowledge about soil properties without emphasis on geographic limits employ the basic model of soil and a small reference volume or arbitrary individual that is independent of taxonomic criteria.

CONCEPTS OF SOIL IN SOIL SURVEY

There is an apparent dichotomy of thought when considering soil geography. On one hand, soil is thought of as a continuum of surficial material that meets the definition of soil and as such, the landscape is segmented into different kinds of soil. As with any method of segmenting a continuum, attention is focused on the limiting profiles or boundaries produced by applying class limits to the continuum. On the other hand, soil is thought of as a collection of natural bodies which focuses attention on central or typifying concepts of the natural bodies. In this perspective, soils are described by a range of properties deviating from a central concept and, as such, are natural bodies not only as profiles but as landscapes occupying space.

The basic model of soil, namely $s = f\ (cl,\ b,\ pm,\ r,\ t)$, implies that soils are dynamic, geographical systems and, in fact, provides the basis for the geographic distribution of soils themselves. Each factor of soil formation has a geographic distribution on the earth's surface and the patterns resulting from their overlapping give rise to those unique combinations which are recognized as different soils. This overlapping of geography implies that not only are soils areally distributed but that they also form a continuum of soil-forming processes, or functional relationships, in landscapes. Within this continuum no two spots have exactly the same combination or interaction of factors, thus, geographic variability is inherent in our model of soil.

Soil survey is a predictive study of soils as geographic bodies, however they are conceived, and determines the unique relationships of sets of soil properties that are observed in nature (Soil Survey Staff, 1975b). It identifies bodies of soils that can be recognized as natural units, predicts and delineates their areas on maps, and identifies the delineated areas in terms of defined kinds of soils. Through the years, soil mapping has helped emphasize the need to predict and plot soil boundaries in more detail, and the need for interpreting these landscapes has led to the realization that profiles with little or no genetic horizons should also be considered soil.

Perceptions of taxonomic classes

Most soil surveys are made with a particular taxonomy in mind that guides the naming of delineated areas, and in some instances the location of boundaries that are not readily visible by external features. Even though soils are commonly believed to be part of a continuum, they are also thought of as a collection of natural bodies which differ from place to place. Using these concepts, each soil is thought to have a limited range of variability, both in terms of landscape and in terms of internal composition.

A taxonomic soil class is a defined segment within a multidimensional array of sets of soil properties that are known from studying pedons or other sampling units of landscapes. As such, a taxonomic class is not conceived as a group of bodies of soil, but as a segment of a continuum of related soil properties with focus on the defined limits that bound the segment (Soil Survey Staff, 1975b).

To a soil mapper, a taxonomic class is generally viewed as a group of physical entities and even though the idea of the group is a concept or a model, the constituent bodies of soil are real things. For him the natural bodies of soil are being studied to determine acceptable relationships on which to predict their distribution and then the areas are classified and named with taxa that have predetermined limits.

The representatives of taxa that occur in nature have been given different names by soil scientists. The boundaries of these representatives are marked by real differences in sets of soil properties but the limits that restrict their extent and determine their boundaries are fixed by concepts derived from studies of reference bodies — i.e., concepts derived from samples (Soil Survey Staff, 1975b).

The art and scale used in map making, and the recognition of intermingled soil bodies having contrasting qualities preclude delineating areas containing the same limits of variability as taxonomic classes. The need for a bridge from the structured taxa of soil-classification schemes to the projected boundaries of naturally occurring variability in landscapes has promoted the search for a basic soil geographic unit.

The search for a basic geographic unit

Basic geographic units serve a unique function in soil survey; they link the physical reality of bodies of soil in nature to the mental concepts of taxonomic classes, especially those of the lowest category. These units are not entirely independent of taxonomy and, therefore, differ according to the criteria employed in a classification system. As such, the units proposed do not serve equally well as reference bodies to compare soil taxonomies. Some proposals for basic geographic units of pedologic soils include:

(a) Soil-area units (Muir, 1962): areas that have a similar pattern of soil morphology compared to a standard profile form of a classification system.

(b) Soil body (Hole, 1953): a specimen of a taxonomic unit such as a soil type; limiting profile units with characteristic profile faces constitute a soil body.

(c) Artificial soil body (Van Wambeke, 1966): an individual that is a coherent segment of soil created by the classifier to approximate the natural soil body which is one that is distinct and independent of the observer.

(d) Elementary soil area (Fridland, 1965): an area that has characteristics of the soil that identify the taxonomic unit but also is defined by area, degree of dissection, and form. It is a primary constituent of soil cover which belongs to some classification unit of the lowest rank.

(e) Polypedon (Johnson, 1963; Soil Survey Staff, 1975a): a group of contiguous similar pedons that are bounded on all sides by "not soil" or by pedons of unlike character. The limits of the polypedons are also the conceptual limits between soil series which are classes of the lowest category in the U.S. Soil Taxonomy.

(f) Land component (Gibbons and Downes, 1964): an area where climate, parent material, topography, soil and vegetation are uniform within the limits significant for a particular form or kind of land use; lower limit of size is the minimum size to which a farmer can give different treatments.

(g) Component of ground surface (Van Dijk, 1959): a subdivision of a ground surface based on nature and variation of parent material, in particular, whether the material is erosional or depositional. A ground surface includes all erosional and depositional surfaces and layers which have developed in a landscape during one interval of time and on which a mantle of soil without stratigraphic breaks has developed (Butler, 1959).

(h) Pedomorphic form (Dan and Yaalon, 1968): a unit of soil characterized by a definite horizon sequence which reflects its degree of maturity and history of erosion or sedimentation; conceived as being a member of a catenary sequence of pedomorphic forms, related by the influences of topography on genesis, and arranged along a topographic "pedomorphic surface".

(i) Soil stratigraphic unit (Am. Comm. of Stratigraphic Nomenclature, 1961): a soil with physical features and stratigraphic relations that permit its consistent recognition and mapping as a stratigraphic unit.

Combinations of these small soil bodies, which relate to classes of the lowest category of a reference taxonomy, are common in mapping larger geographic areas. Terms such as soil association, catena (Milne, 1935; Bushnell, 1943) pedomorphic surface, ground surface and land unit have been employed by different surveyors.

In conclusion, it is noted that the basic pedologic model of soil is genetic and provides general guidelines for defining soil but that geographic bodies represented on maps may be different due to the criteria of the taxonomy to which the units are referenced.

There is no consensus of opinion on theoretical grounds for defining a basic or fundamental unit of soil as a geographic body. There is probably reasonable agreement of such units among field-soil mappers who delineate soils at map scales from about 1:6000—1:12,000. Insofar as practical, boundaries of landscape segments utilize external features that are consistently recognized and capable of delineation, and are well correlated with real differences in sets of soil properties that are commonly used to describe soils in the field. Changes of these sets of properties are based on conceptual models relating soil features to landscape features and are derived from samples rather than complete knowledge of any geographic unit. Whatever the geographic body, it is a prediction based on the knowledge and skill of the pedologist as influenced by both the perceptions of the reference classification system and the expected soil behavior.

Thus, the diversity of units employed by soil surveys is mainly the result of superimposing taxonomically concerned criteria that subdivide a universe of a soil continuum. At our current stage of comprehension it is very difficult to aggregate the knowledge about soils and their landscapes obtained in large-scale soil mapping into a hierarchical system of classification of soils as geographic entities. Pedology is surely a discipline destined to live with change as it strives to become an important part of science. The genetic concepts of soil development and distribution will markedly influence classification endeavors because of man's innate desire to explain as well as to describe the phenomena he conceives of as soils.

REFERENCES

Afanasieff, J., 1928. Soil classification problems in Russia. Proc. Pap. First Int. Congress Soil Sci., Comm. V., 1927, pp. 498—501.

American Commission of Stratigraphic Nomenclature, 1961. Code of stratigraphic nomenclature. Bull. Am. Assoc. Pet. Geol., 45: 645—665.

Arnold, R.W., 1965. Multiple working hypotheses in soil genesis. Soil Sci. Soc. Am. Proc., 29: 717—724.

Barshad, I., 1964. Chemistry of Soil Development. In: F.E. Bear (Editor), Chemistry of the Soil. Reinhold, New York, N.Y., pp. 1—70.

Buol, S.W., Hole, F.D. and McCracken, R.J., 1973. Soil Genesis and Classification. The Iowa State Univ. Press, Ames, Iowa, 360 pp.

Bushnell, T.M., 1928. To what extent should location, topography or physiology consti- tute a basis for differentiating soil into units or groups? Proc. Pap., First Int. Congress Soil Sci., Comm. V., 1927, pp. 158—163.

Bushnell, T.M., 1943. Some aspects of the soil catena concept. Soil Sci. Soc. Am. Proc., 7: 466—476.

Butler, B.E., 1959. Periodic phenomena in landscapes as a basis for soil studies. Aust. CSIRO Soil Publ., 14: 1—20.

Cline, M.G., 1949. Principles of soil classification. Soil Sci., 67: 81—91.

Cline, M.G., 1963. Logic of the new system of soil classification. Soil Sci., 96: 17—22.

Cline, A.J. and Johnson, D.D., 1963. Threads of genesis. Soil Sci. Soc. Am. Proc., 27: 220—222.

Coffey, G.N., 1912. A study of the soils of the United States. USDA Bur. Soils Bull., 85: 7—40.

Dan, J. and Yaalon, D.H., 1968. Pedomorphic forms and pedomorphic surfaces. 9th Int. Congress Soil Sci., Trans., 4: 577—584.

Fridland, V.M., 1965. The structure of soil cover. Soviet Soil Sci., 4: 343—355.

Gibbons, F.R. and Downes, R.G., 1964. A Study of the Land in Southwestern Victoria. Soil Conserv. Auth., Melbourne, N.S.W., 289 pp.

Glinka, K.D., 1927. The Great Soil Groups of the World and their Development. Edwards, Ann Arbor, Mich., 150 pp.

Haseman, J.F. and Marshall, C.E., 1945. The use of heavy minerals in studies of the origin and development of soils. Mo. Agric. Exp. Stn., Res. Bull., 387: 1—75.

Hilgard, E.W., 1892. The relations of soil to climate. USDA Weather Bur. Bull., 3: 1—59.

Hilgard, E.W., 1906. Soils. Macmillan, New York, N.Y., 593 pp.

Hole, F.D., 1953. Suggested terminology for describing soils as three-dimensional bodies. Soil Sci. Soc. Am. Proc., 17: 131—135.

Jenny, H., 1958. Role of the plant factor in the pedogenic functions. Ecology, 39: 5—16.

Jenny, H., 1961. Derivation of state factor equations of soils and ecosystems. Soil Sci. Soc. Am. Proc., 25: 385—388.

Joffe, J.S., 1949. The ABC of Soils. Pedology Publications, New Brunswick, N.J., 383 pp.

Johnson, W.M., 1963. The pedon and the polypedon. Soil Sci. Soc. Am. Proc., 27: 212— 215.

Kellogg, C.E., 1936. Development and significance of the Great Soil Groups of the United States. USDA Misc. Publ., 229: 1—40.

Kellogg, C.E., 1937. Soil Survey Manual. USDA Misc. Publ., No. 274, Washington, D.C., 136 pp.

King, F.H., 1902. The Soil. Macmillan, New York, N.Y., 303 pp.

Knox, E.G., 1965. Soil individuals and soil classification. Soil Sci. Soc. Am. Proc., 29: 79—84.

Lebedeff, A.F., 1928. The desirability of mapping specific soil properties. Proc. Pap., First Int. Congress Soil Sci., Comm. V., 1927, pp. 494—497.

Lyon, T.L. and Buckman, H.O., 1938. The Nature and Property of Soils (3rd ed.). Macmillan, New York, N.Y., 392 pp.

Lyon, T.L., Fippin, E.O. and Buckman, H.O., 1916. Soils, Their Properties and Manage- ment (2nd ed.). Macmillan, New York, N.Y., 764 pp.

Marbut, C.F., 1921. The contribution of soil surveys to soil science. Soc. Prom. Agric. Sci., Proc. 41st Annu. Meeting, pp. 116—142.

Marbut, C.F., 1922. Soil classification. Am. Soil Surv. Assoc., Bull., III: 24—32.

Marbut, C.F., 1928. A scheme for soil classification. Proc. Pap. First Int. Congress Soil Sci., Comm. V., 1927, pp. 1—31.

Milne, G., 1935. Some suggested units of classification and mapping, particularly for East African soils. Bodenkund. Forsch., Rech. sur le Sol, IV (3): 183—198.

Muir, J.W., 1962. The general principles of classification with reference to soils. J. Soil Sci., 13: 22—30.

Nikiforoff, C.C. and Drosdoff, M., 1943. Genesis of clay pan soil. Soil Sci., 55: 459—482.

Ollier, C.D., Drover, D.P. and Godelier, M., 1971. Soil knowledge amongst the Baruya of Wonenara, New Guinea. Oceania, XLII (1): 33—41.

Protz, R., Presant, E.W. and Arnold, R.W., 1968. Establishment of the modal profile and measurement of variability within a soil landform unit. Can. J. Soil Sci., 48: 7—19.

Ruhe, R.V., 1956. Geomorphic surfaces and the nature of soils. Soil Sci., 82: 441—445.

Simonson, R.W., 1959. Outline of a generalized theory of soil genesis. Soil Sci. Soc. Am. Proc., 23: 152—156.

Simonson, R.W. and Gardner, D.R., 1960. Concepts and function of the pedon. 7th Int. Congress Soil Sci., Trans., 4: 127—131.

Smith, G.D., 1963. Objectives and basic assumptions of the new soil classification system. Soil Sci., 96: 6—16.

Soil Survey Staff, 1951. Soil Survey Manual. USDA Agric. Handbook, No. 18, 503 pp.

Soil Survey Staff, 1975a. Soil Taxonomy. A Basic System of Soil Classification for Making and Interpreting Soil Surveys. USDA Agric. Handbook, No. 436, 754 pp.

Soil Survey Staff, 1975b. Concepts of Soils. (Ch. 1 of unedited 5th draft of Soil Survey Manual, SCS, Washington.) Mimeo, pp. 3—19.

Strzemski, M., 1975. Ideas Underlying Soil Systematics. Trans. 1971 Polish ed. TT73-54013, Foreign Scientific Publ. Dept. of National Center for Scientific, Technical and Economic Information, Warsaw, 541 pp.

Van Dijk, D.C., 1959. Soil features in relation to erosional history in the vicinity of Canberra. Aust. CSIRO Soil Publ., 13: 1—41.

Van Wambeke, A., 1966. Soil bodies and soil classification. Soils Fert., 29: 507—510.

Weir, W.W., 1928. What is the relative weight that should be given field and laboratory data in the definition of the several categories in a comprehensive scheme of soil classification? Proc. Pap., First Int. Congress Soil Sci., Comm. V., 1927, pp. 113—121.

Whitney, M., 1925. Soil and Civilization. Van Nostrand, New York, N.Y., 278 pp.

HISTORICAL DEVELOPMENT OF SOIL TAXONOMY — BACKGROUND

G.D. SMITH

THE EARLIER CLASSIFICATIONS

The development of Soil Taxonomy (Soil Survey Staff, 1975) was so strongly influenced by the earlier classifications used in the United States that it cannot be understood without a brief review of their history. At the start of the soil survey under Milton Whitney, in 1899, the cartographic units were the soil types, but by 1903 the types were grouped into soil series, e.g. *Miami loam* (Simonson, 1964). *Miami* was the series name, taken from the locality where the series was first mapped. *Loam* was the type name, describing the texture of the whole soil. Texture at first was a combination of grainsize, organic matter and structure, so that such types as *Miami loam* and *Miami black-clay loam* were used. Very shortly, the meaning of the type was restricted to the grainsize of the whole soil. The original concept of the soil series and type was very different from the present concept, Simonson (1959) quotes from the 1903 instructions to field parties the following "...the object has been to establish certain series in the different physiographic divisions of the United States, and we are finding that there are a few general classes of soils that are in a way related. Prominent among these are the Norfolk, Miami, Fresno, Cecil and Hagerstown series. In each of these we have found or expect to find a stony loam, a gravel, gravelly loam, sand, fine sand, sandy loam, fine sandy loam, silt, clay loam and clay...".

"When the Norfolk sand is being deposited, the conditions somewhere in the area will undoubtedly be favorable to the deposition of gravel, of silt, of fine sand, of loam and of clay, and wherever material of these characters is encountered, presumably coming from the same source and being deposited essentially at the same time, they should be given this distinctive (series) name so as to show their relation to one another...".

Marbut (Marbut et al., 1913) defined a soil series "as a group of soils having the same range in color, the same character of subsoil, particularly as regards color and structure, broadly the same type of relief and drainage, and a common or similar origin". The meaning of the type shifted gradually to the grainsize of the plow layer or its equivalent in undisturbed soils. Soil was regarded in the United States at the time largely as weathered rock, so the geologic origin of the mineral fraction was considered one of its most important properties. Marbut (Marbut et al., 1913) wrote: "It is of vast importance, therefore, in the classification of soils to recognize not only the character of the rock from which the material has been derived but also the agencies which have acted in the transportation and deposition of the soil material and the changes which have taken place since its deposition''. A given series was restricted to a broad geologic province such as the Glacial and Loessial Province.

The purpose of mapping soil series and types was, and still is, to facilitate the transfer of results of research and experience with the use of soils gained in one place to the other places where it has applicability. The first men to make soil maps had been trained in geology, a related earth science. Basic knowledge of soil—plant relations was extremely limited. Field experiments with soil amendments and crop rotations had been conducted in a few States for about thirty years. It was known that crop responses varied from one soil to another, but the reasons were not understood. Soil chemistry consisted of total analyses. Field workers had to learn from their own observations which properties of the soils they mapped were important to plant growth and how to identify the important properties in the field. Their problems were discussed by Marbut (1928) and Ableiter (1949b).

Knowledge came slowly. Many of the original soil types were given series status. For example, the black color of the Miami black-clay loam became the basis for another series in 1904 (Ableiter, 1949a). As new areas were mapped, more series were added. In 1912 (Marbut et al., 1913) there were 534 series and 1650 types. The number of series grew steadily from a few hundred to a very few thousand between about 1912 and 1927, but they were grouped only by the geologic provinces. The series was the highest category.

The influence of Dokuchaiev

In Russia, between 1870 and 1900, a very different classification of soils arose from the work of Dokuchaiev and his followers (Glinka, 1914). Soils were conceived as independent natural bodies with properties that resulted from the effects of climate and living organisms acting on parent materials over time as conditioned by relief. The early Russian mapping of soils had a different purpose from that in the United States. It was primarily that of assessing taxes. The soil types of the Russian school were broadly conceived groups of soils that had a similar genesis but could form in a variety of parent materials. Coffey (1912) was influenced by this school. He published a classification of United States soils using the Russian concepts, but his ideas were too advanced for the time. Some of his groups were very similar to some of the present orders of Soil Taxonomy.

The classification of Marbut

When the Russian concepts were published in German (Glinka, 1914), Marbut was influenced to accept the Russian concept of the soil type. Instead of emphasizing the geologic origin of the parent materials, he emphasized that the soils should be classified on the basis of the characteristics of the profile (Marbut, 1921). He listed eight properties which, broadly interpreted, include virtually all properties used in Soil Taxonomy except soil temperature and moisture regimes and the lateral continuity of horizons. Marbut's eight characteristics considered to be significant for the differentiation of a soil series were:
(1) Number of horizons in the soil profile.
(2) Color of the various horizons, with special emphasis on the surface one or two.
(3) Texture of the horizons.
(4) Structure of the horizons.
(5) Relative arrangement of the horizons.
(6) Chemical composition of the horizons.
(7) Thickness of the horizons.
(8) Geology of the soil material.
Because soil type had an established meaning in the United States, the Russian type became known as the great soil group. Marbut developed a multicategoric classification of United States' soils which he published first in outline form (Marbut, 1928) and later in more detail (Marbut, 1935). Marbut's arrangement of soil groups is shown in Table 2.1 (Marbut, 1928). He emphasized that the classification in the higher categories should be based on the soil properties of the *mature*, or *normal* soil, a freely drained soil having clearly expressed horizons. He introduced great soil concepts to the United States using a mixture of Russian, European and United States' names (Table 2.1). Soils that were not "normal" had no place in the higher categories. These included soils on recent surfaces, hydromorphic soils other than tundra, alkali soils, organic soils, and others, including soils which overlie developed profiles. The soils without normal profiles had places at the type and series level and in the next higher category, Category III. In Category III, Marbut's groups 2 and 4 (Table 2.1) could not be clearly distinguished by their own properties but had to be classified by the properties of the surrounding *normal* soils.

The theories of soil genesis that were held by Marbut had a great influence on his classification of United States soils. His groups V-4 and V-5 (Table 2.1, now mostly Udults) and his group V-3 (now mostly Udalfs) were separated on his small-scale map by temperature. He said: "They are not differentiated therefore on the basis of differences in characteristics produced by differences in moisture. Their differences correspond on the other hand to differences in temperature". He thought the differences in color

TABLE 2.1

Arrangement of the soil groups of Marbut (1928)

Category VII	1. Pedalfers	2. Pedocals
Category VI	1. Podzolic Soils 2. Lateritic Soils	3. Pedocals of Temperate Zone 4. Pedocals of Tropical Zone
Category V	1. Tundra 2. Podzols 3. Brown Forest Soils 4. Red Soils 5. Yellow Soils 6. Prairie Soils 7. Laterites 8. Ferruginous Laterites	9. Northern Temperate Pedocals 10. Mid-Latitude Temperate Pedocals 11. Southern Temperate Pedocals 12. The various still unknown groups of Tropical Pedocals

Category IV

Sub-groups of Group 10 in Category V
1. Tschernosem
2. Chestnut Colored
3. Brown
4. Gray
5. Sub-groups of groups 9, 11 and 12 of Category V, none of which have yet received distinctive names

Category III	1. Soils with perfectly developed profiles 2. Soils with imperfectly developed profiles	3. Soils with perfectly developed profiles 4. Soils with imperfectly developed profiles
Category II	1. Soil Series Groups (a very great number)	2. Soil Series Groups (a very great number)
Category I	1. Soil units based on texture of surface horizon	2. Soil units based on texture of surface horizon

were due to differences in temperature in contrast to the present belief that they are due to differences in the ages of the soils. He included with his groups V-4 and V-5 the broad belt of soils formed in late Wisconsinian loess lying to the east of the Mississippi River and south of the Ohio River because they were warmer than the soils formed in loess to the north of the Ohio River. In Soil Taxonomy these soils are separated only at a low category (family) because present beliefs are that the genesis and horizons are the same, and the principal differences are in the lack of freezing temperatures in the soil and the longer growing season in the south.

The concepts of the groups of Categories IV and V were quickly accepted in the United States. Marbut (1935) used a few series as examples of the properties of his groups in Categories IV and V, but did not develop guidelines for the classification of the series into the groups of Category III. So there arose two classifications of soils in the United States, one into soil types and series and the other into great soil groups. The relations between the two were never developed, but both carried over into the next classification (Baldwin et al., 1938).

The classification of 1938

The 1938 classification had to be prepared hurriedly for inclusion in the 1938 Yearbook of the U.S. Department of Agriculture, Soils and Men (Kellogg, 1960, 1974). Only about one year was available for its preparation. New great soil groups, such as Lithosols, Alluvial soils, Bog soils and Planosols, were provided for Marbut's soils with imperfectly developed profiles. Marbut's orders of Pedocals and Pedalfers had to be abandoned as such because some soils fit both classes and others fit neither. The concepts of Zonal, Intrazonal and Azonal soils were substituted. These were adapted from the 1895 classification of N.M. Sibertsev (cited by Glinka, 1914) which were the outgrowth of Dokuchaiev's earlier classification of soils into normal, transitional and abnormal orders. Sibertsev's concept of the zonal soils was one of soils that "are on the whole distributed according to zones or belts on the surface of the continents, which correspond to the latter's zones of physical geography". (Glinka, 1931.) Intrazonal soils occur whereever the local and particular factors of soil formation are predominant over the general zonal factors. Azonal soils are incomplete or not fully developed and are not distributed according to any zones. Following publication of the 1938 classification, an attempt was immediately started to relate soil series to the great soil groups. Problems were difficult. Some series fit no great soil group, so additional great soil groups were created, such as Ando soils and Grumusols. Other series fit more than one great soil group. Not only had there been no time to prepare definitions of the great soil groups, but the terminology needed for their definition still has to be developed. This required another decade (Soil Survey Staff, 1951). No differentiae had been suggested for the family category. The Zonal and Intrazonal orders could not be defined in terms of soil properties. Nor could more precise definitions of the great soil groups be written without overlaps and gaps. Riecken (1945) summarized some of the difficulties with the 1938 classification, pointing out that the lack of definition of the great soil groups made it difficult to relate them to the soil series of Iowa. He thought the concepts of the great soil groups were useful and should be retained, but needed to be broadened to permit the unequivocal inclusion of various kinds of intergrades between the groups.

The Chester series of Maryland may be used as an example of the problems of definition.of the great soil groups. During a joint field study about 1950 between the correlation staffs of the southern and northeastern regions, it was classified as a Gray-Brown Podzolic soil by the southern staff and as a Red-Yellow Podzolic soil by the northeastern staff. It was similar to the Norfolk series, which some considered a typical Red-Yellow Podzolic soil, in base status and in kind of clay. It differed from the Norfolk in the thickness of horizons, distribution and amount of organic matter, and in weatherable minerals. In these respects it resembled the Miami series, which some considered to be the typical Gray-Brown Podzolic soil. No agreement was reached about its classification at the great soil-group category. Many of the problems with the 1938 classification were discussed by Thorp and Smith (1949) and Riecken and Smith (1949). The higher categories of the modified 1938 classification are shown in Table 2.2 (Thorp and Smith, 1949).

The numbers of series increased rapidly between Marbut's introduction of the great soil groups in 1928 and 1951 when the decision was made to attempt the development of a new system. There were three important reasons. One was the changing concept of the soil series. Marbut's emphasis on the importance of the profile of the soil to its classification (Marbut, 1921) and his 1928 introduction of a hierarchical classification stimulated the re-examination of many of the concepts of existing series. New series were defined for many of the intergrades between his great soil groups. There were major advances in soil chemistry and physics, and in clay mineralogy, and the new knowledge required new series. Farming practices changed drastically and ranges in properties of series had to be reduced for advisory work. The aerial photograph and larger scales for soil surveys made it possible to delineate more series. Concepts of the catena (Bushnell, 1945) and other sequences (Riecken, 1945) led to splitting of many of the older series.

Kellogg (1937), in the first edition of the Soil Survey Manual, defined a soil series as follows: "A series is a group of soils having genetic horizons similar as to differentiating characteristics in the soil profile, and developed from a particular type of parent material. Except for texture, especially that of the A horizon, the morphological features of the soil profile as exhibited in the physical characteristics and thickness of soil horizons are not allowed to vary significantly in the series...". This definition does not vary greatly from that in the second edition of the Soil Survey Manual (Soil Survey Staff, 1951) but the word "genetic" was dropped.

The second reason was the need for increasingly quantitative interpretations, both for the growth of plants and for engineering uses. Some soil series still had very wide ranges in particle size in horizons below the plow layer, ranges such that almost no engineering and only general farming interpretations were possible. These ranges were gradually reduced. Series of wet soils were separated if their wetness was due to shallow ground water or to slow hydraulic conductivity. The changes in concepts of series were not

TABLE 2.2

Arrangement of the great soil groups of Baldwin et al. (1938) into suborders and orders as modified in 1949 (Thorp and Smith, 1949)

Order	Suborder	Great soil groups
Zonal soils	1. Soils of the cold zone	Tundra soils
	2. Light-colored soils of arid regions	Desert soils
		Red desert soils
		Sierozem
		Brown soils
		Reddish-brown soils
	3. Dark-colored soils of semi-arid, subhumid and humid grasslands	Chestnut soils
		Reddish chestnut soils
		Chernozem soils
		Prairie soils
		Reddish prairie soils
	4. Soils of the forest—grassland transition	Degraded chernozem
		Non-calcic brown or
		Shantung brown soils
	5. Light-colored podzolized soils of the timbered regions	Podzol soils
		Gray wooded, or
		Gray podzolic soils*
		Brown podzolic soils
		Gray-brown podzolic soils
		Red-yellow podzolic soils*
	6. Lateritic soils of forested warm-temperate and tropical regions	Reddish-brown lateritic soils*
		Yellowish-brown lateritic soils*
		Lateritic soils*
Intrazonal soils	1. Halomorphic (saline and alkali) soils of imperfectly drained arid regions and littoral deposits	Solonchak, or
		Saline soils
		Solonetz soils
		Soloth soils
	2. Hydromorphic soils of marshes, swamps, seep areas and flats	Humic-glei soils* (includes Wiesenboden)
		Alpine meadow soils
		Bog soils
		Half-bog soils
		Low-humic glei* soils
		Planosols
		Groundwater podzol soils
		Groundwater laterite soils
	3. Calcimorphic soils	Brown forest soils (Braunerde)
		Rendzina soils
Azonal soils		Lithosols
		Regosols (includes Dry Sands)
		Alluvial soils

*New or recently modified great soil groups.

uniform across the country. As late as 1942 (Roberts, 1942), a published soil survey included one series that was based on the 1910 concept of series and types, and had types that ranged from a sand texture throughout the soil to a heavy clay.

The third reason was a great expansion in the areas in which soil surveys were being made. The Soil Conservation Service had been founded and had expanded its soil surveys of individual farms into nearly every county in the country during this period. The correlation of their mapping units with soil series and types finally became impossible and had to be abandoned. Some 5500 series had been recognized by 1951, a number far too large to comprehend without an orderly grouping into successively higher categories of a general classification.

The early approximations

The abandonment of the Zonal and Intrazonal orders, which could not be defined in terms of common soil properties, required a more or less complete revision of the 1938 classification. The series were too numerous to comprehend. Consequently, they could not be grouped into successively higher categories. It was necessary first to form concepts of new orders, and then to test the concepts to see how the series might be grouped by one definition or another.

The logic of the 1938 classification required some small adjustments. Cline (1949) wrote "The purpose of any classification is to so organize our knowledge that the properties of objects may be remembered and their relationships may be understood more easily *for a specific objective*". (author's italics.) For Soil Taxonomy, this means the purposes of the soil survey. His statement was, and still is, valid. However, he also wrote "A class is a group of individuals bound from within, not circumscribed from without". In most senses this is also still valid, but because the series were so numerous, it was necessary to define classes by their limits as well as to develop a central or modal concept, if that were possible. Otherwise, the gaps and overlaps would carry over into the new classification, and the problems of grouping the series into successively higher categories would not be diminished. The logic used in the development of Soil Taxonomy was discussed by Cline (1963).

The classification of soils into series was entrenched by 1951, not only with those who made soil surveys, but with those who used them. Advertisements of farms for sale in Iowa, for example, commonly carried the name of the dominant soil series and type. Highway engineers were using the soil maps with the series names to plan the secondary roads. Many tax assessors were using phases of soil series as a basis for equalizing taxes. Many extension services used the series names to interpret soil tests. The Highway Research Board asked the author to allay its fears that the new classification, rumoured in development, would disturb the soil series. Wholesale changes in concepts of series were not only unwarranted but unacceptable. The series had been tested and found useful. But, because of their number they were unmanageable. These were some of the problems that faced the soil survey staff in 1951.

Before work was started on Soil Taxonomy, it was agreed that it could be developed only through a series of approximations. These would be circulated for criticism to as large a group as possible and would be revised to meet as many as possible of the criticisms and suggestions that were received.

The first two approximations were reviewed by only a limited number of the soil survey staff. These had only a faint resemblance to the present taxonomy. Soil moisture and soil temperature were used, and the definitions were intended to include both cultivated and virgin soils. These innovations were not accepted quickly.

In the first approximation, the order of Histosols was proposed (under another name) and the order of Entisols was foreshadowed as an order with AC or C profiles. More or less freely drained soils with ABC (or BC profiles to provide for eroded soils) constituted an order, and poorly drained soils with ABGC or AGC without pans constituted another. Soils with pans constituted the fifth order, called Durobods. This order was subdivided into four suborders, Natrisols, Planosols, Durosols and Fragisols. Great groups had names ending in *em*. Temperature and moisture were criteria for suborders. The present orders of Alfisols, Spodosols and Ultisols were separated only as great groups. The first approximation was prepared hurriedly in order to have something to discuss at a meeting of the senior correlation staff. Many of the classes of the first approximation had been developed with James Thorp for a paper published in 1949 (Thorp and Smith, 1949), but the authors had concluded that it was premature to publish it.

Most of the discussion at the meeting centered on the names rather than the concepts of the proposed taxa. Therefore, starting with the second approximation, a decimal system of numbers was used to identify the taxa.

The second approximation dropped the orders of hydromorphic soils and of soils that had a pan. The hydromorphic soils were distributed among the orders as suborders, and soils with pans were distributed among suborders as great groups. However, most soils were grouped in a single order, one of soils with ABC or BC profiles with or without a G horizon. Temperature was retained but only at the family category.

The next step in the development was a field study of the classification systems in use in the seven western European countries that were then making soil surveys. A general system was desired that would not only be useful for the transfer of experience within the United States but that would also facilitate the transfer of experience in other countries to the United States. At the conclusion of this study, Prof. R. Tavernier of the State University of Gent, Belgium, arranged a conference in Gent of representatives from these and other countries. A modification of the second approximation had been prepared for this discussion, much of which centered on the suitability of the use of soil moisture and temperature in definitions of taxa.

The unnumbered approximation discussed in Gent was revised to include as many suggestions as possible (some always conflicted) and was tested in the United States by placing the soil series in taxa of the higher categories according to the proposed definitions. If the definitions produced a wholesale splitting of series because they did not follow the common series limits, attempts were made to fit the definitions to these limits. Some small changes in series limits were unavoidable, and some of the older series obviously had ranges in properties that were too wide. In some parts of the country, the series differed if hard rock was shallower or deeper than 45 cm (18 in). The limit was 50 cm in other parts, and 60 cm in the remainder. The minimum disturbance seemed to come if the limit was set at 50 cm (20 in), the present limit for lithic subgroups. A few of the older series had wide geographic distribution, but most series had rather limited geographic distribution for reasons that will be discussed later.

The testing of the revised 2nd approximation was followed by the 3rd approximation in 1954. This was distributed to those interested at the 5th Congress of the International Soil Science Society at Leopoldville, and was discussed at a meeting in Gent of European pedologists, particularly those with experience with soils of intertropical regions. In this approximation, five of the present orders can be seen dimly, Aridisols, Entisols, Histosols, Mollisols and Spodosols. Definitions of the orders according to the presence or absence of a B horizon continued in the 3rd and 4th approximations. The present concepts of differentiae for subgroups appeared in the 3rd approximation, and differentiae for families were proposed to serve the present purpose of that category. The 3rd approximation was also tested against the soil series by placing them in the proposed taxa of the three highest categories to determine what kinds of groups were formed by its definitions.

The 4th and 5th approximations were developed and tested in the same manner. It was not until the 6th approximation that concepts for families and subgroups had developed far enough to permit testing of the taxa in these categories against the interpretations being made for phases of series and types. But so many revisions were made before the 6th approximation could be issued that it was decided to number it the 7th approximation.

Suggestions for and criticisms of the various approximations came in several ways. Correspondence with many workers in foreign countries was one. But correspondence alone is commonly inadequate for precise communication about soils. A number of languages were involved and subtle meanings can be lost in translation. Discussions in pits are most useful, but travel is expensive and time consuming. Nevertheless, many months of travel were spent in many countries so that difficulties with approximations could be demonstrated in the field and alternatives discussed. State, regional and national work planning conferences and special meetings furnished forums for extensive discussions of the approximations. Each individual contributed by examining the proposals from the viewpoint of their effects on the classification of the soils that he knew personally. Hundreds of people were involved and suggestions came from a very large number of people, too many to be remembered.

The 7th Approximation

The 7th Approximation (Soil Survey Staff, 1960) was the first published approximation and the last in the numbered series. It retained the basic concepts of many of the great soil groups of several existing classifications, modified and rearranged with a few innovations. The latter were introduced at various stages in the series of approximations along with many other innovations that were tested and subsequently dropped. The major innovations retained were the following:

(1) Properties of the whole soil were used in addition to the nature of the horizons. Soil moisture and soil-temperature regimes are examples. These were used as differentiae beginning with the 1st approximation.

(2) Instead of having a separate order for hydromorphic soils, they were divided among the various orders according to the properties that would persist after drainage. This was clearly evident in the 2nd approximation.

(3) Criteria were introduced to bridge the gap between the soil series and the great soil group. Specific proposals for subgroups appeared in the 5th approximation, and class limits for families in the 7th approximation.

(4) Definitions of taxa could be applied to cultivated or to undisturbed soils. The intention was to keep plowed and eroded soils with their virgin counterparts to the maximum extent possible. This had been the practice in the classification of series, but the descriptions of series and great soil groups had concentrated on the undisturbed profiles.

(5) The classification of soils according to the A, B and C-horizon nomenclature was abandoned completely in favor of named diagnostic horizons and features. This was a gradual process, but the 5th approximation illustrates one reason for this decision, saying "The term 'Latosolic B horizon' used in the 4th approximation has been replaced here by 'Sesquioxide horizon' in order to divert discussion from the problem of whether this horizon should be called a B horizon. Most comments on the 4th approximation were concerned with this problem, and the authors were unable to determine whether the concept of the horizon was satisfactory, or whether the correspondents felt the presence or absence of the horizon could be used as a basis for grouping like soils".

(6) The pedon was introduced as the sampling unit in the 7th approxi-

mation to facilitate classification of soils that have intermittent horizons. The emphasis shifted from the classification of profiles to that of soils as three-dimensional bodies called polypedons (Johnson, 1963). A single pedon could have strongly contrasting profiles if the variability was repeating and on a scale such that an area of 10 m² contains some of each. In the polypedon, the different profiles occur in a repeating pattern over linear distances of 7 m or less. The 7-m number was selected because it was thought to be the common maximum in soils subject to movement by shrinking and swelling or by frost. In the normal situation where the horizons are continuous over much greater areas, the pedon size was set at 1 m², an area large enough to encompass the normal variations in thickness of individual horizons.

(7) The Halomorphic suborder of the 1938 classification was dispersed among the various orders to permit more statements to be made about the various orders and suborders. The Solonchaks and Solonetz of arid regions were grouped with the other soils of those regions, the Aridisols. The other Solonetz were divided according to their horizons and moisture regimes as new great groups in several suborders.

(8) A new and systematic terminology was introduced with the 7th Approximation. The older names had been taken from common languages, and over the years had acquired different meanings in different countries. To retain the old names with redefined meanings would compound the existing confusion. Names were coined, using mostly Greek and Latin roots. The names of the diagnostic horizons and features have the same roots as the names of the classes for which they are diagnostic. The construction of the names was described by Heller (1963).

The orders of the 7th Approximation developed largely from the concepts of suborders and great soil groups of the 1938 classification. The Azonal order, which could be defined in terms of soil properties, formed the basis for the concept of Entisols. Generalization of the properties of the suborder of light-colored soils of arid regions led to their early grouping as the order now called Aridisols. Similarly, the suborder of dark-colored soils of semi-arid, subhumid, and humid grasslands led to the concept of Mollisols. However, the suborder of light-colored podzolized soils of the timbered regions included soils with little in common, even the light color and the vegetation. Many of the Podzols are dark in color and had a heath vegetation. The Podzol soils were combined with some Brown Podzolic soils and the Ground-water Podzol soils to form the order of Spodosols. The Gray-Brown Podzolic soils and Gray podzolic soils led to the concept of Alfisols. The Red-Yellow Podzolic soils had many similarities to the Reddish-Brown and Yellowish-Brown Lateritic soils, and they led to the concept of Ultisols. The Laterite soils became the basis for the order of Oxisols. The Grumusols and Bog soils seemed unique for the separate orders of Vertisols and Histosols. The remaining Hydromorphic great soil groups, and the Halomorphic soils were distributed as suborders and great groups among the various orders.

But several of the great soil groups recognized after 1949 remained. The Ando soils and Sols Bruns Acides were examples. Some of the Brown Forest Soils and Low-Humic Gley soils had no place among the orders mentioned, nor did many of the soils on recent surfaces of Puerto Rico. In the earlier approximations, these soils had been distributed in various ways, but none seemed satisfactory. The few statements that could be made about all of the soils in any one order became impossible if they were included. Consequently, they were put together in another order, the Inceptisols.

The supplements

The 7th Approximation was not yet ready for use, even in the United States. It was published to be criticized by as wide an audience as possible. No proposals were ready for the classification of organic soils, and only very tentative proposals were made for the classification of Oxisols and many other soils in intertropical regions. Many criticisms and many suggestions for improvements were received following its publication, and many changes were made in definitions as the result of continued testing against the series limits and the interpretations being made for phases of series and types. Criticisms of the nomenclature resulted in many changed names. There were then about 8000 soil series, and soil maps were being made at the rate of about 30 million hectares (66 million acres) a year. Publication of completed soil surveys was lagging behind completion, partly because of difficulties of comparing proposed new series with the 8000 already recognized. Inquiries to agencies cooperating in the soil survey showed an almost unanimous opinion that the National Cooperative Soil Survey should begin to use the new classification despite its shortcomings and lack of completion. So it was decided to begin use of the system with the start of 1965, and to facilitate this use, a supplement was issued in 1964 listing all of the changes that had been agreed upon.

Smith (1965) published a synopsis of the taxonomy as it stood at that time with emphasis on the reasons for the groupings and their definitions.

During this period of testing, definitions of the soil series became more and more quantitative because quantitative limits in the categories higher than series were also limits of series. Field studies of morphology also became more and more quantitative.

When actual use began, the more rigorous testing against the series limits and interpretations forced many additional changes in definitions. These were summarized in a supplement issued in 1967 in which the present form was almost complete except for the classification of organic soils. The classification of the organic soils was outlined first in a supplement issued in 1968. The writing of the text of Soil Taxonomy was completed by 1970 except for minor changes needed to accommodate new series established after the text was written.

Many modifications are sure to come. More diagnostic horizons will be found, and changes will be made in present definitions. New diagnostic features will come from continuing research in the various fields of soil science. Gaps in Soil Taxonomy, particularly in taxa that are not represented in the United States, will be filled. The text is simply one more step in the search for the most useful taxonomy.

DEVELOPMENT OF DEFINITIONS FOR SOIL TAXONOMY

It should be emphasized that the taxa of categories of order, suborder, great group and subgroup, developed through the various approximations, were intended to reflect differences in the dominance of one combination or another of sets of genetic processes. These taxa had to be conceived first in broad terms. Then definitions had to be written to create the desired taxa. The central problem was to select specific characteristics that would produce the desired groupings. One must consider *all* the characteristics that he knows in deciding on the desired groupings, but only a few characteristics may be used in the definitions if they are to be intelligible. The characteristics selected are not necessarily the most important in themselves, but they are important to the formation of the desired groupings. Attention is focused on the characteristics that were used in the definitions, and those that perhaps should have been used, but were not, are apt to be overlooked. This is why Soil Taxonomy says (p. 10) "The definitions must be continually tested by the nature and functioning of the soils grouped in a taxon. A taxonomy for the use of the soil survey must be tested by the nature of the interpretation that can be made".

The importance of the soil series to the nature of the definitions of Soil Taxonomy has been pointed out. The taxa of the higher categories reflected concepts drawn from earlier classification with some modifications and considerable rearrangement. The definitions were intended to cause the minimum desirable or necessary disturbance to the series. When Soil Taxonomy came into use in 1965, a considerable portion of the more productive farm land and areas of rapidly expanding population had been mapped and either had been published or was in the process of publication. Because these maps had been tested and found useful for many purposes (Kellogg, 1974) wholesale changes in the series definitions were to be avoided. This was one major test of the definitions of the supplements to the 7th Approximation, in which the definitions were made more and more quantitative.

The series served important pragmatic functions. Except for a few of the oldest series, a given series had a limited geographic distribution. If the type of farming differed because of differences in rainfall or in the length of the growing season, the series also differed. Cline and Johnson (1963) have pointed out that the Brown and Chestnut great soil groups also were more pragmatic than genetic or morphologic, separating soils too dry for cultivation from those that could be cultivated. There was little overlap of series between the cotton belt and the corn belt, or between areas used for winter and spring wheat. Without definition, limits of soil temperature and soil moisture existed for most of the series. The lower mean annual soil-temperature limit of the cotton belt was about 15°C, and few series had significant ranges across this limit. The lower soil-temperature limits of maize for grain and of winter wheat was close to 8°C. In the arid regions, 15°C was the limit between the Desert and Red Desert soils. Few series crossed this limit, but a number of Desert series crossed the 8°C limit. The temperature limits existing between series were made explicit.

The amount and pattern of precipitation also had very significant influences on the use of soils. As a consequence, few series had a wide range in either, and the limits of the moisture regimes, though unspecified, were built into the series concepts. These limits and many others were a reflection of the practical purpose for making soil surveys — to facilitate the transfer of experience with the use of soils. Occurrences in different types of farming areas were considered important enough to justify different soil series.

Soil surveys and compiled soil maps are made at many scales. With the larger scales, the individual polypedons and their significant phases are normally delineated. With small scales, this is impossible, and associations of phases of taxa of the higher categories are commonly used. They are used of necessity if series have not been defined. If small-scale maps are to be useful, some pragmatism is required at all categoric levels. If a choice existed, the more important properties that affect the potential uses of soils for growing plants or for engineering purposes were used to define the taxa in the higher categories. This allows more important interpretations to be made for small-scale maps. Among these properties are the soil moisture and temperature regimes, and the amounts of organic matter. Interpretations are needed in various parts of the world for farming with and without the availability of soil amendments. This makes the base status important for soils of the humid intertropical regions. In boreal regions, where few crops can be grown, the importance of the base status is greatly reduced, and the importance of temperature is greater. It is essential to weight the differentiae according to their relative importance in a given taxon and to use the most significant in the higher categories if we are to make the most important interpretations for small-scale maps. Consequently, the definitions use the same differentiae at different categoric levels in different taxa. The colder Alfisols and Mollisols were separated as suborders without regard to their moisture regimes, but the warmer ones were separated as suborders according to their moisture regimes, emphasizing that the relative importance of moisture and temperature (or any other property) is not everywhere the same. Interpretations vary between soils if the growing season is controlled by moisture or by temperature.

Many people must have wondered and not a few have asked about the differences in weighting of properties and how the specific limits between taxa were selected. Why does an Alfisol have $\geqslant 35$ percent base saturation by sum of cations at specific depths? Why does a mollic epipedon have $\geqslant 0.6$ percent carbon? Why is the presence of an argillic horizon required of two orders but only recognized at the subgroup category in other orders? Why?

Only a general answer is possible here, but there were two situations. First, the taxa were represented by a number of series in the United States, and second, they were not. If there were series, limits were needed that would group the series in such a way that the greatest number of the most important interpretations would be possible for the taxa. But, because series limits had been developed largely for pragmatic purposes without being related clearly to any general classification, limits set between taxa in categories higher than the series category commonly split some of the series. The limits selected were the common limits of series that the soil survey staff felt, for one reason or another, should not be split. For the most part, the reason was that interpretations would not be improved, and the split would confuse the users of the soil surveys. It seems sure that no one individual knows the names of many of these series, but the author of this chapter can give a few case histories as examples. The reader must understand that in most definitions somewhere in the United States some series had this approximate limit, and it was thought more important not to split these series than to split other series that had another limit. The origin of the 50-cm depth to a lithic contact for most lithic subgroups (and shallow families) and the 8 and 15°C-temperature limits have already been mentioned.

If there were few or no series, as in most intertropical regions, definitions generally were determined more by theoretical considerations than by series limits. There were too few series in Puerto Rico and Hawaii to permit much testing of the limits between taxa. Many taxa are not represented by any series. The limits for the taxa of intertropical soils were proposed for testing, but most have not yet been tested and undoubtedly require changes to make them useful.

The case histories follow:

(1) *Question.* The limit between Alfisols and Ultisols is the base saturation (by sum of cations at pH 8.2) at specified but variable depths. Why?

Answer. It was decided early in the development of Soil Taxonomy that there was a very important difference between the Red-Yellow Podzolic Soils and Gray-Brown Podzolic soils that later became the Ultisols and the Alfisols. Those that became Ultisols, could be farmed only under shifting cultivation in the absence of soil amendments. Those that became Alfisols could support a permanent agriculture. The former had few or no bases other than those cycled by plants. As a consequence, the base saturation normally decreased with depth in and below the argillic horizon. Normally, in the absence of lime applications, the level was extremely low in the lower part of the rooting zone.

In contrast, most Gray-Brown Podzolic soils had either moderate or high base saturation, and the base saturation increased with depth if there was any change. They had a natural reserve of bases from readily weatherable minerals or from an external source such as dust or water. Attempts in the 4th approximation to relate these differences to clay mineralogy failed, and base saturation was tried as the differentia. Data on base saturation in the United States east of Mississippi River were almost exclusively by sum of cations at pH 8.2. Only fragmentary data by other methods were available, and probable classification of most series would be uncertain if any other method were to be specified. Early attempts to use the decrease or increase in base saturation with depth failed to produce the groupings desired, so the low base saturation at a specified depth was tried as the most promising differentia. Comparisons of data for Red-Yellow and Gray-Brown Podzolic soils suggested that the limit of 35 percent in the B horizon, or saturation that decreased below the B would preserve most closely the distinctions between the great majority of the series previously accepted as members of the two great soil groups. Few series of either group seemed to be close to this limit.

The proposal of the limit of 35 percent base saturation of the B horizon in the 5th approximation stimulated additional studies of base saturation. In New Jersey, Delaware, Pennsylvania, and Maryland, it had been the custom of some farmers for many decades to apply small amounts of burned lime (CaO) during each rotation. The long cultivated fields had base saturation throughout the B horizon of about 60 percent. The woodlands that had not been cultivated had very low base saturation in the B horizon. The cultivated and forested areas of the same series were split. Series boundaries would have to follow fence lines because of liming, and the base saturation in each field would have to be measured or estimated to classify the soils in the field at the series level. This was not only impractical, but it defeated the main purpose of the soil survey. The transfer of experience would be very difficult for the users of the soil survey if the series names differed across fence lines as the result of liming. The use of base saturation at a depth of 1.8 m in uneroded soils seemed to avoid this problem, so it was selected. To select comparable horizons of eroded soils, a depth limit of 1.25 m below the top of the argillic horizon was selected. This seemed to solve the problem of the limed soils but created another problem with soils developed from basic igneous rocks in the southeastern states. At these depths, the base saturation was close to the 35-percent limit but had a narrow range on either side. It seemed possible to avoid splitting these series, which have dark red or dusky red colors and clayey textures, by using a slightly different depth.

(2) *Question*. Why is the soil-moisture regime used rather than other properties that are associated with excess and deficiencies of moisture?

Answer. The most important statements that the soil surveys make about the various taxa are the interpretations concerning the use of the soil for a wide variety of purposes. The availability of water and the presence of oxygen in the soil are critical to these interpretations. If we use morphology in our definitions, we must discriminate between features, such as mottling, that are the result of groundwater that we must lower by drainage and mottles that are the result of groundwater that was present during an earlier geologic time. Climates have changed in the past, and many soils retain features formed under an earlier and different climate.

A second difficulty with the use of morphologic properties that are preserved in samples is that soils with very similar morphology can develop under widely differing climates. The Mollisols formed in loess in the States of Illinois and Washington are difficult to distinguish at the family and series levels. In Illinois they are used to produce maize and soybeans. To produce these crops in Washington, the soils must be irrigated because the warm months are virtually rainless. If the soil moisture regime is not used in the definitions, climatic phases are required for interpretations. The reader should note that the series have been distinguished in the past because they were widely separated geographically, and the land use differences were very great because of the climatic differences. The climatic phases that would be needed are not only difficult to name but are inadequate. With a given climate, adjacent soils commonly differ in the amounts of moisture they receive. Water runs off of some soils and on to others. It is the *soil climate* that is important with rare exceptions.

To prepare the definitions of the moisture regimes, a model was developed to calculate, from climatic records, the soil moisture conditions for soils that receive their moisture from the atmosphere by precipitation. The classification of the soils of the various parts of the country was predetermined by the morphology and the interpretations. Calculations of the moisture conditions for the critical parts of the country permitted the fitting of the definitions to the predetermined boundaries. The definitions have obvious weaknesses. The first is in the model. The correlation coefficient between calculated and measured moisture conditions over a 30-year period was only 0.8. The second is that many combinations of precipitation and temperature do not exist in the United States, and the limits in the definitions could not be tested against these combinations. But the changes are more apt to come in the definitions than in the classification in the United States. Testing of the definitions against interpretations in Venezuela by the author showed several serious deficiencies in definitions of subgroups of soils with an ustic moisture regime in intertropical regions.

(3) *Question.* The mollic epipedons are required to have only 0.6 percent organic carbon, but many ochric epipedons greatly exceed this value. Is not this value too low?

Answer. The limit of 0.6 percent organic carbon is very low. There are series of dark-colored sands in the drier parts of the Great Plains. They are used both for grazing and production of winter wheat. The organic carbon of those that have not been cultivated is considerably higher than 0.6 percent. Under cultivation, the organic carbon has been reduced both by oxidation and by soil blowing, but the color and apparent texture are not significantly affected. The low limit was set to avoid splitting the series. It is possible that a more complicated limit, varying with the texture, would have been better, but the data to draft and test such a definition were too few.

One intent of the definition of the mollic epipedon was to provide a differentia to distinguish the soils that have traditionally been used to produce grain, from those that are too dry to cultivate without irrigation. If this can be done by the presence or absence of a mollic epipedon in arid and semi-arid regions, the classification of the soils in the field can be more consistent. It is impossible to determine the moisture regimes of each mapping unit in the field if the differences are very small.

(4) *Question.* There is a limit of 35 percent clay between loamy and clayey particle-size classes, and of 18 percent clay between fine-loamy and coarse-loamy and between fine- and coarse-silty. Didn't these limits, not previously recognized in the textural triangle, split a great many series? Why were they introduced?

Answer. Soil surveys are being used increasingly to reduce soil testing by engineers. For engineering interpretations, the recognition of non-plastic soil is very important. While there is no exact limit in terms of percentage of clay between plastic and non-plastic soil, the limit of 18 percent clay sorts out the important differences. A considerable body of data was available on the engineering classifications and percentages of clay. The data showed clearly the importance of a limit, near 18 percent.

Many series, by their definitions, had an argillic horizon with a texture of silty clay loam or of clay loam. A comparison of the estimated texture and the measured clay of samples submitted for laboratory analyses showed that plasticity was commonly being used by field workers to estimate textural classes. Silty clay loam textures were commonly described for samples that had only 20 percent clay, not 27 percent or more. The change disturbed some series definitions but made them more descriptive of the soils as they had been mapped.

The choice of the limit of 35 percent clay between loamy and clayey particle-size classes was more difficult. Some series had limits of 35 percent clay while others had 40 percent. Regressions between the engineering classifications and clay percentages seemed to show a small advantage for the 35 percent limit for all soils as a group and for each individual order. The advantage was not large, but the use of the same limit for all families seemed important.

(5) *Question*. Salinity is very important to interpretations but is rarely used in definitions of taxa. Why?

Answer. Salinity *is* an important property and is not difficult to measure, even in the field. Interpretations cannot be made for many uses without considering it. Under irrigation, salinity can vary from season to season and from year to year in the same soil, depending on the amount and quality of the irrigation water used. Non-saline soils can become salty and saline soils can be reclaimed. The salinity had been shown by phases in the soil surveys and did not enter into series definitions. Use of salinity in definitions of taxa would have resulted in wholesale splitting of series that are commonly irrigated.

(6) *Question*. Why must an oxic horizon have 15 percent or more clay as well as a sandy loam or finer texture?

Answer. This limit is one that could not be tested in the United States. The Oxisols in the United States have clayey oxic horizons, but it was known from the literature that the Oxisols grade into Quartz ipsamments. No soils of the United States were known to approach this limit. It was thought that the amounts of silt in soils near this limit would be very small and could be disregarded. The proposed limit was never criticized. An intergrade between Oxic Quartzipsamments and Psammentic Oxisols might have 5 percent silt and 13 percent clay. By the present definitions, it would have to be classified as an Orthent, and its relations to the other taxa would be concealed. The limit of 15 percent clay of the oxic horizon must either be reduced to allow for small amounts of silt or be dropped from the definition. It is now known that such soils exist in Venezuela, and they may be presumed to exist elsewhere.

GENETIC IMPLICATIONS OF SOIL TAXONOMY

Soil Taxonomy assumes that many processes go on in any soil (Simonson, 1959) and the horizons that are formed as a result of soil genesis reflect their relative strengths, at least some of which tend to offset others. If a given set of processes has been dominant for a significant time, they will have left their marks in the soil in the form of distinctive horizons or features of horizons. These horizons or features can be defined in terms of measurable or observable properties though the definitions may be more difficult to apply than the features are to recognize in the field, just as there is no problem in recognizing a dog or a cat at a glance. Nevertheless, if the definitions are properly written and carefully applied, competent pedologists should arrive at the same classification of a given soil, even though they hold widely divergent opinions about genetic processes. This was one of the objectives of Soil Taxonomy (Smith, 1963), necessitated by the large number and diversity of training of the men making soil surveys in the United States.

The genesis per se, cannot be used to define taxa and meet this objective. The processes that go on can rarely be observed or measured. They vary with the season and with the year. They change if the climate changes or as the result of new cycles of landscape dissection. They leave their marks in the soil, but the marks may persist long after the processes that produced them have ceased to act. Thus, mottles in the lower soil horizons may be the marks of groundwater that is currently present at some season, or of ground water that disappeared some tens of hundreds or thousands of years ago.

The marks are always the result of processes that existed in a past which may be recent or distant. The genesis of most soils must therefore be inferred. It happened in the past. Beliefs about it differ between individuals with varying experiences and change with new knowledge.

Nevertheless, the genesis of soils is extremely important both to the taxonomy of soils and to the mapping in the field. Genesis is important to the classification partly because it produces the observable or measurable differences that can be used as differentiae. These normally have some known accessory properties and probably have others that are important but are still unknown. The known properties are too numerous to be used as differentiae except in the lowest category. Only a few can be used in the higher categories, but their accessory properties make some general interpretations possible for most of the orders and suborders.

The genesis is also important to accurate and efficient mapping. The mapper uses his knowledge of genesis to extend his very limited sampling observations to the whole landscape. He knows that he can expect the soils to differ where one of the soil-forming factors differs.

Genesis does not appear in the definitions of the taxa but lies behind them. It was the intent to keep the soils of similar genesis in the same taxa to the maximum extent possible by using properties that either result from or control soil genesis. Obviously, in the order category, with only ten classes for all soils, the similarities in some orders are either very general or do not exist. In the series category the similarities can be as close as knowledge permits. The use as differentiae of diagnostic horizons that are the result of soil genesis brings the genesis indirectly into the definitions of the taxa, even though the processes that produced the horizons are unknown. Some diagnostic horizons such as the silica-cemented duripan can be formed in the presence of other widely differing sets of processes. It was thought that if the other processes differed greatly, their effects would be reflected by the presence of other diagnostic horizons or features. Thus, some duripans overlie a spodic horizon. Others underlie an argillic horizon. The genesis of the duripan in such different soils probably is not the same, but the associated differentiae keep the soils separated in the taxonomy.

If soils of unlike genesis were grouped in one category, an attempt was made to distinguish them in the next lower category. The Aridisols may be used as an example. They were grouped in the order by their dryness and its effects. They were dry too much of the time to support vegetation other than xerophytic plants and ephemeral grasses and herbs. Any water that entered the surface horizons would be completely exhausted by evapotranspiration. Additions of organic matter were too small to produce a mollic epipedon. There was also the added pragmatic reason that they require irrigation for cultivated crops. But some Aridisols are ancient soils in the sense that they have been stable soils, without erosion, since early Pleistocene time. Others are in Holocene deposits. The soils of the more stable surfaces seemed mostly to have an argillic horizon, having gone through one or more glacial and interglacial pluvial and dry periods. They were soils that at some time had undergone leaching of carbonates and more soluble salts, and they were grouped as the suborder of Argids, Aridisols that have an argillic or natric horizon. However, some of the Argids that have a natric horizon seemed never to have lost their primary carbonates. They were of Holocene age. At the great group level, they were distinguished from the other Argids as Natrargids. The Argids on late Pleistocene and early Holocene surfaces were grouped as Haplargids, and the oldest Argids were grouped as Paleargids. Amongst the Paleargids, there were soils that have a thick petrocalcic horizon and others that are non-calcareous throughout; these were distinguished as subgroups of Paleargids.

Most of the important genetic differences were thought to have been sorted out as taxa in the subgroup category or a higher one. Some Spodsol subgroups include soils that have a cemented spodic horizon along with others that do not. The genetic reasons for the differences that exist were not clear, so they were distinguished in the family category. It is possible that they will be distinguished at a higher categoric level in the future when the genesis of the cemented spodic horizons is better understood.

The order of Entisols may also be used as an example of distinctions among soils whose genesis is minimal. Entisols have few or no diagnostic horizons, but the reasons differ. Some consist of very recent alluvium. Some have undergone too rapid erosion for horizons to form. Some consist of quartz sand in which few horizons can form. Some have been so deeply disturbed that all the horizons have been mixed but fragments remain. The suborders of Entisols represent an attempt to sort the soils according to the reasons for their lack of horizons. The sorting into the five suborders of Entisols was inadequate to distinguish all of the major genetic differences. Some Psamments consist of very recent eolian sand with many weatherable minerals. Others are ancient sands consisting almost entirely of quartz. At the great group category, the quartz sands were grouped as Quartz-ipsamments. Here, the sorting partly stopped. Although some Quartzipsamments are very recent deposits of quartz sand and some are very old, no practical reason or method for their separation could be found if the sand was uncoated. If the sand had thin coatings of clay, distinctions continued to the lower categories between the young and the old sand deposits using the nature of the clay as the differentia, not the age.

The reason emphasis was given to diagnostic properties produced by soil genesis or affecting genesis was that these would have the greatest number of accessory properties. The aim of Soil Taxonomy was to devise taxa about which the largest number of important statements could be made. The statements that were important to the purposes of the soil survey were interpretations about the use and management of the soils, not about their genesis. A classification intended to reflect genesis alone could be very different from Soil Taxonomy. Knowledge about soil genesis lags far behind knowledge and experience with soil behavior. Soil Taxonomy was developed in response to the pressing practical problems of the soil survey with its publications and the needs for interpretations by its users.

The definitions of Soil Taxonomy focus attention on the particular diagnostic horizons and features that were selected. There is danger that this will detract attention from their accessory properties or from other properties, still undefined. If two soils arrive at the same combination of diagnostic properties through different genetic routes, differences normally exist between them but can easily be overlooked. We all tend to see what we have been trained to see. Even the obvious can be overlooked until someone points it out to us. Because of the bias against properties that were not selected for use as differentiae, the definitions must be continually tested by the functioning of the soils grouped in a taxon. Taxonomy is not simply a process of applying definitions; it requires some thought about the objects that are grouped. Does the grouping that results permit the greatest number of the most important statements for the purposes of the classification about the objects that are grouped? This is the central problem of taxonomy. For Soil Taxonomy, these statements concern the interpretations about responses to use and management. Genesis plays its role indirectly.

An example may help the understanding of the situation. The Postpodzols of Belgium (Tavernier and Ameryckx, 1957) are sandy soils that are believed to have been Spodosols, formed under heath. Under cultivation for flax, with fertilization which included applications of lime and manure, the spodic horizon was destroyed more or less completely by biologic oxidation of its organic fraction. Where little or no iron was present, only the aluminum of the spodic horizon could remain. But aluminum has no color and cannot be seen in the field. Its presence as an illuvial horizon has not been used in any definition. Where iron was present, it was concentrated in concretions or mottles whose presence likewise has not been used in any definition. Therefore, the Postpodzol is a *Udipsamment by definition* if the epipedon is ochric.

Very similar sands of the same age and mineralogy that never supported heath and never had a spodic horizon are not distinguished by the definitions of Soil Taxonomy, even at the family level. If important different statements must be made about the Postpodzols and the other Udipsamments, the definitions would be faulty, and the two kinds of soil would need to be distinguished by adding a new diagnostic property, possibly that of the illuvial aluminium or the traces of iron that remain. Such a definition might be difficult to apply in the field, but ways could be devised for its application. If the statements we can make about the two kinds of soil are identical, no harm is done by grouping them.

The concept of the Postpodzol's genesis is very important because of its implications about the long-time effects of cultivation on the spodic horizon. Nevertheless, for the purposes of the soil survey nothing is gained by the delineation of the areas where the spodic horizon has been completely destroyed unless different statements can be made. If they are delineated, nothing is lost except the time required. If this is small, the areas should be distinguished at the series level because new knowledge may later require new statements that are different. After the Postpodzols had been distinguished from other kinds of sands, it was learned that differences exist in problems with potato scab (R. Tavernier, pers. commun.).

USE OF SOIL TAXONOMY

Reporting research results

The taxa of Soil Taxonomy are used increasingly to report results in many countries. Thus, one of the original objectives of transferring research results from other countries to the United States is being reached. It was for this purpose that a system of classification that could be applied to all soils was devised. Not only studies of soil genesis but, more importantly, studies of soil management are being reported in terms of taxa ranging in category from order to family.

Soil surveys in other countries

The importance of soil surveys is recognized in the ministries of most of the older countries and in many new countries. The recognition in many countries of the importance of large-scale soil surveys for advisory work and for town and country planning began about the end of World War II. The interest of ministries of the newer countries in small-scale soil suveys began soon after independence.

Soil surveys at any scale are expensive and, in one way or another, are supported by the funds of national governments, commonly with help from technical assistance programs of international agencies. The governments are concerned with the use of their own natural resources, so each national soil survey has the limited objective of classifying the soils of a single country. One exception is the Food and Agriculture Organization of the United Nations which has supported large-scale soil surveys for specific development projects in a number of countries. Each national soil survey requires a classification and had devised one or more for the kinds of soil in its own country. Thus, many classifications exist.

Generally, those countries that had developed a national classification before the publication of the 7th Approximation have retained them. Some have been modified, as must all classifications, and have adopted some of the innovations of the 7th Approximation.

The new countries generally have not devised new classifications but have adapted one or another taxonomy to fit their particular needs. Soil Taxonomy, with its many specific limits between taxa, is a relatively sophisticated system that requires considerable laboratory and field data for application. New national soil surveys that have just started have inadequate data for the classification of many soils. There is little collected information about the response to use of the various kinds of soil. Few interpretations are possible except on a qualitative basis.

The series category permits the greatest number and most quantitative interpretations. The experience in the United States suggests that this category is too refined for newly started soil surveys. Not only were most of the early soil types in the United States given series status during the first thirty years of the soil survey, but these series were divided and subdivided a number of times. New knowledge in the fields of soil genesis, soil chemistry, soil fertility and soil physics required the splitting of the older series if reasonably quantitative interpretations were to be made. With continued research in these fields, the splitting of the present series can be expected to continue.

The family category is probably the lowest practical category for large-scale soil surveys that are being made in countries where soil surveys are new. The categoric level appropriate to small-scale soil maps depends both on the scale and the pattern of soil variability. If the latter differs greatly within the area being mapped, the maps can carry the maximum information only if the legend units are defined in terms of more than one category. The generalized soil map of the United States (Soil Survey Staff, 1975, p. 412) is an example of a very small scale map that uses associations of phases of suborders, great groups and subgroups in the legend, depending on the soil pattern.

The quantitative limits between the taxa of Soil Taxonomy have complicated its use. It is much easier to measure the color of a soil horizon than to determine the activity of the clay or the base saturation. Since the properties of the exchange complex are of major importance to the use of a soil for growing plants, maps that do not reflect those properties have limited use.

The important properties should be known generally *when* the legend is being developed for a soil survey of a specific area. This requires knowledge of a number of chemical and mineralogical properties, most of which can now be measured in a pit using portable equipment that can readily be carried by hand. Just as pH meters using a glass electrode have been miniaturized, so has the equipment for chemical determinations. Salinity problems, gypsum, lime, base saturation, permanent and buffered cation exchange capacities, bases and aluminum can all be determined in the soil pit with reliability that approaches that of the laboratory. These are properties that should be known when constructing a legend, and the measurements made in the field are more useful than those made in the laboratory. Results are immediately available. Unexpected results can be checked at once to determine the variability between samples. Measurements that require time, such as that of COLE, can be made roughly at a local field headquarters. Lack of data should not hamper the use of Soil Taxonomy. Rather, it should motivate the collection of the data needed to construct a soil map that can be used for the purposes intended.

REFERENCES

Ableiter, J.K., 1949a. Trends in soil classification and correlation at the series level. Soil Sci. Soc. Am. Proc., 14: 320—322.
Ableiter, J.K., 1949b. Soil classification in the United States. Soil Sci., 67: 183—191.
Baldwin, M., Kellogg, C.E. and Thorp, J. 1938. Soil Classification. Soils and Men, U.S. Dept. Agric. Yearbook, U.S. Govt. Printing Office, Washington, D.C., pp. 979—1001.
Bushnell, T.M., 1945. The catena caldron. Soil Sci. Soc. Am. Proc., 10: 335—340.
Cline, A.J. and Johnson, D.D., 1963. Threads of genesis in the seventh approximation. Soil Sci. Soc. Am. Proc., 27: 220—222.
Cline, M.G., 1949. Basic principles of soil classification. Soil Sci., 67: 81—91.
Cline, M.G., 1963. Logic of the new system of soil classification. Soil Sci., 96: 17—22.
Coffey, G.N., 1912. A Study of the Soils of the United States. Bull. 85, Bur. of Soils, U.S. Dept. Agric. Washington, D.C., 114 pp.
Glinka, K.D., 1914. Die Typen der Bodenbildung, ihre Klassifikation und geographische Verbreitung. Borntraeger, Berlin, 582 pp.
Glinka, K.D., 1931. Pochvovedenie, Moskva — Leningrad (Transl., Treatise on Soil Science, Publ. for the National Science Foundation, Washington, D.C., by the Israel Program for Scientific Translations, Jerusalem, 1963), 674 pp.
Heller, J.L., 1963. The nomenclature of soils, or what's in a name. Soil Sci. Soc. Am. Proc., 27: 216—220.
Johnson, W.M., 1963. The pedon and the polypedon. Soil Sci. Soc. Am. Proc., 27: 212—215.
Kellogg, C.E., 1937. Soil Survey Manual. U.S. Dept. Agric., Misc. Publ., 274, 135 pp.
Kellogg, C.E., 1960. Foreword. Soil Classification, a Comprehensive System 7th Approximation. Soil Conserv. Serv., U.S. Dept. Agric., U.S. Govt. Printing Office, Washington, D.C., p. iv.

Kellogg, C.E., 1974. Soil genesis, classification, and cartography, 1924—1974. Geoderma, 12: 347—362.

Marbut, C.F., 1921. The contribution of soil surveys to soil science. Soc. Promot. Agric. Sci. Proc., 41: 116—142.

Marbut, C.F., 1928. A scheme for soil classification. IV. Proc. 1st Int. Congress Soil Sci., IV: 1—31.

Marbut, C.F., 1935. Soils of the United States, Part III. In: Atlas of American Agriculture. U.S. Dept. Agric., pp. 1—98.

Marbut, C.F., Bennett, H.H., Lapham, J.E. and Lapham, M.H., 1913. Soils of the United States. U.S. Bur. Soils Bull., 96: 1—791.

Riecken, F.F., 1945. Selection of criteria for the classification of certain soil types of Iowa into great soil groups. Soil Sci. Soc. Am. Proc., 10: 319—325.

Riecken, F.F. and Smith, G.D., 1949. Lower categories of soil classification: family, series, type and phase. Soil Sci., 67: 107—115.

Roberts, R.C., 1942. Soil Survey of Puerto Rico. USDA Printing Office, Washington, D.C., Ser. 1936, 8, 503 pp.

Simonson, R.W., 1959. Outline of a generalised theory of soil genesis. Soil Sci. Soc. Am. Proc., 23: 152—156.

Simonson, R.W., 1964. The soil series as used in the U.S.A. Trans. 8th Int. Congress Soil Sci., 5: 17—24.

Smith, G.D., 1963. Objectives and basic assumptions of the new soil classification system. Soil Sci., 96: 6—16.

Smith, G.D., 1965. Lectures on soil classification. Pedologie, 4: 1—134.

Soil Survey Staff, 1951. Soil Survey Manual. U.S. Dept. Agric., Handbook. 18, U.S. Govt. Printing Office, Washington, D.C., 503 pp.

Soil Survey Staff, 1960. Soil Classification, a Comprehensive System, 7th approximation. Soil Conserv. Serv., U.S. Dept. Agric., U.S. Govt. Printing Office, Washington, D.C., 265 pp.

Soil Survey Staff, 1975. Soil Taxonomy, a Basic System of Soil Classification for Making and Interpreting Soil Surveys. Soil Conserv. Serv., U.S. Dept. Agric. Handbook, 436. U.S. Govt. Printing Office, Washington, D.C., 754 pp.

Tavernier, R. and Ameryckx, J., 1957. Le postpodzol en Flandre sablonneuse. Pedologie, VII: 89—96.

Thorp, J. and Smith, G.D., 1949. Higher cateogories of soil classification. Soil Sci., 67: 117—126.

DYNAMICS AND GENETIC MODELLING OF SOIL SYSTEMS

NEIL E. SMECK, E.C.A. RUNGE and E.E. MACKINTOSH

DYNAMICS

Dynamic nature of soils

Soils comprise a dynamic system, constantly perturbated by internal and external forces. The distinction between internal and external perturbations is dependent upon the boundaries which are imposed on the system being considered. Arnold (Chapter 1) discusses natural boundaries which have been applied to units considered to represent a soil. Landscapes, catena, poly-pedon, pedon, profile, horizon, ped and sample are all terms which represent a hierarchy of soil systems with appropriately defined boundaries. Dijkerman (1974) has described a hierarchy of soil systems at increasingly lower levels of organization of pedological research which has been developed further in Table 3.1. All systems are composed of subsystems of a lower order and also form part of a larger supersystem. It is necessary to develop and test theories and hypotheses for the various levels of the system in terms of the laws of the system at that level (Anderson, 1972). Properties important in describing one level of a system may become quite irrelevant at successively higher or lower levels. The hierarchical level and associated boundaries chosen to define a soil system are dependent on the scope of the problem being investigated. Unless otherwise specified, the soil system considered in this chapter will essentially correspond to a "pedon" as defined in Soil Taxonomy (Soil Survey Staff, 1975).

Even though pedologists may view soils as dynamic systems, man, in general, perceives soil to be one of the more stable components of our environment. The distinction between these divergent viewpoints involves either the time frame in which soils are considered or the detail involved in observation. From a morphological viewpoint, most soils change very little, if undisturbed by man, during a lifetime. Conversely, the composition of the soil solution is constantly changing in response to nutrient uptake, weathering, adsorption—desorption reactions, leaching, or changes in moisture content of the soil.

Dynamics is more appropriate than statics in soil systems because of implied processes or driving forces. Since dynamics implies change, such concepts help separate cause from effect in soils. Morphological properties of

TABLE 3.1

A hierarchy of soil systems for modelling soil development (modified after Dijkerman, 1974)

Level	System	Definition
1	Pedological province	Part of a region, isolated and defined by its climate and topography and characterized by a particular group of soils.
2	Compound landscape unit	An area whose spatial distribution corresponds to a natural watershed or subwatershed and contains 1st to nth order streams.
3	Simple landscape unit	A regular repetition of a sequence of soils in association with a certain topography (Milne, 1935).
4	Pedon/polypedon	Pedon is the smallest, three-dimensional unit at the surface of the earth that can be considered a soil. A polypedon is a contiguous group of similar pedons (Soil Survey Staff, 1975).
5	Soil horizons	A layer of mineral or organic soil material approximately parallel to the land surface that has characteristics formed by pedogenetic processes (Canada Soil Survey Comm., 1978).
6	Peds (macrostructural units)	Natural soil aggregates consisting of a cluster of primary particles and separated from adjoining peds by surfaces of weakness which are recognizable as natural voids or by the occurrence of cutans.
7	Microstructural units	Includes micromorphological features, aggregate and microaggregate features (<5 mm), sand and silt particles and domains.
8	Physical phases	Mineral, gaseous or aqueous phases.

soils develop as a result of processes acting on parent materials; however, only a few processes are likely to be dominant at any one time. An understanding of the relative importance of various processes will yield a more accurate prediction of man's influence on soil through management practices. Management input into soils must be consistent with anticipated results even though evaluation might take place only over long time intervals (generations). Understanding soils is clearer and man's impact on soils is more predictable if an appreciation of energy fluxes or processes is part of our thought process.

Thermodynamics

In order to identify stable states of natural systems and understand how energy affects natural systems, a knowledge of the fundamental laws of thermodynamics is necessary. A brief review of the pertinent laws will be given so that these laws can be used to better understand soil systems. At this point, it needs to be mentioned that the following discussion of thermodynamics is applicable only to closed[1] systems. Thermodynamic concepts will be related to open systems in the next section on fluxes of the soil system.

The First Law of Thermodynamics concerns the conservation of energy. A general statement of the law is that energy can neither be created nor destroyed. A mathematical expression of the First Law follows:

$$\Delta E = \Delta q + \Delta w$$

This equation states that the change in internal energy (ΔE) of a closed system is equal to the sum of the heat flux (Δq) and work inputs or outputs (Δw). The internal energy of a system exists in many forms such as mechanical, kinetic, thermal, chemical, electrical, or matter. Irreversible processes result in the spontaneous conversion of internal energy to heat and work so that at equilibrium, a state of minimum internal energy is attained. This is an important point which will be returned to shortly.

In systems where no work is done other than pressure—volume ($P\Delta V$) work, such as in most naturally occurring chemical reactions, another term can be conveniently introduced. This term, enthalpy (H), can be thought of as an indicator of relative heat contents and is defined as:

$$H = E + PV$$

By convention, an enthalpy value of zero is assigned to elements in their stable states under standard conditions (25°C and 1 atm pressure). The heat of formation (relative enthalpy level) for many compounds and ions has been determined calorimetrically by measuring the heat of the reactions by which the compounds or ions are formed from their elements in their standard states. Heats of formation (ΔH°_f) for many compounds and minerals have been compiled by Garrels and Christ (1965) and in most physical chemistry texts. The standard heat of any reaction at 25°C (ΔH°_r) is equal to the difference between the standard heats of formation of the products and the reactants:

$$\Delta H^{\circ}_r = \Sigma \Delta H^{\circ}_f \text{ products} - \Sigma \Delta H^{\circ}_f \text{ reactants}$$

Reactions in which heat is evolved (exothermic) have a negative ΔH whereas reactions which absorb heat (endothermic) have a positive ΔH.

A general statement of the Second Law of Thermodynamics is that all

---

[1] In this chapter, the definitions of Prigogine (1961) will be used to distinguish between isolated, closed and open systems. Isolated systems can exchange neither energy nor matter through their boundaries, closed systems can exchange energy but not matter, and open systems can exchange both energy and matter with the exterior.

isolated systems will spontaneously approach a state of equilibrium. Consideration of the First Law revealed that processes occur spontaneously if energy, in the form of work or heat, is released in the process; however, some processes are known to occur spontaneously without moving toward a state of minimum energy. A commonly cited example is the dissipation of a concentration gradient as a function of time. Such spontaneous processes are attributed to the thermal motion of particles which tends to increase the randomness or disorder of systems. In order to quantify the Second Law, another term, entropy (S), needs to be introduced. Entropy increases as randomness or disorder in a system increases. For a reversible (equilibrium) process in an isolated system, $\Delta S = 0$, whereas for an irreversible (spontaneous) process in an isolated system, $\Delta S > 0$. In effect, the entropy (disorder) of an isolated system always increases during an irreversible process and attains a maximum value at equilibrium. The concept of entropy implies that any process which results in an entropy increase will be subject to spontaneous occurrence. Thus in an isolated system, entropy can never decrease and entails the irreversibility of nature and the never-ending march toward universal equilibrium. Since the only completely isolated system which occurs naturally is the entire universe, entropy has been equated with time's arrow. This latter phrase refers to entropy as an indicator of the relative degree of universal energy dissipation. As entropy tends toward a maximum, ultimately everything in the universe will become completely random. In regard to soil systems, this implies that all minerals will be destroyed, temperature and concentration gradients will be non-existent, and landscapes will not only be completely leveled but will be non-distinguishable due to the lack of any interface between earth, water and air. All processes will cease as all energy will have been dissipated to space and universal equilibrium will have been attained.

From the preceding discussion, two driving forces emerge for all processes. Systems will spontaneously approach a state of equilibrium by tending toward minimum energy or maximum entropy. However, due to the boundary constraints of closed systems, only in cases where energy is constant can entropy achieve a maximum and only where entropy is held constant can energy achieve a minimum. Thus another function is necessary to define equilibrium when a compromise is reached between the drive toward maximum entropy and minimum energy. At constant temperature (T) and pressure, free energy (G) serves this purpose and is defined as:

$$\Delta G = \Delta H - T\Delta S$$

From this equation, it is apparent that entropy increases and enthalpy decreases will result in a negative free-energy change. Reactions occur spontaneously until free energy attains a minimum; at equilibrium, $\Delta G = 0$. Thus a reaction with a negative ΔG will occur spontaneously in moving the system toward equilibrium and a state of minimum free energy.

As with ΔH values, ΔG values are relative with the most stable state of an element at standard temperature and pressure being assigned a value of zero. The standard free energy of formation of a compound or ion is equal to the free energy required or released during formation of one mole of compound or ion from its stable elements under conditions of standard temperature and pressure. Standard free energies for most compounds and ions are readily available. One of the first attempts to calculate free-energy values for some common minerals in natural geologic systems was by Garrels (1957). Since then, free-energy values for many naturally occurring oxides and silicates have been determined. Robie and Waldbaum (1968) present one of the most complete compilations of such thermochemical data. Using known free energies and the following two equations:

$$\Delta G_r = \Sigma \Delta G_f \text{ products} - \Sigma \Delta G_f \text{ reactants}$$

$$\Delta G_r = -RT \ln K$$

where R is the gas constant and K is the equilibrium constant, stability diagrams can be constructed for many naturally occurring mineral suites. Since both Garrels and Christ (1965) and Kittrick (1977) present excellent discussions on the construction of such diagrams, the details will not be given here.

Thermodynamic stability diagrams can be used to predict: (1) mineral stabilities; (2) mineralogical components which will occur at equilibrium; (3) changes in the composition of solutions and mineralogical suites; and (4) the direction in which reactions will spontaneously move. Although much information concerning mineralogical systems in soils can be readily gained from stability diagrams, several limitations need to be pointed out. Kittrick (1977) points out that there is a lack of reliable basic thermochemical information for many minerals and ionic species which are common constituents of soils. Aluminum species in soils are cited as an example. Not only are the free energies for many of the polynuclear hydroxy aluminum species unknown, but even the ΔG value for Al^{3+} is uncertain. The reliability of ΔG values is also complicated by the variable chemical compositions of many naturally occurring minerals, such as the smectites and chlorites, which result in variable free energies. These problems lead to low quality or, in some cases, even erroneous thermochemical data for many minerals of interest in soils (Kittrick, 1977). Another problem concerns the collection of reliable data for micro-environments surrounding mineral grains. The micro-environments with which mineral grains tend to equilibrate are certainly not the same as the macro-environments of soils. A third problem is our ability to handle only a limited number of components and a narrow solution composition which may limit applicability to multicomponent, natural mineralogical systems. Nevertheless, Kittrick (1967) suggests simple mineral mixtures can be expected to approach equilibria predicted by the stabilities of individual minerals. Whereas stability diagrams illustrate relationships at equilibrium, still another problem concerns the attainment of equilibrium in natural mineralogical systems in soils. Although Kittrick (1977) reviews some work which suggests that soil minerals may attain equilibrium with soil solution, he concludes that it is doubtful if equilibrium is commonly achieved between all soil minerals and the surrounding solution (equilibrium in soil systems will be addressed in more detail later in this chapter). Still, Kittrick (1967) points out that equilibrium relationships for essentially non-equilibrium soil mineral mixtures will predict the condition toward which mineralogical systems in soils will alter. So in spite of the problems, the thermodynamic approach to understanding soil mineralogical systems has tremendous potential.

Fluxes of the soil system

In the preceding section, it was shown that all closed systems will move toward a state of minimum free energy (maximum entropy and/or minimum energy) and the application of these concepts to soil mineralogical systems was discussed. Whereas classical thermodynamics, discussed above, applies only to closed systems and to equilibrium conditions generally obtainable only in a laboratory, most natural systems are, in fact, open systems. Denbigh (1951), Prigogine (1961) and Tykodi (1967) have all adapted classical thermodynamics to open systems. The thermodynamics of open systems is generally referred to as non-equilibrium thermodynamics, thermodynamics of steady states, or thermodynamics of irreversible processes. Pertinent points from these works will be discussed since open systems appropriately describe soil systems at high levels of abstraction.

From a statistical viewpoint, the concept of entropy can be equated with a measure of randomness or disorder of a system. As entropy increases, disorder of systems also increases. Thus the drive toward maximum entropy implies a tendency toward system disorder. However, it has been recognized that living systems represent both an energetic and configurational improbability since living systems are highly ordered and energy-rich (Morowitz, 1971). This is only possible by the import of energy and matter into the system. The same reasoning can be applied to soil development. The ordering of parent materials into pedons by horizonation is due to fluxes of energy and matter and conceptually leads to a decrease in entropy. Thus it would seem that biological and soil systems do not obey the Second Law of Thermodynamics. But it must be remembered that the Second Law is only applicable to isolated systems; in order to apply the Second Law to open systems, the system's surroundings must be considered as well as the system itself. Accordingly, Prigogine (1961) indicates that the total change in entropy of open systems can be written as:

$$\Delta S = \Delta S_e + \Delta S_i$$

ΔS_e denotes the change of entropy due to interactions with the surroundings and ΔS_i denotes the production of entropy due to irreversible processes within the system. Whereas the term ΔS_i is always positive, ΔS_e may be either negative or positive. Therefore depending on the magnitude of ΔS_e, the total entropy change in an open system can be negative as well as positive.

For biological and soil systems (pedons) which both represent more ordered states than their precursors, entropy will decrease as a result of cell and profile development, respectively. Thus in accordance with the Second Law, entropy of the surroundings must increase. In effect, entropy flows from such open systems to the surroundings. Processes which lead to ordering and/or high potential energy levels in open systems are driven by energy flow into the system or by the degradation of matter entering the system. Whereas the Second Law defines a universal drive toward complete randomness, there can be local ordering of open systems such as pedons due to entropy flow to the surroundings.

With this information in mind, the concept of soil-profile development as an energy-consuming process with an accompanying flow of entropy to the external environment will be explored. In Table 3.2, the relative contribution of generalized soil-forming processes is related to each of the ten soil orders of Soil Taxonomy (Soil Survey Staff, 1975). The soil-forming processes listed encompass many specific processes and, as such, the importance of each to the development of soils in each order is speculative. Specific processes which belong to one of the generalized groupings in Table 3.2 may affect soil systems quite differently. For example, the formation of secondary minerals is taken to include the formation of secondary oxides which is important in Spodosols as well as the precipitation of soluble salts, common in Aridisols; nevertheless, the importance of secondary mineral formation in both soils is interpreted to be similar even though the processes involved are quite different.

The change in entropy (ΔS) of soil systems due to the various soil-forming processes listed in Table 3.2 is assigned a positive or negative value by conceptually evaluating the change in randomness or disorder in the soil as affected by the soil-forming processes. Physical mixing, due to shrink-swell pressures, biological activities, colluviation or other processes, increases the spatial randomness of soil components and consequently is assigned a positive ΔS. Whereas mineral weathering involves the breaking of chemical bonds, resulting in the release of bond energy and an increase in disorder and ΔS, the formation of secondary minerals has just the opposite effects. Eluviation—illuviation refers to the preferential removal of constituents such as clays, organic chelates and oxides from one zone and their subsequent accumulation in another zone within the profile. Since these processes tend to sort soil constituents, eluviation—illuviation increases order within soil and must be assigned a negative ΔS. Ordering associated with organic matter accumulation will decrease entropy. Since leaching preferentially removes soluble components from soil, it will increase order by concentrating the

58

TABLE 3.2

Relative entropy changes as a function of the contribution of selected soil-forming processes to the development of the 10 taxonomic soil orders

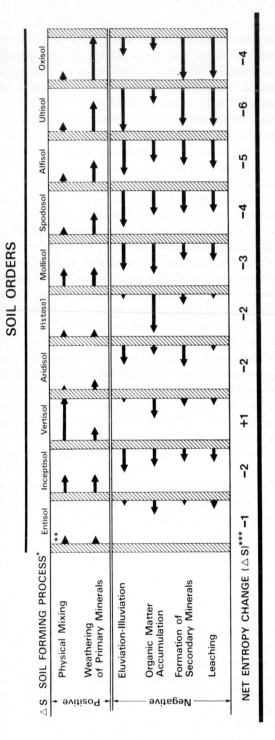

* The processes selected are of necessity very general but may not be comprehensive and are not necessarily mutually exclusive. The processes are intended to account for major changes accompanying profile development.

** The length of the arrows is directly proportional to the importance of the various processes in each order.

*** An indication of the net entropy change as a result of all soil forming processes active in the development of each order (the numbers provided simply indicate a relative ranking of entropy changes accompanying pedogenesis).

soluble components in the leachate and insoluble components in the soil. Considered thusly, leaching will decrease entropy. However, it could be argued that once the leachate leaves the solum, the homogeneity (randomness) of the leached soil has increased due to removal or partial removal of the soluble components. For the purposes of Table 3.2, the former hypothesis is accepted and leaching is assigned a negative ΔS.

A net entropy change for soils in each order due to pedogenesis is estimated by subjectively summing the individual entropy changes for all processes listed in Table 3.2 which contribute to the development of soils in an individual order. The entropy change for each generalized soil-forming process is weighted by its relative contribution to the formation of soils in each order. It must be kept in mind that the net entropy changes listed in Table 3.2 are dependent upon the relative importance assigned to the various soil-forming processes. In Table 3.2, processes which yield positive entropy changes and those which yield negative entropy changes are considered to be of comparable importance. Since more processes are listed which yield negative entropy changes, the net entropy change for most orders is negative. However, if physical mixing and weathering of primary minerals were much more important in soil development than the other processes listed, the net entropy change for most orders could turn out to be positive. But the relative relationships among the orders could remain the same as that given in Table 3.2. It is the opinion of the authors that the negative entropy changes given in Table 3.2 are conceptually reasonable. Thus it is suggested that pedogenesis results in an entropy decrease for most soils. Only Vertisol formation is interpreted to result in a positive entropy change; the formation of soils in the other orders, such as Spodosol, Alfisol and Ultisol, will yield negative entropy changes due primarily to the development of horizonation. The decrease in entropy which most soil systems incur as a result of pedogenesis must be attributed to the addition of external energy or matter. As discussed previously, entropy always increases in a closed system (spontaneous processes move the system toward equilibrium); however, since soil constitutes an open system, energy and material flow into the system can drive processes which result in negative entropy flow. It then follows that soil formation is basically an energy-consuming process. Although many soil-forming processes such as chemical weathering (hydrolysis, hydration, dissolution and diffusion) can occur spontaneously in the absence of external energy inputs, horizon differentiation is primarily driven by energy and material fluxes.

External energy fluxes which drive soil-forming processes are ultimately derived from either solar radiation or gravity. The effect of radiant energy on pedogenesis will be considered first. The most obvious utilization of radiant energy occurs in photosynthesis wherein vegetative tissue is formed. When vegetation dies, the energy captured in plant tissues is available to soil micro-organisms which are directly responsible for many reactions involved in mineral weathering, particularly oxidation-reduction. Decomposition products of organic materials are important in adsorption and translocation of metallic elements. Of course, the organic materials formed, both plant and microbial, contribute to the accumulation of organic matter in soils. Besides providing energy for photosynthesis, radiant energy is also responsible for biocycling (the upward translocation of elements via plant roots). Upward translocation in plants is due to transpiration. The components incorporated into plant tissues are returned to the soil surface when the plant dies or the leaves fall off, thereby concentrating plant nutrients and accessory compounds such as plant opal at soil surfaces. In many areas, evaporation of water at soil surfaces is just as effective as transpiration in moving soluble materials to soil surfaces. A moisture gradient is established at the soil surface by the evaporation of water by radiant energy; water moves upward by capillarity in response to that gradient, carrying with it all soluble components. The latter are concentrated at the soil surface as the water evaporates. Recently, the absorption of solar energy has been equated with landscape stability. Lanyon and Hall (1982) suggest that above average solar radiation favors landscape stability in southeastern Ohio due to evaporation of excessive soil moisture. The lack of sufficient radiant energy inputs can allow soil temperature to drop and cause freezing of the soil. Alternate freezing and thawing can dramatically alter morphological features of soils. On the other hand, a high incidence of solar radiation in tropical climates enhances pedogenesis due to the high energy supply. This is apparent in some tropical soils by the high degree of weathering and the subsequent concentration of only the most resistant components in sola.

Gravity imparts the other external energy flux to soil systems. Mass movements (colluviation, solifluction, mud flows, slips, etc.) in response to gravitational pull provide some of the most apparent perturbations of soils. Geomorphic influences on soil development are discussed in Chapter 5. Other than mass movement, the most significant effects of gravitational pull on horizon differentiation occur as a result of the downward movement of water through the earth's surface. This does not imply that all moisture movement in soils can be attributed to gravity. At moisture contents less than field capacity, moisture within the soil moves primarily by capillarity (forces of adhesion and cohesion). However, in soils where precipitation exceeds evaporation, there is generally a net movement of moisture down through the solum. Whereas the amount of water available to leach through the soil is conditioned by topographic position and climate, the extent of leaching is determined by internal characteristics such as permeability and the occurrence of water tables or restricting layers. Nevertheless, the downward percolation of water is primarily responsible for translocation of constituents within the soil and removal of constituents from the solum. Translocation of clays and translocation of organic matter and aluminum are responsible for the formation of some of the most distinctive horizons in soils, argillic and spodic horizons, respectively. Leaching of soluble components from sola promotes soil development in nearly all soils. Chemical weathering is enhanced by leaching due to the removal of reaction products from the weathering zone. In summary, the work done on soil systems by water movement responding to the force of gravity is very significant.

It is interesting to note at this point that, for the most part, solar radiation tends to concentrate soil constituents at the soil surface whereas gravity tends to move soluble or suspended soil components further down into or from the solum. As a result of these opposing tendencies, some soil components, such as phosphorus, show a bimodal distribution. In Iowa, phosphorus characteristically shows a concentration at soil surfaces due to the accumulation of organically bound phosphorus, a minimum content from 30 to 100 cm due to eluviation and plant uptake, and a maximum concentration at 100 to 200 cm depth due to illuviation (Runge and Riecken, 1966).

Besides the energy inputs discussed above, soil development is also affected by fluxes of matter across soil-system boundaries. Matter is commonly added to soils by mass movement, wind, and precipitation and lost by erosion, throughflow and volatilization. In this regard, stable upland positions must be selected for study if examinations of soil systems in which fluxes of matter are minimized are desired. However, in order to evaluate what is crossing soil-system boundaries, solutions at the base of sola, debris at the foot of slopes, and/or valley basin discharge must be considered.

In summary, a representation of a soil system illustrating energy and matter fluxes which affect pedogenesis is shown in Fig. 3.1. It is important to note that soil systems experience outfluxes as well as influxes of energy and matter. However, the net balance must favor energy influxes in order to drive soil-forming processes for soil development to proceed.

Equilibrium versus steady state

The terms equilibrium and steady state are often loosely applied to soil systems without rigorous definition. The following discussion will first address the question of the existence of equilibrium in soil systems. *Equilibrium* is a static and time-invariant state of a system ($\Delta G = 0$ and $\Delta S = 0$) where no irreversible processes take place and all macroscopic quantities of the system remain unchanged (Denbigh, 1951). Other criteria for equilibrium are that enthalpy (H) and free energy (G) attain minima and entropy (S) a maximum. However, as indicated earlier, these criteria (and thus equilibrium) are only applicable to isolated systems. Denbigh (1951) indicates that equilibrium does not exist in nature since the only isolated system is the entire universe. In a rigorous thermodynamic sense, equilibrium is not a meaningful concept for an open system such as a pedon. Furthermore it is interesting to note that if one accepts our previously suggested premise that soil formation is an energy-consuming process wherein entropy decreases due to ordering within the system (bounded by the definition of a pedon), soil development results in the system moving away from equilibrium (Fig. 3.2).

Gibbs' phase rule provides an alternate method to evaluate the possibility of equilibrium in soil-mineral systems. Kittrick (1977) applied the phase rule to a hypothetical, but realistic, soil composed of 9 minerals and 10 phases (including the soil solution). According to the phase rule, such a system would be invariant, meaning that the chemical composition of the soil

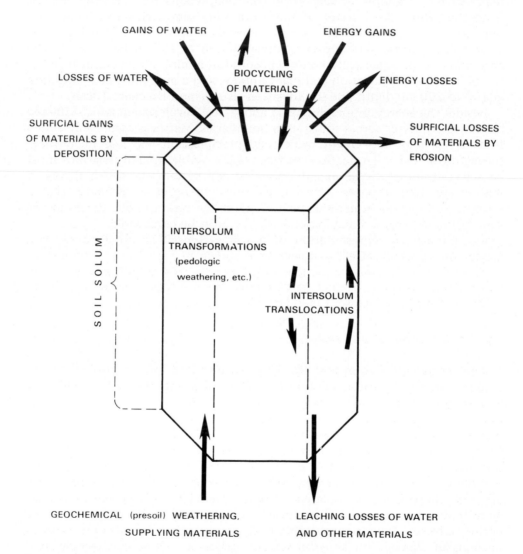

Fig. 3.1. Schematic representation of the solum of a soil pedon as an open system (Reprinted from Buol et al., 1973, with permission of the Iowa State University Press).

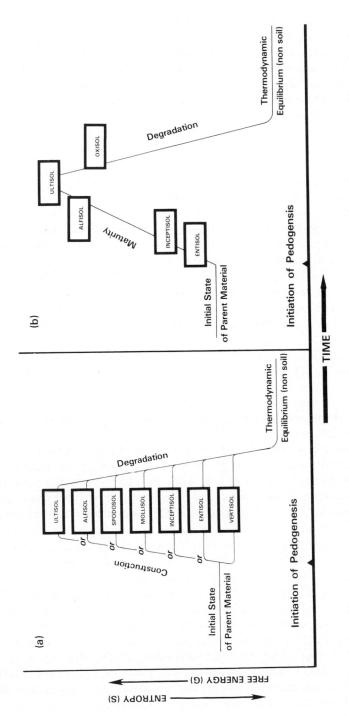

Fig. 3.2. A schematic representation of free-energy and entropy content of soils in selected orders as a function of time: (a) Assumes the existence of steady states; (b) represents the continuous evolution of soils toward equilibrium.

solution could not be changed without changing the number of phases. Since the chemical compositions of soil solutions are not constant, this implies that soil-mineral systems are not at equilibrium. Kittrick (1977) states that "it is likely that all soil minerals are seldom, if ever, simultaneously in equilibrium with the soil solution". However, he does allow that where soil solution has appreciable contact with a mineral, the subsystem composed of the mineral and the surrounding solution appear to attain equilibrium.

After recognizing that soils do not represent equilibrium systems, we will now examine the concept of steady state. Pedological literature contains many references to "equilibria" between soils and their environment or between soil-forming processes and the down-wearing of landscapes (Cline, 1961). Both relationships suggest an interaction between soil bodies and external fluxes which results in essentially a time-invariant condition for the soil; that is, soil properties do not change as a function of time. These observations essentially define a condition of steady state. Denbigh (1951) indicates that at steady state, macroscopic parameters, such as chemical composition, have time-independent values at every point in the system despite the occurrence of dissipative processes. At steady state, all state variables (H, G, S) of the system are independent of time. Whereas equilibrium is appropriate for closed systems, steady state is applicable to open systems such as soils (illustrated by the plateaus in Fig. 3.2a).

The ensuing discussion of steady states in biological systems is adapted from Von Bertalanffy (1950) and Morowitz (1971). It is our working hypothesis that biological systems and soils are similar in that both systems are net importers of energy and matter during constructional stages and only exhibit a net loss of energy following death of the living system or degradation of the soil profile, respectively. Also in both soils and living organisms, there is a drive toward states of higher order and differentiation (loss of entropy) during constructional stages (Fig. 3.2a). During constructional stages, entropy production within the system due to irreversible processes $(\Delta S_i,$ p. 56) is more than compensated for by entropy flow from the system to the surroundings $(\Delta S_e,$ p. 56). Prigogine (1961) has shown that at steady state, entropy production within an open system reaches a minimum which just equals entropy flow from the system. Thus at steady state, entropy as well as all the other state variables of the system become constant (Fig. 3.2a). Maintenance of steady states through negative entropy flow is due to the system receiving more energy than given off or by influx of matter with less entropy than that of the matter given off by the system to the external world. In the latter case, open systems "degrade" matter received in order to maintain the steady state. It should be apparent that entropy levels of the steady state can be less than that of preceding states due to negative entropy flow (Fig. 3.2a). In summary, at steady state, energy and/or matter influx is just sufficient for maintenance of the properties of the soil. In other words, constructional processes just balance degradational processes at steady state (Fig. 3.2a).

As illustrated in Fig. 3.2a, not all steady states of soils occur at similar energy nor entropy levels. The characteristics of a system at steady state is dependent upon the initial state of the system and the fluxes of the system. Generally parent materials subjected to high-energy influxes will attain steady state at a higher free-energy or lower entropy levels than those subjected to low levels of energy influxes. This suggests that soils in humid, warm climates will reach higher levels of organization and potential energy than soils in cooler, more arid areas. Considering only stable landscape positions, soils which are subject to intense leaching will be more highly ordered than soils subject to less intense leaching.

In view of the constantly changing flux of material and energy entering soil systems, the time-invariant state exhibited by soils in steady states needs to be considered. In contrast to isolated systems which move toward a state of maximum entropy (equilibrium), open systems move toward a state of minimum entropy production which is the steady state (Prigogine, 1961). Furthermore, Prigogine (1961) has shown that a system cannot leave a state of minimum entropy production by spontaneous irreversible processes. If a system deviates from the steady state due to changes in external flux, spontaneous internal changes take place which return the system to the steady state. This offers some explanation for the stability of soil systems at steady state despite the variation of external fluxes such as the seasonal variation of solar radiation. An alternate explanation for the invariant nature of soil features is the sluggishness with which some soil features are altered by pedogenic processes. Other soils develop features which limit further change; Yaalon (1971) refers to such features as self-terminating. The most common example of the latter is the formation of an argillic horizon which limits water percolation due to decreased permeability of the Bt horizon which, in turn, retards further leaching and illuviation of clays.

Arguments have been presented against the possibility of steady states in soil systems. Chesworth (1973a, 1976b) indicates that steady states in soil systems can only be ephemeral due to constantly changing external fluxes and thermodynamic gradients. It follows then that the soil system must be in a state of constant adjustment to varying fluxes. However, it can be countered that steady states do not require constant fluxes, only a time-independent state of the system. As stated above, systems at steady state subjected to varying fluxes will undergo irreversible internal adjustments wherein the steady state is maintained. The real arguments, pro and con, for the existence of steady states in soil systems involves the time scale considered and the detail involved in observation of system parameters. On a microscale, small changes in soil properties such as soil solution composition as affected by rainfall variation over time periods of days to months would rule out the existence of steady state. Likewise, when considering a geologic time scale, as Chesworth (1973a, 1976b) does, wherein there are major changes in external fluxes (climatic changes) with corresponding changes in soil properties, the existence of steady states in soils must again be dismissed. However, the time-invariant nature of macroscopic soil properties such as horizonation and morphological properties over periods of a few hundred to thousands of years would support the existence of steady states in soils. Thus it is suggested herein that from a morphological viewpoint and within a pedogenic time-frame, soil systems can represent steady states which are time-invariant with respect to normal fluctuations in environmental conditions.

Nevertheless, it must be acknowledged that not all soils have attained a condition of steady state. Many are, undoubtedly, dynamically approaching steady state. It has been suggested that Alfisols are only an infantile stage of Ultisols (Cline, 1961; Novak et al., 1971). Others suggest that time is the only independent variable of soil formation and that all soils are in a state of continuous evolution (Rode, 1961; Chesworth, 1973b). The occurrence of soils of some orders within a framework of continuous evolution is suggested in Fig. 3.2b. Undoubtedly many soils represent transient states whereas others represent steady states. Inceptisols (Foss et al., 1983) provide classic examples of both situations. Thus steady states and evolution may both play a role in the formation of soils; consequently soil development can best be depicted as a combination of Figs. 3.2a and 3.2b.

Role of kinetics in pedogenesis

As has been previously indicated, the thermodynamic concept of equilibrium is not directly applicable to soil systems. Although classical thermodynamics provide some insight regarding the end-point toward which soil processes are tending, an appreciation of kinetics is essential to understanding soil systems. The field of kinetics is not as well developed as that of thermodynamics. Many factors contribute to the difficulty in dealing with kinetics including the interactions of two or more simultaneous reactions in many processes, the occurrence of impurities and catalysts which can greatly alter reaction rates, and the variation of reaction rates with time. All of these factors affect the kinetics of soil reactions.

Nevertheless, the role of kinetics in soil processes can be readily appreciated. Equilibrium conditions do not exist in soils because they constitute open systems subjected to a continual external flux. Thus the rate at which soil systems adjust to perturbations is very important to our understanding of the systems. As indicated at the beginning of this chapter, the dynamic nature of soil systems can be attributed to nutrient uptake and release; variations in moisture content due to rainfall, evapotranspiration and drainage; adsorption and desorption of ions; mineral weathering and precipitation; gaseous exchange; and biological activity. In soil systems, there are countless reactions to any single change in the system.

Another factor which contributes to non-equilibrium conditions in soils is sluggish reaction rates of some processes in soil systems. In contrast to the relatively rapid ionic desorption—adsorption phenomena in soils, the rates of dissolution and precipitation of many common soil minerals are quite slow. The influence of kinetics on the soil mineralogical system will be illustrated with the silica components of soils. Thermodynamic considerations indicate that the concentration of soluble components in a system is controlled by the solubility of the least soluble component. Using such reasoning, the concentration of soluble Si in soils containing quartz should be 3 mg l^{-1}, the solubility of quartz which is the least soluble Si component in soils. However, soluble Si levels in soils generally range from 15 to 20 mg Si l^{-1} (Wilding et al., 1977). Quartz does not control the concentration of soluble Si in soils due to its slow rate of dissolution and negligible precipitation rate. The sluggishness with which quartz equilibrates with the surrounding solution is related to a high activation energy required to alter the Si—O—Si bonds. Although the dissolution of amorphous SiO_2 is faster than quartz, the concentration of Si in soil solution cannot be attributed to amorphous SiO_2 since soluble Si levels in soils are intermediate between equilibrium values for amorphous SiO_2 and quartz (Elgawhary and Lindsay, 1972). Soluble Si levels in soils must be related to more reactive Si components of soils. Using thermodynamic calculations, Kittrick (1969) shows that the soluble Si level in equilibrium with kaolinite and montmorillonite is of the same magnitude as that found in soils. This implies that clay minerals may control Si levels in soil solution; however, most of the evidence seems to indicate that soluble Si is in equilibrium with reactive Fe and Al silicates which most probably occur as coatings on mineral grains (Wilding et al., 1977). Thermodynamic considerations alone predict that quartz will precipitate in soils until soluble Si levels reach 3 mg l^{-1} but due to the negligible precipitation rate of quartz, soluble Si concentrations are a function of the faster adsorption—desorption phenomena of the Fe and Al silicates. Soluble Si concentrations in soils are more closely allied to kinetic considerations than to thermodynamic considerations. Silica relationships in soils provide an excellent example of the importance of kinetics in soil mineralogical systems.

MODELS

Modelling soil systems

As illustrated in the foregoing sections, soils constitute very complex, dynamic systems which can be discussed in terms of the fundamental laws of the basic sciences. However, in order to adequately study complex systems, simpler frameworks need to be devised to guide investigations and assimilate information. Denbigh (1951) states that the idea of equilibrium is one of the simplifying concepts employed in chemistry to make systems more amenable to analysis; unfortunately equilibrium is not applicable to open systems such as soils. Thus other simplifying concepts or models are essential to investigating soil systems. Whereas the collection of pedologic data and the publication of genetic schemes generally follow an isomorphic approach in contributing to our knowledge of soils, soil systems can best be understood by the development of homomorphic concepts[1]. Only with use of the latter can the response of whole soil systems to fluxes be predicted with any degree of confidence. Although there is relatively little published on the homomorphic approach to understanding soils, such modelling attempts are vital to advancement and understanding of genetic pathways in soils.

Present pedogenetic models attempt to organize, simplify and enumerate factors affecting soil systems or processes occurring in soil systems. To be of any value, a model must belong to a more familiar realm than the soil system to which it is applied. Models are used to collect data in a systematic manner, describe systems or to predict relationships or behavior in order to extend our knowledge of soils. However, models can be limiting to progress if the model is accepted as fact rather than as a source of hypotheses. All models should ultimately destroy themselves in whole or in part as models simply represent a series of approximations toward the "truth". A good model will instill in the scientist a probing attitude toward the system of concern in order to improve, redefine, and expand the model to gain a complete understanding of the system.

In discussing the roles of models in natural soil systems, Dijkerman (1974) lists four types of conceptual models: mental, verbal, structural and mathematical. Whereas most of our working models have been of a verbal nature, more emphasis is now being shown in mathematical models due to the availability of computers. Huggett (1976) refers to the former models as factorial or functional approaches whereas the latter is referred to as the systems approach. Factorial models explain system characteristics in terms of external variables but reveal little about details of soil-system dynamics. The systems approach which is process oriented is concerned with fluxes of material and energy through soil systems and thus relates driving forces of pedogenesis to soil-system dynamics.

The ensuing discussion will examine the pros and cons of the most popular models employed in pedogenetic studies. A careful examination of models presently available should, optimistically, lead to the formulation and development of more advanced and testable models of soil systems. Application of such models will, in turn, lead to a better understanding of processes operative in soil systems.

---

[1] Huggett (1975) introduces Patten's (1971) terminology to the soils literature. Isomorphic models describe systems as a combination of all individual processes in the system (a forest is described by describing each tree) whereas homomorphic models develop relationships for the system as a whole (a forest is described as a group of trees without describing each tree).

State-factor analysis

The best known and most frequently employed factorial model of soil systems is the soil-forming factors popularized by Jenny (1941). The model indicates that soils are a function of five factors which define the state and history of soil systems and are therefore referred to as state factors. The five soil-forming factors suggested by Jenny (1941) are: (1) climate (cl); (2) organisms (o); (3) topography (r); (4) parent material (p); and (5) time (t). The model is commonly expressed as

$$S = f(cl, o, r, p, t, ...)$$

where the dots indicate additional unspecified factors. The factors essentially define the soil system in terms of variables which control the characteristics of the system and not in terms of processes, causes, or forces which are active in the system. In order to place the model on a broader base, Jenny (1961) reduced his model to three state factors: initial state of the system (L_o), external flux potentials (P_x), and age of the system (t). Thus the general state factor equation for soils is expressed as:

$$S = f(L_o, P_x, t)$$

Any other property of the ecosystem such as vegetation and animal life can also be expressed with the same general equation. External fluxes include solar radiation, heat transfer, entropy transfer, gaseous diffusion, water flow, colluviation, biotic immigration and many others, but all are essentially determined by climate and the biosphere. The initial state of soil systems is defined by the physical, chemical, mineralogical and organic composition of the system which is commonly referred to as parent material. The initial state is also conditioned by topography. Thus the general state-factor equation in an extended form is identical to the five soil-forming factors.

Since the soil-forming factors are assumed to vary independently, the equation can be theoretically differentiated. However, as indicated by Runge (1973), difficulty in solving the equations arises since some factors are discrete, nonoverlapping units which offer no means for obtaining rates of change and some factors are of such a composite nature that it is difficult to conceive of collecting data necessary to solve the expression. Kline (1973) indicates that the equation is of unprecedented complexity and completely intractable. Although Yaalon (1975) believes the extended state-factor equation is too large for a simple quantitative solution, he suggests that with the availability of computer simulation, the remaining constraint is collection of suitable data for solving the equations. If possible, the collection of suitable data to solve the equation would be a formidable task.

Realistically, Jenny (1961, 1980) suggests that the model best be employed to understand soils by ordination of the state factors. Using ordination, changes in the soil system are attributed to changes in one state factor by holding all other state factors constant. Relationships derived from climo-, bio-, topo-, litho- and chronofunctions are common in pedologic literature; however, to date, no one has developed a mathematically rigorous, quantitative solution to any univariant state-factor equation. One problem with univariant state-factor equations is the partial dependence and frequent interactions among the factors (Stephens, 1947). Stevens and Walker (1970) question the reliability of chronofunctions, which are generally considered to be the easiest univariant functions to establish, due to the staggered onset of soil formation which casts doubt on the claim of climatic constancy. Even Jenny (1961) recognizes the interaction between soils and the vegetation growing on them; consequently he defines the biotic factor as the potential floristic list as opposed to the actual growing vegetation. Yaalon (1975) points out that not even topography and parent material factors are independent due to the flux of materials in landscapes. Chesworth (1976a) indicates that all factors vary as a function of time and suggests that time alone is the only independent variable of soil formation. Conversely, time can be considered to be an element in the essence of being and thus is not really a factor of formation. Every change in a system requires time, but change is not caused by the mere passing of time (Nifkiforoff, 1959). Thus, semantically, pedologists should not refer to time as a soil-forming factor, a point recognized by Schelling (1970).

State-factor analysis provides a useful, homomorphic, conceptual model of soil systems; however, as previously indicated, factorial approaches yield little possibility for enumerating and assimilating the processes active in soil systems. Crompton (1967) states that correlations between soils and state factors, even when clearly shown to be causative relationships, do not in themselves explain any of the mechanisms whereby factors such as climate and organisms are active in soil systems. Furthermore, such conceptual models are extremely difficult if not impossible to test and validate. Nevertheless, it must be emphasized that the factors of soil formation have had more impact on pedogenetic studies than any other soil model and have contributed to our understanding of soil formation. One of the most important attributes of the state-factor model is that it provides a means to dissect landscapes into segments along vectors of state factors which in turn provides an avenue for understanding (Jenny, 1980).

Energy model

Runge (1973) has proposed a factorial model which refines the factors of soil formation (Jenny, 1941) by giving priority to certain factors because not all factors deserve equal rank. The model emphasizes two intensity factors, water available for leaching (w) and organic matter production (o), and time (t). The model can conveniently be expressed as:

$$S = f(o, w, t)$$

The intensity factors are conditioned by a number of capacity factors. Water available for leaching is conditioned by such factors as duration and intensity of rainfall, runon, runoff and soil permeability. Organic-matter production is conditioned by nutrient, air and water availability, and the characteristics and growth of the vegetation. Thus in effect, organic matter production can be correlated with parent material (source of nutrients) and vegetation and water available for leaching with climate and relief in Jenny's model. However, Runge's model places more emphasis on processes active in soil systems rather than environmental variables external to the soil.

The model proposed by Runge (1973) is called the energy model because it stresses energy fluxes to the soil system. Water available for leaching is essentially an effective agent for utilizing gravitational energy whereas organic matter production is an expression of radiant energy. The former is referred to as the developing vector whereas the latter is referred to as the renewing vector. As indicated in the first part of this chapter, entropy can only decrease in soil systems due to entropy flow to external sources. In this model, the principal energy source for increasing order in soil systems is attributed to the movement of water through the soil. In this context, soils are a record of the impact of entropy and energy fluxes.

Conceptually, Runge (1973) suggests that soil formation is analogous to energy fluxes acting on a chromatographic column. Such a description of soil systems provides a mental model which is easy to visualize. Furthermore the model stresses energy relationships and, although it is a factorial model, is more process oriented than Jenny's original model. Nevertheless, Huggett (1975) indicates that Runge's three factors are just as difficult to quantify and express in mathematical expressions as Jenny's five factors. In addition, both Huggett (1975) and Yaalon (1975) indicate that parent material is inadequately handled in the model and Yaalon (1975) also suggests that leaching is not a suitable substitute for weathering. Another problem pointed out by Yaalon (1975) is that although the model is professed to be based on energy relationships, all references to energy are in verbal or graphical terms; no units of energy are used anywhere. The mental picture of soils as chromatographic columns also presents somewhat of a problem in visualizing the effect of lateral fluxes on soil development. In spite of these limitations, the energy model has proved to be useful in formulating hypotheses for several studies. Ballagh and Runge (1970) employed the model to develop a crucial test to determine the origin of clays in beta horizons over limestone or calcareous outwash. They concluded that the clayey horizons were illuvial rather than residual in origin. Hinkley et al. (1970) utilized the model in explaining the development of soils across forest—prairie boundaries in Illinois in terms of organic-matter production. The amount of water available for effective leaching was found to be responsible for the development of regional and local maturity sequences on the loess mantled Illinoian till plain in Illinois (Smeck and Runge, 1971). In these studies, the energy model has been very helpful in separating cause and effect, proposing hypotheses, and designing crucial tests.

Residua and haplosoil model

A further simplification of the five factors of soil formation is proposed by Chesworth (1973b) who views soils as systems spontaneously moving toward a state of equilibrium. Chesworth (1973a) contends that the soil-forming factors are not independent variables and thus can not be expressed in differential form. Particularly in areas affected by glaciation, Chesworth (1976b) states that it is only reasonable to conclude that climate, vegetation and relief have changed when viewed in the perspective of geologic time. In addressing the influence of parent materials in soil genesis, Chesworth (1973a) states that "time has the result of modifying and ultimately of nullifying the parent material effect so that only in young or relatively immature soils will the parent material exert its strongest influence on the soil-forming process; an influence that will be an inverse function of time". To illustrate this he indicates that soils derived from as dissimilar parent materials as granite and basalt will become indistinguishable given sufficient time to attain equilibrium. Thus it is speculated that time is the only independent variable of soil formation or any other process occurring spontaneously in nature (Chesworth, 1973a, 1976b).

During soil development, weathering preferentially removes mobile components and concentrates the relatively immobile components. Thus Chesworth (1973b) suggests that the four-component system consisting of $SiO_2-Al_2O_3-Fe_2O_3-H_2O$ constitutes a chemical sink or residua system toward which mineral composition trends during weathering. Chesworth (1973a) supports this theory by suggesting that as soils approach the residua system which most closely correlates with soils of the Oxisol order, the degree of horizon differentiation increases. However, most pedologists would argue that horizonation is not as well expressed in Oxisols as in less weathered soils (Fig. 3.2). Chesworth (1973a) indicates that intensity factors such as temperature, water status and landform simply control the rate at which soil composition moves toward the residua system. Of course, the existence of steady states in soils, which are time-independent by definition, would rule out the applicability of the residua theory to soil development in a pedogenic scale of time; however, Chesworth (1976a) believes that steady states rarely, if ever, exist in soils.

Nevertheless, Chesworth (1973b) does recognize that a limitation of the residua system is that it lacks a means to evaluate soil systems and mineral stabilities at points along the evolutionary pathway other than at the ultimate end-point and thus lacks general usefulness. Consequently, Chesworth (1980) proposes a haplosoil system which consists of a six-component system (SiO_2—Al_2O_3—Fe_2O_3—MgO—K_2O—H_2O). The activities of the mobile components, (MgO and K_2O) added to the residua system, will depend on the chemistry of the surroundings which governs their concentration in the system. The addition of the mobile components greatly increases the number of mineralogical possibilities which can be considered. The haplosoil system permits evaluation of the stabilities of systems containing most of the common authigenic minerals found in soils. Even though Chesworth (1980) indicates that few if any soils have attained strict thermodynamic equilibrium, he suggests that equilibrium models are worth considering if for no other reason than helping to systematically study weathering at the earth's surface. Chesworth (1980) also suggests that the humid tropics, due to a combination of high temperatures, adequate moisture and long term stability of many landforms, provide the best opportunity for attaining equilibrium and that common mineral assemblages found in the humid tropics are consistent with the haplosoil system.

Since both the residua and haplosoil models emphasize changes in the chemical composition of soil systems with time, they present an overly simplified view of soil genesis; soil formation not only involves mineral weathering but many other processes such as eluviation—illuviation, biologic cycling, organic-matter accumulation and mineralization, and mass movement of soil materials on slopes. Yaalon (1975) implies that selecting a terminal state consisting of SiO_2—Al_2O_3—Fe_2O_3 tends to mask desilication of soil systems during weathering. Furthermore since the models only indicate the terminal state (equilibrium state) toward which soil systems are moved by weathering, the models contribute little to our knowledge of the actual weathering processes active in soil systems. However, the existence of steady states and lack of equilibrium in soil systems pose the most serious threats to the utility of the residua and haplosoil models. Realizing that soils do not represent a state of equilibrium and suggesting that steady states can be no more than ephemeral, Chesworth (1980) indicates that the real value of the residua and haplosoil systems is that they indicate the states natural soil systems will attain if given sufficient time and provide a deductive check on the inductive reasoning of conventional pedology.

A generalized process model

All of the models previously discussed were basically factorial models in that soil properties are related to external conditions, initial material, or time (progress toward an equilibrium state). In factorial models, the mechanisms by which state factors influence soil properties are not addressed. The model suggested by Simonson (1959) and discussed herein represents one of the earliest attempts to model soil formation using a systems or process-response approach. The model suggests a generalized scheme for organizing and studying processes operative within soil systems.

According to Simonson (1959), soil genesis consists of two steps: (1) parent material accumulation; and (2) differentiation of horizons in the profile. Although most of the discussion in Simonson's article concerns the latter, he stresses the fact that parent-material accumulation is important in soil formation. Huggett (1975) indicates that Simonson's process model is only applicable if the soil landscape has remained geomorphically inactive since the initiation of soil genesis. However, the process model can accommodate the influence of geomorphic instability of parent materials by considering geomorphic material gains and losses as an active process in soil development (Arnold, 1965). Simonson (1959) suggests that horizon differentiation is a function of additions, removals, transfers and transformations within soil systems. These four processes are, of necessity, very general in order to cover the entire range of specific processes active in soil genesis. Nevertheless, the general processes do provide a framework for conceptually organizing processes to facilitate understanding. Simonson postulates that all processes are proceeding simultaneously in all soils and that only rates differ among soils. The ultimate nature of soils is governed by the balance among all the processes.

Obviously one of the limitations of a general model is that all the processes contributing to soil formation are not specifically identified. In fact, with our present state of knowledge, this would be an impossible task; even if all processes active in soil systems could be identified, the magnitude and complexity of such a compilation would contribute little to our understanding of soil genesis. Of more importance is the need to evaluate the relative importance of various processes in classes of similar soils. In order to develop a more complete or detailed model of soil genesis with the systems approach, additional quantitative information is necessary so that mathematical relationships can be developed for the most pertinent processes active in soils. A quantitative systems approach seems to be the most fruitful avenue for development of the most meaningful and useful models of soil formation.

Soil-landscape model

Huggett (1975) points out that one of the most serious deficiencies of previous homomorphic models is that the models never actually define the functional boundaries of the soil systems which are being modeled. In order to accommodate the flux of materials through soil systems, Huggett (1975) suggests the use of a "valley basin" or "soil-landscape system" as the basic three-dimensional functional unit of soil systems. He defines the soil-landscape system as being bounded by drainage divides, the surface of the land and the weathering front at the base of the soil profile. Huggett believes that any functional unit must include movements tangential to the surface as well as the normally considered vertical movements. The soil-landscape model can accommodate such geomorphic processes just as readily as pedogenetic processes whereas other models have traditionally stressed the latter. Huggett considers the soil-landscape system to consist of three materials: soluble, plasmic and skeletal. These components are transmitted through and transformed within the system. Plasmic components are basically affected by pedogenesis whereas the skeletal components are affected by geomorphogenesis.

The soil-landscape system functions as an open system which can be viewed as a black box or plant containing a complex store of materials and energy. The soil-landscape system is driven by a constant flux of material and energy between the system and its environment. To paraphrase Huggett, the soil-landscape system is a storing, transforming and transmitting plant whose inputs are material and energy and whose outputs are clastic sediments and colloidal and soluble material to a stream or local sink.

The soil-landscape system, as presented by Huggett, does exhibit two weaknesses. First, Huggett seems to emphasize material balances at the expense of energy balances and transformations. Secondly, the model contributes little to our understanding of processes operative within the system or even little detail concerning the inputs and outputs which affect the system. Nevertheless, Huggett indicates that soil-landscape systems exhibit all the features of a dynamic system model: system components, boundaries, interrelationships, transport and conservation of material and energy, and time flow. As such the model provides an excellent definition of system boundaries and thus provides a realistic framework for pursuing computer simulation of soil systems.

General systems theory

Systems concepts

Systems and concepts derived from systems theory are not new in pedological literature. Yet, there are inconsistencies and misunderstandings in the way these concepts have been applied and indeed, often a clear understanding of general systems theory is lacking. Therefore, it is worthwhile to clarify some of these issues prior to discussing their application to soil genesis models.

General systems theory is a philosophy of approach, or a paradigm, rather than a cookbook formula. It provides a framework which facilitates the integration of fundamental knowledge across a broad spectrum of sciences. The whole idea of systems theory is to study "systems" as entities (homomorphic approach) rather than as a conglomerate of parts, thereby providing a balance to the tendency in contemporary science to isolate "parts" and investigate their properties in greater and greater detail.

Before proceeding further, a number of terms require definition.

System. A system is an organized or complex whole made up of an assemblage or combination of parts (Kast and Rosenzweig, 1972). A hierarchy of systems extends from the single cell studied by the biologist to the astronomer's universe with level in the hierarchy being an obvious discriminant. Hierarchical organization is fundamental to the understanding of systems (see Table 3.1).

Systems approach. This refers to a paradigm of study with four distinctive but interrelated features defined (after Wright, 1975) as follows: (1) *systems thinking*: the ability to perceive some degree of order or interconnectedness in complex situations; (2) *systems concepts*: series of properties that can be used to describe or help demarcate the relevant system(s); (3) *systems methodology*: a plan for working through a problem in an orderly manner; (4) *systems techniques*: a set of unambiguous rules which is applicable to well-defined problems.

Model. In its broadest sense, a model is a form of synthesis and integration. Conceptual word and picture models are commonplace in literature on soil genesis but few attempts have been made at constructing quantitative, mathematical models. There is an obvious relationship between the terms system and model. In effect, a model is an idealized system, an attempt to abstract the essential detail from real-world situations and construct a simplified and therefore more manageable likeness.

Pertinent properties of systems as used in general systems theory and which apply to the development of soil genesis models are listed in Table 3.3. Whereas most of these properties have been adequately discussed earlier in this chapter, some additional comments are necessary. As previously indicated, soils are most appropriately defined as open systems. The hierarchical level and set of subsystems chosen are primarily determined by the purpose of the model. Boundaries should be chosen which divide the system into subsystems where interactions within subsystems are stronger and more numerous than those among subsystems. Explicit definition of boundary conditions is critical because validation of a model is dependent upon being

TABLE 3.3

Properties of systems

Property	Characteristics
Type	Open, closed
Hierarchy of systems	High to low levels of abstraction (Table 3.1)
Boundaries	Permeable, impermeable
Environment	Everything outside system boundaries
Feedback mechanisms	Negative, positive
Equifinality	Multiple pathways (multicausality)

able to measure inputs and outputs across boundaries. Feedback control systems are ubiquitous in nature. Through the process of feedback, systems continually receive information from the environment which causes readjustment to changing external conditions. The concept of equifinality asserts that the final state may be reached from different initial conditions and in different ways. Equifinality implies that various combinations of soil-forming processes interacting at different intensities can produce similar soils from parent materials of similar or dissimilar composition.

Application of systems concepts to mathematical modelling in soil genesis

Almost all of the physical and biological sciences, including pedology, are based on models. Scientists deal with a multiplicity of models which are often vague; usually deal with only limited aspects of the system being studied; and may even be mutually contradictory. Models should play a clarifying role by pointing out what is being described or perhaps more importantly, what is being left out. This is particularly true as one proceeds through a progression from word and picture models to mathematical and computer simulation models.

Mathematical models are particularly useful in forcing one to make explicit assumptions that are only implied in mental models and to resolve contradictions and ambiguities that exist. Modelling and simulation[1] is really the classical method of science in operation. The model serves as the hypothesis; simulation and experiment serve to test it. Thus, the very existence of a model should eventually lead to its obsolescence. It follows then that unless experiments can be set up to invalidate a model, the model should be scrapped or its original purpose reevaluated.

Constraints set by the need for validation largely determine the hierarchical levels to appear in models. Perhaps we should recognize that with our present state of knowledge the development of general mathematical models to describe soil genesis processes is too complex of an undertaking. Kline (1973) illustrates this point quite effectively. However, this does not preclude further effort in the field, rather it emphasizes the need to formulate models that are commensurate with our abilities to test and validate them.

Accepting this latter premise for the moment, how can general systems theory and more specifically, systems concepts aid our ability to model soil development? As stated earlier, general systems theory is a paradigm or philosophy of approach rather than a cookbook formula. It provides the modeller of soil genesis with a systematic framework (systems thinking, systems concepts, systems methodology and systems techniques) within which to introduce rigor into what can only currently be described as a

---

[1] Simulation expresses the dynamics of the system rather than the statics.

qualitative/semiquantitative science. Moreover, it emphasizes the need to study systems as entities and to investigate the interrelationships of parts rather than to isolate phenomena and investigate their properties in greater and greater detail.

Not all of the properties of systems outlined in Table 3.3 are necessarily going to be used in the construction of every soil-genesis model. Nevertheless, in order to successfully develop mathematical models to describe soil genesis, the successful modeller must at a minimum explicitly define the type, hierarchical level(s), boundary conditions and environment of the system. Arnold and De Wit (1976) and Van Dyne and Abramsky (1975) provide useful background information to the reader in this respect.

CONCLUSIONS

The preceding review of soil-genesis models indicates that although there are no totally acceptable models, all do have conceptual value. Whereas most models exhibit an awareness of systems concepts, there is a lack of continuity in their application. Most modellers recognize that soils are open systems, but there is no consistent pattern in the application of other systems properties (Yaalon, 1971; Kline, 1973; Runge, 1973; Hugget, 1975; Conacher and Dalrymple, 1977). Several of the more popular models (Jenny, 1941; Simonson, 1959) have been developed for general purposes, but in doing so, have violated the basic principle of hierarchies: hypotheses, laws and principles that are developed and tested for one level are not necessarily applicable at another level. The mere fact that few models explicitly state the hierarchical level at which they are directed leads to a lack of well-defined hypotheses and objectives which can be tested.

The problem of dealing with thermodynamics in soil-genesis models is even more difficult to address, particularly from the standpoint of validation. Yet this must not preclude the modeller from using thermodynamic terms in the classical sense nor defining the terms if used in a non-thermodynamic manner to prevent confusing semantic problems from arising.

In part, the inconsistent application of system concepts to soil-genesis models stems from the fact that most of the models are conceptual in nature and can not be tested in any rigorous experimental fashion. Efforts to overcome this deficiency are beginning to appear in print (Kline, 1973; Runge, 1973; Scrivner et al., 1973; Huggett, 1975), but most still lack mathematical solutions. The major constraint to model development is adequate qualitative and quantitative data regarding soil-forming processes. The use of such data, as generated, with systems concepts will lead to more realistic models of soil genesis.

ACKNOWLEDGEMENT

The thoughts presented in this chapter have evolved over a period of years in discussions among the authors and graduate students. In regard to the latter, recognition is due to M.L. Thompson and C.T. Hallmark. Both former students contributed greatly to the development of the material in this chapter.

REFERENCES

Anderson, P.W., 1972. More in different. Science, 177: 393—396.
Arnold, G.W. and De Wit, C.T., 1976. Critical Evaluation of Systems Analysis in Ecosystems Research and Management. Pudoc, Wageningen, 108 pp.
Arnold, R.W., 1965. Multiple working hypothesis in soil genesis. Soil Sci. Soc. Am. Proc., 29: 717—724.
Ballagh, T.M. and Runge, E.C.A., 1970. Clay-rich horizons over limestone — illuvial or residual? Soil Sci. Soc. Am. Proc., 34: 534—536.
Buol, S.W., Hole, F.D. and McCracken, R.J., 1973. Soil Genesis and Classification. The Iowa State Univ. Press, Ames, Iowa, 360 pp.
Canada Soil Survey Committee, 1978. The Canadian System of Soil Classification. Can. Dept. Agric. Publ., 1646. Supply and Services Canada, Ottawa, 164 pp.
Chesworth, W., 1973a. The parent rock effect in the genesis of soil. Geoderma, 10: 215—225.
Chesworth, W., 1973b. The residua system of chemical weathering: A model for the chemical breakdown of silicate rocks at the surface of the earth. J. Soil Sci., 24: 69—81.
Chesworth, W., 1976a. Conceptual models in pedogenesis: A further rejoinder. Geoderma, 16: 265—266.
Chesworth, W., 1976b. Conceptual models in pedogenesis: A rejoinder. Geoderma, 16: 257—260.
Chesworth, W., 1980. The haplosoil system. Am. J. Sci., 280: 969—985.
Cline, M.G., 1961. The changing model of soil. Soil Sci. Soc. Am. Proc., 25: 442—446.
Conacher, A.J. and Dalrymple, J.B., 1977. The nine-unit landsurface model: an approach to pedogeomorphic research. Geoderma, 18: 1—154.
Crompton, E., 1967. Soil Formation. In: J.V. Drew (Editor), Selected Papers in Soil Formation and Classification. Soil Sci. Soc. Am., pp. 3—15.
Denbigh, K.G., 1951. The Thermodynamics of the Steady State. Wiley, New York, N.Y., 103 pp.
Dijkerman, J.C., 1974. Pedology as a science: The role of data, models, and theories in the study of natural soil systems. Geoderma, 11: 73—93.
Elgawhary, S.M. and Lindsay, W.L., 1972. Solubility of silica in soils. Soil Sci. Soc. Am. Proc., 36: 439—442.
Foss, J.C., Rieger, S. and Moormann, F.R., 1983. Inceptisols. In: L.P. Wilding, N.E. Smeck and G.F. Hall (Editors), Pedogenesis of Soil Taxonomy. II. The Soil Orders. Elsevier, Amsterdam.
Garrels, R.M., 1957. Some free energy values from geologic relations. Am. Mineral., 42: 780—791.
Garrels, R.M. and Christ, C.L., 1965. Solutions, Minerals, and Equilibria. Harper and Row, New York, N.Y., 450 pp.
Hinkley, K.C., Runge, E.C.A. and Pedersen, E.J., 1970. Effect of soil on vegetation in NE Illinois. Am. Soc. Agron., p. 137 (abstract).

Huggett, R.J., 1975. Soil landscape systems: A model of soil genesis. Geoderma, 13:1—22.
Huggett, R.J., 1976. Conceptual models in pedogenesis — A discussion. Geoderma, 16: 261-262.
Jenny, H., 1941. Factors of Soil Formation. McGraw-Hill, New York, N.Y., 281 pp.
Jenny, H., 1961. Derivation of state factor equations of soils and ecosystems. Soil Sci. Soc. Am. Proc., 25: 385—388.
Jenny, H., 1980. The Soil Resource, Origin and Behavior. Springer, New York, N.Y., 377 pp.
Kast, F.E. and Rosenzweig, J.E., 1972. The modern view: a systems approach. In: J. Beishon and G. Peters (Editors), Systems Behaviour. The Open University Press, London, pp. 14—28.
Kittrick, J.A., 1967. Gibbsite-kaolinite equilibria. Soil Sci. Soc. Am. Proc., 31:314—316.
Kittrick, J.A., 1969. Soil minerals in the Al_2O_3—SiO_2—H_2O system and a theory of their formation. Clays Clay Mineral., 17: 157—167.
Kittrick, J.A., 1977. Mineral equilibria and the soil system. In: J.B. Dixon and S.B. Weed (Editors), Minerals in Soil Environments. Soil Sci. Soc. Am., pp. 1—25.
Kline, J.R., 1973. Mathematical simulation of soil—plant relationships and soil genesis. Soil Sci., 115: 240-249.
Lanyon, L.E. and Hall, G.F., 1982. Land surface morphology: II. Predicting potential landscape instability in eastern Ohio. Soil Sci. (in press).
Milne, G., 1935. Composite units for the mapping of complex soil associations. Trans. 3rd Int. Congress Soil Sci., 1: 345—347.
Morowitz, H.J., 1971. Entropy for Biologists, An Introduction to Thermodynamics. Academic Press, New York, N.Y., 195 pp.
Nikiforoff, C.C., 1959. Reappraisal of the soil. Science, 129: 186—196.
Novak, R.J., Motto, H.L. and Douglas, L.A., 1971. The effect of time and particle size on mineral alteration in several Quaternary soils in New Jersey and Pennsylvania, U.S.A. In: D.H. Yaalon (Editor), Paleopedology. Israel University Press, Jerusalem, pp. 211—224.
Patten, B.C., 1971. Systems and Simulation in Ecology, 1. Academic Press, New York, N.Y., 607 pp.
Prigogine, I., 1961. Introduction to Thermodynamics of Irreversible Processes. Wiley-Interscience, New York, N.Y., 119 pp.
Robie, R.A. and Waldbaum, D.R., 1968. Thermodynamic properties of minerals and related substances at $298.15°K$ ($25°C$) and one atmosphere (1.013 Bars) pressure and at higher temperatures. Geol. Surv. Bull., 1259, 256 pp.
Rode, A.A., 1961. The Soil-forming Process and Soil Evolution. Israel Program Sci. Transl., Jerusalem, 100 pp. (translated from Russian).
Runge, E.C.A., 1973. Soil development sequences and energy models. Soil Sci., 115: 183-193.
Runge, E.C.A. and Riecken, F.F., 1966. Influence of natural drainage on the distribution and forms of phosphorus in some Iowa prairie soils. Soil Sci. Soc. Am. Proc., 30: 624-630.
Schelling, J., 1970. Soil genesis, soil classification and soil survey. Geoderma, 4:165—193.
Scrivner, C.L., Baker, J.C. and Brees, D.R., 1973. Combined daily climatic data and dilute solution chemistry in studies of soil profile formation. Soil Sci., 115: 213—223.
Simonson, R.W., 1959. Outline of a generalized theory of soil genesis. Soil Sci. Soc. Am. Proc., 23: 152—156.
Smeck, N.E. and Runge, E.C.A., 1971. Factors influencing profile development exhibited by some hydromorphic soils in Illinois. In: E. Schlichting and U. Schwertmann (Editors), Pseudogley and Gleys. Trans. Comm. V and VI Int. Soc. Soil Sci., Chemie Verlag, pp. 169—179.
Soil Survey Staff, 1975. Soil Taxonomy. A Basic System of Soil Classification for Making and Interpreting Soil Surveys. USDA Agric. Handbook No. 436, U.S. Govt. Printing

Office, Washington, D.C., 754 pp.

Stephens, C.G., 1947. Functional synthesis in pedogenesis. Trans. R. Soc. S. Aust., 71: 168—181.

Stevens, P.R. and Walker, T.W., 1970. The chronosequence concept and soil formation. Q. Rev. Biol., 45: 333—350.

Tykodi, R.J., 1967. Thermodynamics of Steady States. Macmillan, New York, N.Y., 217 pp.

Van Dyne, G.M. and Abramsky, Z., 1975. Agricultural Systems Models and Modelling: An Overview. In: G.E. Dalton (Editor), Study of Agricultural Systems. Applied Science Publishers, Barking, pp. 23—106.

Von Bertalanffy, L., 1950. The theory of open systems in physics and biology. Science, 111:23—29.

Wilding, L.P., Smeck, N.E. and Drees, L.R., 1977. Silica in soils: Quartz, cristobalite, tridymite, and opal. In: J.B. Dixon and S.B. Weed (Editors), Minerals in Soil Environments. Soil Sci. Soc. Am., pp. 471—552.

Wright, T., 1975. Systems, Models and Decisions. The Open University Press, Leeds, 72 pp.

Yaalon, D.H., 1971. Soil-forming processes in time and space. In: D.H. Yaalon (Editor), Paleopedology. Israel University Press, Jerusalem, pp. 29—39.

Yaalon, D.H., 1975. Conceptual models in pedogenesis. Can soil-forming functions be solved? Geoderma, 14: 189—205.

SPATIAL VARIABILITY AND PEDOLOGY

L.P. WILDING and L.R. DREES[1]

INTRODUCTION

Soil variability is no stranger to a pedologist; in fact, landscape variability is the very essence of this discipline and dates to antiquity (Arnold, see Chapter 1). Over the past 15 to 20 years greater attention has been focused on soil variability as a means to further quantify the pedogenic concepts and to better understand the causal factors for soil distribution patterns and landscape evolution. The development and implementation of Soil Taxonomy (Soil Survey Staff, 1975) have furthered pedogenic quantification. Those sciences which have progressed rapidly in recent years have done so primarily through changing from a qualitative to a quantitative emphasis. Geology is an excellent example (Griffiths, 1967; Harbaugh and Merriam, 1968) and pedology is progressing in the same direction (Webster, 1977; Wilding and Drees, 1978; Miller et al., 1979).

The transfer of technology from laboratory models to field conditions presents serious difficulties. Mass and energy flow, chemical reactions, mineralogical transformations and biological activity can sometimes be predicted satisfactorily in homogenous, isotropic laboratory experiments but field conditions are anisotropic and non-homogeneous. Predictive capability of models is thus lost in the spectrum of spatial variability, not because the model failed, but because it does not accommodate reality.

Models are material specific but soils as landscape bodies contain wide ranges of physical, chemical, morphological and mineralogical properties, laterally and vertically. In addition, many parameters are not single valued (i.e. water retention, hydraulic conductivity) but vary with transient soil features. Many do not vary randomly in space and thus are not normally distributed. Inability to adequately cope with spatial variability remains a major obstacle to interpretations of field research.

Identifying the magnitude and loci of spatial variability, its systematic versus random origin and the pedologist's role in communicating such information to users of soil surveys is the purpose of this chapter. Previous

[1] Contribution from the Texas Agricultural Experiment Station and Texas A&M University, College Station, Texas, U.S.A.

reviews by the authors (Wilding, 1972; Wilding and Drees, 1978; Smeck and Wilding, 1980) are used extensively. Literature on the subject is voluminous and space does not permit a comprehensive coverage; for more detailed compilations see excellent summaries available elsewhere (Beckett and Webster, 1971; Nielson et al., 1973; Fridland, 1976; Campbell, 1979; Miller et al., 1979).

Reasons why pedologists continue to pursue spatial variability include the following:

(1) To estimate central tendency and variance statistics for specified classes and class differentiae.

(2) To quantify pedogenesis as related to soil-forming factors and processes.

(3) To determine soil composition of mapping units.

(4) To develop more sensitive and acceptable sampling designs and statistical models for soil survey and pedogenic applications.

(5) To determine optimum allocation of sampling units for the most efficient statistical design.

(6) To differentiate systematic from random error in landform analysis.

(7) To determine spatial variability in three dimensions so pedogenesis and soil behavior can be easily visualized.

SYSTEMATIC VERSUS RANDOM VARIATION

Systematic variation

Spatial variability can be grouped into two broad categories, systematic and random. Systematic variability is a gradual or marked change in soil properties (or sign of trend effects) as a function of landform, geomorphic elements and soil-forming factors and/or soil management by man (Jenny, 1941; Belobrov, 1976). Systematic soil variability occurs at the microlevel in terms of microfabric and physical-chemical composition (Miller at al., 1971; Brewer, 1976). Pedologists have long concentrated their efforts on systematic changes rather than random changes. This is understandable and deemed justifiable because soil distribution patterns must be related to landscapes and geomorphic entities for effective soil survey operations and pedological investigations; such features provide the most reliable, effective and predictive measures to differentiate soils and to extrapolate our current body of knowledge (Van Wambeke and Dudal, 1978; Moormann and Kang, 1978; Arnold and Schargel, 1978). Thus natural systematic variability is a function of the following:

(1) Landforms: mountains, plateaus, basins, plains, terraces, fans, valleys, moraines, etc.

(2) Geomorphic elements: summit, shoulder, backslope and toeslope.

(3) Soil-forming factors: (a) chronosequences — a function of geomorphic-age and landscape stability; (b) lithosequences — a function of parent material or bedrock types; (c) toposequences — a function of topography on similar parent materials; (d) biosequences — a function of biology (changes in macro- or microflora and fauna), i.e. forest versus grassland or organic versus mineral sequences; (e) climosequences — function of macro- or micro-climate.

(4) Interactions of above factors.

Traditionally, *local* differences in soils have been attributed primarily to the "active" factors of vegetation and climate; more recently in some areas it has been recognized that differences in parent material lithology and geo-morphic position are more important local control factors (Campbell, 1978; Northcliff, 1978).

Random variation

Systematic variability often becomes highly complex, difficult to discern and impossible to express analytically. Associated with it, simultaneously and concurrently, are those changes in soil properties that cannot be related to a known cause; these are termed random or chance variation. When the soil system is investigated in greater detail, a part of the variation originally considered random may be recognized as systematic. In reality, if our state of knowledge were perfect, perhaps all variation in soil properties would be recognized as systematic; critical to this consideration is the sampling scheme. If the spacing of observations is too far apart, then even systematic variability may appear as random. Thus, differentiation of these two concepts is intended to focus on the proportion of soil variability that can now be related to know causes versus that which is yet to be discerned.

Causes of vertical and lateral soil anisotropy that yield spatial variability of a random, non-visual, or unidentified nature over short-range or indeterminate distances and of a temporal or permanent nature include:

(1) Differential lithology: function of physical, chemical and mineralogical composition of parent material reflecting modes of origin, mechanisms of transport and sedimentary histories.

(2) Differential intensity of weathering: function of modes and mechanisms of weathering, formation and transfer of weathering products and landscape evolution.

(3) Differential erosion and accretion: function of landscape stability (erosional versus constructional surfaces) and geomorphic processes.

(4) Biological factors: function of flora and fauna (including man's influence).

(5) Differential hydrology: function of climate, relief, vegetation and geomorphic position at specific sites.

(6) Sampling and analytical errors: function of population characteristics,

sampling design and errors of field and laboratory determinations.

All of the above factors except 6 may contribute to systematic variation. However, such effects may be too subtle to be visually identified or measured, or they may represent combined interactions allocated to random error.

STATE OF KNOWLEDGE

Quantification of spatial variability is a product of this century. Only within the past two decades have statistical approaches been applied to describe soil spatial variability. In the early 1900's, statistical treatment of spatial variability was primarily related to agronomic research and analysis of field plot data (Beckettt and Webster, 1971). While not solely restricted to surficial horizons, the upper 20—30 cm of rooting volume were emphasized. Soils were generally viewed as changing gradually with increased field-plot area; sometimes marked changes in soil properties were observed over very short distances, but rarely were experimental areas mapped in sufficient detail or series sufficiently restrictive to relate research results to soil series, types or specific soil properties.

Many of our current statistical methods come from Snedecor (1940). The major focus of experimental designs was to interpret the significance of main treatment effects (yield or fertility responses) with little or no effort to understand the results in terms of soil conditions. Variance due to soil parameters was extracted as blocking or replication errors and given little more attention. Statistical theory did not lead to direct correlation of soil properties with plant response or with landform parameters. Sequential testing appears to be more appropriate for this purpose; marked changes in plant response are directly correlated with soil properties observed or measured along a transect or series of plots located normal to the response or topographic gradient (Moormann and Kang, 1978). Campbell (1978) also argues that analysis of variance procedures do not permit concise and complete descriptions of soil changes over distance; therefore, he offers semi-variance or autocorrelation as alternatives.

Robinson and Lloyd (1915), Davis (1936) and Harradine (1949) were among the first to investigate soil variability within survey areas and soil series, but series concepts have become much more restrictive since these studies. In the early 1950's and 1960's, major efforts were made to document physical, chemical and morphological variability within and between taxonomic and cartographic units of soil series. Most of the pre-1970 investigations were summarized by Beckett and Webster (1971); more recent work includes that by Ball et al. (1970), Klute (1972), Crosson and Protz (1974), Amos and Whiteside (1975), Lee et al. (1975), Adams and Wilde (1976a,b), Ball (1976), Belobrov (1976), Karpachevskii (1976), Kiseleva (1976), Tidball

(1976), Vznuzdaev (1976), Cameron (1978) and Wagenet and Jurinak (1978). Variability within and between morphologically similar pedons has been documented by Drees and Wilding (1973), Smeck and Wilding (1980) and Mausbach et al. (1980). Magnitudes of variability observed in the above investigations have been summarized diagramatically in the section "Magnitude of Soil Variability" of this chapter. As a consequence of this significant body of work, efforts were spurred to determine optimum allocation of sampling levels, commonly employing a nested sampling design. For example, how many areas should be sampled? How many observations within an area should be chosen? How many subsamples within observations are needed?

Subsequent to the mid-1960's and coincident with the implementation of Soil Taxonomy, cartographic units representative of soil series were found to seldom comprise more than 40—50% (sometimes only 20%) of the soil(s) designated in the mapping unit name (Powell and Springer, 1965; Wilding et al., 1965; McCormack and Wilding, 1969; Amos and Whiteside, 1975). This is a measure of the degree of fit between the taxonomic system as a conceptual model and the cartographic units as real landscape counterparts. Many of the inclusions in mapping units were not sufficiently different from the central concept to detract significantly from the interpretative value of the maps for soil performance. Taxonomic purity of map units is not a proper measure of quality or precision of a soil survey (Miller et al., 1979). In the future, much greater effort must be placed on the interpretative accuracy of mapping units. There is a growing pressure by users of soil surveys for quantification of spatial variability and assignment of confidence limits for soil composition, specific soil properties, and soil performance within mapping units (Miller, 1978).

To a greater extent in the future, geomorphology will be utilized to elucidate systematic spatial variation (Daniels et al., 1971; Ruhe, 1975). More observations and sampling will be conducted with elevation control and in a geometry permitting diagnostic horizons, geomorphic surfaces and stratigraphic units to be identified and projected in three-dimension. Computer plotting techniques have been used by Hock et al. (1973), Huddleston and Riecken (1973) and Crosson and Protz (1974) for this purpose.

Geostatistics is a new field based on the theory of regionalized variables which uses the semi-variogram and a method of prediction or extrapolation known as "kriging" (Journel and Huijbregts, 1978; Burgess and Webster, 1980a,b; Royle, 1980). Regionalized variables are those variables whose values are related in some way to their positions—spatial dependence. No attempt will be made herein to review this emerging body of statistics; rather important citations and examples will be presented to encourage pedologists to consider the value of this tool for our future growth. Statistical treatment of geosurfaces have been applied to many mining fields and should provide useful approaches in pedology. For example, it should permit further differentiation of systematic versus random errors; it should aid in an unbiased assessment of sampling interval; it should be useful in determining the geometric configuration of subsurface morphological features as a function of landform parameters; and it should permit extrapolation from a data set with more precision and at a defined level of confidence.

Statistical theories called autocorrelation and semi-variance are now being explored as a means to more concisely and completely describe changes in soil properties over distance (Webster and Cuanalo, 1975; Campbell, 1978, Burgess and Webster, 1980a; Lanyon and Hall, 1981; Vieira et al., 1981). The purpose of this approach is to determine optimum observational intervals in designing sampling schemes. For example, how far apart should samples be spaced to fully encompass the spatial variation of continuous geographic distributions so that successive observations will not be dependent on previous ones? Burgess and Webster (1980a) suggest that the semi-variance approach has advantages over autocorrelation in that the autocorrelation coefficient depends on sample variance which must be finite for differing areas of interest while semi-variance is free from this restriction. An idealized semi-variogram is illustrated in Fig. 4.1A. The range (L) is the distance at which the semi-variance (γ_h) approaches the maximum variance (K_0) of the data set and at which observations no longer indicate systematic variability. The total distance is given as (h) over which multiple, equally spaced observations have been made in a straight line. Such straight-line transects can be composited from grid studies to yield two-dimensional control (Campbell, 1979; Burgess and Webster, 1980a). Alternatively, from grid data x, y and diagonal transects can be examined to determine geometric homogeneity.

Burgess and Webster (1980a) and Campbell (1978) show that semi-variance for soil properties rarely follows the idealized model. Rather the average semi-variance between points a given distance apart consists of two components; a *structural* component that represents both systematic and random error and is a function of increasing separation distance. A second component represents a limiting variance between two sampling points as their separation approaches zero; this is often called the *nugget variance* (Fig. 4.1B). Nugget variation represents random sampling error within observational units; the greater the magnitude of this error, the less precise extrapolative estimates can be made from the data set. The total of the structural component, C, and the nugget variance, C_0, is called the *sill* (Fig. 4.1B).

The semi-variogram can be used to estimate point values of a property with associated variance estimates of unrecorded points by an interpolative procedure called punctual *kriging*. Vieira et al. (1981) have employed kriging along with semi-variance to demonstrate how spatial variability of field-measured infiltration rate could be described with about one-tenth the number of samples as observed.

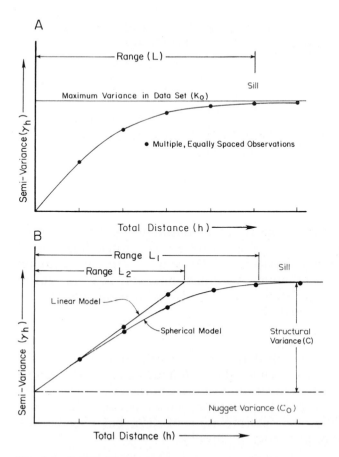

Fig. 4.1. A. Idealized semi-variogram (modified from fig. 1 from Campbell, 1978). B. Observed semi-variograms for soil properties (modified from fig. 1b from Burgess and Webster, 1980a).

Often in soil survey work, we may be more interested in average values over an area rather than point expectation. A procedure which integrates block cell units called *block kriging* has been proposed by Burgess and Webster (1980b) for this purpose. Such a procedure smooths out erratic *isarithms* (line contours of equal property value) and large estimated variances caused by large nugget variances. Isarithmic maps of sodium content, cover-loam thickness, and stoniness have been developed by these kriging methods.

Webster and Burgess (1980) also illustrate a procedure called *universal kriging* for soil electrical resistivity that is designed to accommodate continuous drift or trends in the data from one small neighborhood of values to the next. The universal kriging method may not be particularly useful if short-range point to point variation (nugget variance) is so great that changing drift is almost indistinguishable from constant drift.

STATISTICAL CONCEPTS

A good discussion of the application of statistics to the earth sciences is given by Griffiths (1967) and Webster (1977). Among other texts, Snedecor and Cochran (1967) also provide an excellent coverage of theoretical and applied statistical concepts.

Population parameters

In pedology, the population consists of a continuum of objects rather than discrete classes. The classes represent arbitrary constructs imposed by man with rationale for boundary placement. We cannot sample all attributes of a variable through its continuum. A sample, however, is a convenient selection taken from the population for study. We wish to understand the population but we actually observe the sample.

Kinds of population distribution

Normal distribution. A bell-shaped frequency distribution in which the mean, mode and median have the same value is defined as a normal distribution (Fig. 4.2). In statistical treatment of most data, normal distributions are assumed without testing the population for this characteristic. This fosters ease of calculation, analysis and interpretation of data, but may be misleading if the assumptions of normality are invalid.

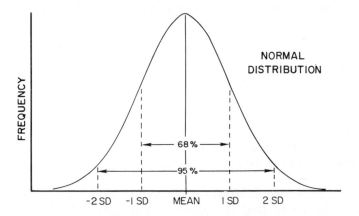

Fig. 4.2. Schematic form of a normal distribution and areal percentages as a function of ± 1 and ± 2 of standard deviations (*SD*).

Skewed distribution. Many soil properties do not approximate normality; for example, they may be skewed asymmetrically to higher or lower values from the mode such that the mean, mode and median do not have the same value (McIntyre and Tanner, 1959; Leone et al., 1961; Pomerening and Knox, 1962; Protz et al., 1968; Cassel and Bauer, 1975). For example, 15 atm moisture percentages, horizon thickness, depth to carbonates, bulk density and penetrability follow skewed distributions (Fig. 4.3). Wagenet and Jurinak (1978) and Schroth (1969) report organic carbon, total N, exchangeable K and soluble salt distributions best fit log-normal distributions (Fig. 4.3) while CEC, total bases, exchangeable Ca, Mg and C/N ratios are closer to gamma distributions which approximate chi-squared functions (Fig. 4.3). Skewness is especially noted for minimal values which are truncated at zero, such as sand content in a silty clay-loam texture. In fact, all soil parameters probably exhibit some degree of non-normality. Wagenet and Jurinak (1978) discuss a method to graphically test transformed data to see if the selected transformation function yields a normally distributed variable.

Polymodal distributions. Some soil properties exhibit a frequency distribution with more than one mode. For example: calcite, garnets, amphiboles-pyroxenes and feldspars in basal till deposits occur in bimodal size distributions; quartz-size distribution is trimodal (Dreimanis and Vagners, 1971). Smeck and Wilding (1980) indicate that calcium-carbonate equivalents in glacio-fluvial derived soils of Ohio are bimodally distributed. Similar distributions have been reported by Belobrov (1976) for organic matter content.

Polymodal distributions may reflect insufficient data to adequately define the population, but such does not seem to be the case in the examples cited above. The application of statistical concepts to polymodal populations is

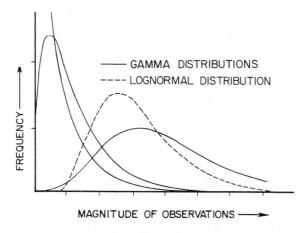

Fig. 4.3. Schematic forms of a log-normal distribution and three gamma distributions.

92

difficult because of non-normality. However, each mode may be treated as a separate population in defining central tendency and variance statistics.

Coefficient of variation

For the purpose of comparing dispersion among different soil properties, it is convenient and appropriate to express variance free from units of measurement. Coefficient of variation (CV) is such a statistic and is defined relative to standard deviation (SD) and the mean $(\overline{X})$ as: $CV(\%) = (SD/\overline{X})100$. Coefficient of variation is a useful and meaningful index to compare variability among different soil properties. However, caution should be exercised in interpreting its significance. When a direct relationship exists between the magnitude of X and SD (i.e. they covary), CV is an invalid index. This is most prevalent when measured values are within the range of laboratory errors. Caution must also be exercised with transformed data (i.e. to a log basis) or where data may have both positive and negative values with a consequent mean near zero. For the purpose of this text, most documentation of spatial variability will be reported in terms of CV without transformed data. Figure 4.4 illustrates the exponential relationship between CV and number of samples necessary to estimate the population mean within given confidence limits. The number of observations necessary to achieve an accuracy of ± 10% for any CV is about four times that for ± 20%.

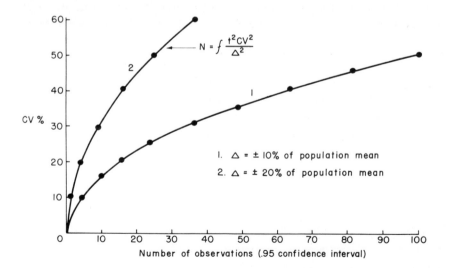

Fig. 4.4. Coefficient of variability (CV) versus number of observations necessary to estimate the population mean within specified limits.

Confidence limits

In most pedologic investigations, we would like to make probability statements concerning expected variance by continued or repeated sampling. The "*t*" distribution was developed to accommodate such extrapolation from small sample sizes at specified confidence levels (Thornburn and Larsen, 1959; Griffiths, 1967). The "*t*" value is selected from prepared statistical tables based on the number of observations and desired accuracy (Snedecor and Cochran, 1967).

Confidence limits over which 95% of the observations (*n*) would be expected to occur are given by $\overline{X} \pm t \cdot SD$ (*t* = 2.26 for *n* = 10 at 95% level). Corresponding confidence limits for the mean are given by $\overline{X} \pm t \cdot SE$; where $SE = SD/\sqrt{n}$. The confidence limits for a given set of observations may be narrowed only by accepting a lower probability level or an increased sample size.

Limit of accuracy

Standard error of the mean (*SE*) multiplied by *t* is also termed limit of accuracy. Since *SE* has an inverse relation to *n*, the number of observations can be allowed to fluctuate in order to observe the corresponding changes in the limit of accuracy; it is assumed that the *SD* of the population in question remains constant. Limit of accuracy curves versus number of samples for a specified level have been presented by a number of workers (Jacob and Klute, 1956; Thornburn and Larsen, 1959; Hampton et al., 1962; Wilding et al., 1965; McCormack and Wilding, 1969; Drees and Wilding, 1973). Limit of accuracy curves or tables permit the determination of number of observations necessary to estimate the mean within absolute (Fig. 4.5) or relative (Table 4.1) limits at desired confidence levels. With *CV*'s of about 25% or greater, the number of observations necessary to achieve a high degree of accuracy becomes prohibitive. In such situations, it may be more realistic to select a lower mean accuracy (±20 or ±30%) or accept a lower confidence level (i.e. 70% rather than 95%) as illustrated in Table 4.1.

SAMPLING SCHEMES

A pedologist using statistics should have a much better concept of soil-property relationships and covariance of soil distribution patterns with landscape features than a statistician without soils experience. With such prior knowledge, care must be exercised not to confound systematic and random variability in design of the sampling scheme. For example, if soils systematically change as a function of relief, then the most efficient sampling scheme will be one that transverses drainage systems at right angles. Like-

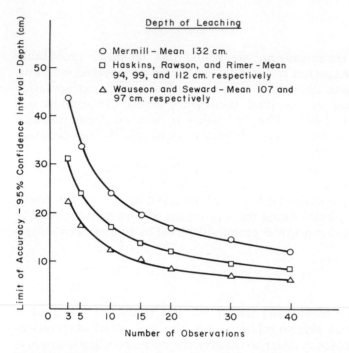

Fig. 4.5. Number of observations needed to estimate the population mean for depth of leaching in three different soils developed from glacio-lacustrine deposits in Ohio (reprinted from fig. 3, McCormack and Wilding, 1969, with permission from Soil Science Society of America).

TABLE 4.1

Number of samples required for 95 and 70% confidence intervals as a function of differing probable mean error limits and coefficients of variation (CV)

CV (%)	Limit of accuracy*					
	10**	20**	30**	10***	20***	30***
5	1	1	1	1	1	1
10	4	1	1	1	1	1
15	9	2	1	2	1	1
20	15	4	2	4	1	1
25	24	6	3	7	2	1
30	35	9	4	10	2	1
40	62	15	7	17	4	2
50	50	24	11	27	7	3

* Relative percentage of population mean.
** Number of samples (observations) needed at 95% confidence interval.
*** Number of samples (observations) needed at 70% confidence interval.

wise, sampling within a pedon, either laterally or vertically, should not be at random. No useful purpose is gained in compositing soil materials of known morphological, physical, chemical or mineralogical difference. Random sampling is suitable only when soil differences are not evident.

Space does not permit a comprehensive appraisal of sampling schemes that can be used in variability investigations. Perhaps the major consideration revolves about the kinds of questions to be answered, the objectives of the work and the nature of the class being sampled. Three general principles should be kept in mind when selecting sampling units (Cline, 1944). These are:

(1) Samples should be representative of the entire population; even a large sample confined to a part of the population contains no information on the excluded parts.

(2) An unbiased estimate of the mean requires that every *sampling unit* have an equal chance of being drawn.

(3) An unbiased estimate of significance and fiducial limits requires that every sample of *n-sampling units* have an equal chance of being drawn.

Random sampling

Random point sampling has been employed to determine soil compositional aspects of mapping unit delineations (Wilding et al., 1965) and to evaluate the utility of specific class criteria as operational differentiae (McCormack and Wilding, 1969). It is also used as a means to withdraw subsample replicates in analytical analysis. Random sampling schemes are unbiased, statistically sound and commonly preferred by statisticians; however, they tend to cluster spacially. That is, the density of observations per unit area and the dispersion of the sites over the delineation are not uniform. Further, with a limited number of observations, many observations may occur at the boundary of the class. In addition, if systematic variation does exist, it will not likely be identified.

For determining mapping unit composition, specific delineations and sites within delineations can be drawn at random from potential delineations screened for areal extent, slope, erosion, cultural features or other bases to stratify the sample. Sites are located in the office on aerial photographs or field sheets so that actual field conditions do not bias the choice of sample sites. A suitable-sized grid with numbered squares can be superposed on the mapping unit delineation at random and sampling points chosen from a random numbers table (Fig. 4.6A). All sites (not just those that fit a particular concept) are observed and recorded. If sufficient observations are made to yield a randomly located point within each grid cell, the sampling scheme would be termed "a stratified random areal sample" (Berry and Baker, 1968) and be similar to grid sampling discussed later.

Characterization of intraclass central tendency and dispersion statistics of

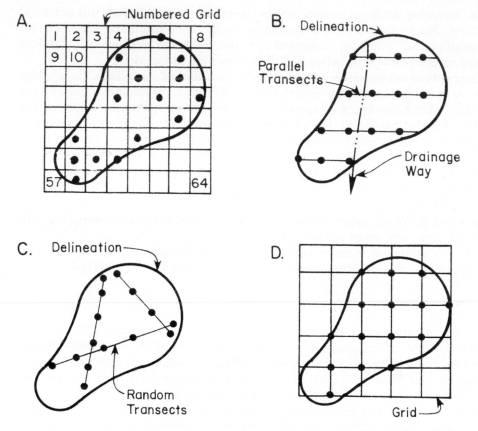

Fig. 4.6. Sampling schemes to determine composition of mapping unit delineations. Observations (●) located at random (A), along parallel point transects (B), along random point transects (C) and at intersection of grid lines (D). Same number of observations in each scheme.

an established taxonomic unit (i.e. soil series) can be accomplished similarly, but the boundary limits are pre-set (Knox, 1965); no sampling scheme will provide information about fiducial limits or ranges for differentiating characteristics because these are defined by the series concept. However, such statistics can be gained on "accidental" or non-covarying properties within the class. When determining the intraclass composition of soils reflecting a given concept, observations can be drawn at random within landscape segments or mapping unit delineations, but sufficient alternate sites must be provided to accommodate observations clearly outside the series range.

In contrast, if a series concept is defined in terms of central tendencies of the nucleus and variability about such a mode (Cline, 1944), boundary limits are not pre-set and differences in class concepts can be statistically differentiated on basis of central tendency and variance statistics; the confidence limits of differentiae can likewise be formulated from this data.

Transect sampling

Point-intercept and line-intercept transect sampling techniques have been used extensively for determining mapping unit composition (Powell and Springer, 1965; Steers and Hajek, 1979), in geographic sampling (Berry and Baker, 1968), and in petrographic analyses (Brewer, 1976). The line-intercept method is appropriate when an observer can visually recognize class boundaries. More commonly, the point-intercept method is used in studying soil-landscape patterns because differentiae demarcating soil boundaries are not readily observable. Transect methods depend on the principle that the total length of a given class along straight-line segments is directly proportional to the area of the class within the limits of the larger area transected. The line-transect method has been criticized because the number of observations necessary for reliable mean estimates is impractically high (White, 1966). Transect sampling, however, can take advantage of various trenches, powerlines or highway excavations which frequently have been pre-aligned independent of soil bias. It has also been used to advantage in remote regions to construct reconnaissance soil surveys where mobility or other restrictions make conventional procedures impractical.

The question of preferred (systematic) versus random transect orientation and the observational interval often arises. Where systematic changes in soil patterns follow landscape features, transects should be oriented normal to such changes for greatest efficiency and maximum extrapolation of results (Fig. 4.6B). Conversely, where landscape features are not apparent (i.e. nearly level, featureless plains) or where vegetation obliterates such features, random transects are in order (Fig. 4.6C). Transects may be oriented parallel to one another with observational intervals adjusted to form a grid pattern (Fig. 4.6B) or they may take the form of a cross to yield three-dimensional control. The observational interval should be dictated by the nature and complexity of the spatial variation. When preliminary sampling indicates close-interval complexity, the magnitude of variability expected in a pedon is first identified; once pedon variability is established, the observational interval can be extended such that reoccurrence of similar conditions is sufficiently frequent that landscape functions, systematic relationships and random error can be partitioned. Establishment of observational intervals may be aided by semivariance (Campbell, 1978) or autocorrelation techniques (Webster and Cuanalo, 1975). Initial observations will be at intervals of a meter or less and increase progressively to tens of meters or more (Schafer, 1979). The spacing of observations is often argued to be independent of statistical probability, but this ignores practical implications of close-interval variation and considerations set forth above. Under given conditions, maximum efficiency may result from intensive sampling of a short segment of a given transect at the expense of multiple transects. Before the question of transect numbers can be answered, close-interval spatial variation must be documented.

Grid sampling

In many studies, the grid sampling scheme (Fig. 4.6D) is preferred because it provides equally spaced observations which are better suited for certain statistical and computer plotting applications (Hock et al., 1973; Burgess and

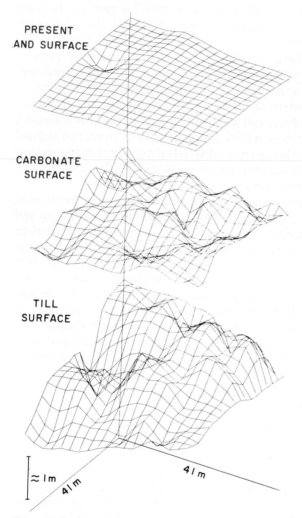

Fig. 4.7. Three-dimensional computer-simulated surface nets of land surface, carbonate surface and till surface (reprinted from fig. 4, Hock et al., 1973, with permission of Soil Science Society of America).

Webster, 1980a). Likewise, this scheme is better adapted to geomorphic—pedogenic interpretations. With elevation control at each sampling site, three-dimensional manual or computer-simulated surface nets can be constructed for limiting zones, diagnostic horizons, stratigraphic and geomorphic elements, pedogenesis, water transmission, chemical transfer and vegetative distribution (Fig. 4.7). The optimum in three-dimensional control is provided with the flexibility to examine a cross-sectional segment at any reference point of interest. Systematic variation as a function of topography is most readily deduced from this design.

Berry and Baker (1968) illustrate several grid-sampling schemes that differ by the method used to select the observational point within the grid. If chosen on the intersection of the grid axes, then it is termed *"systematic aligned"*; if the point is elected within the grid cell such that one of the x or y coordinate lengths is fixed and the other is determined at random, then the sampling scheme is termed *"stratified systematic unaligned"*. They suggest that if the shape of the autocorrelation function (or semi-variance) is unknown and linear trends or periodicities are expected to occur, coupling of stratification and randomization to the systematic unaligned sample appears to yield both the greatest efficiency and safety to estimation procedures. Presumably, the systematic aligned sample network would be the simplest system to interpret for semi-variance because sample distances and direction are rigidly fixed and specific from point to point.

Another sampling design that can be constructed from grid or coordinate overlaps is the *two-stage hierarchical sample* (Berry and Baker, 1968; Nortcliff, 1978). Study areas or blocks are selected with random pairs of coordinates, and then points are selected at random within blocks. Such a sampling scheme nicely accommodates a nested sampling design (Nortcliff, 1978).

MAGNITUDE OF SOIL VARIABILITY

Why study soil variability? Basically, the reason for soil surveys is to delineate units which contain less-variable soil conditions than the population of soils as a whole. The utility of any classification system depends upon the precision of statements that can be made about taxa at lower versus higher categorical levels. Likewise, the utility of any soil map depends upon the precision of statements that can be made about delineated units versus the area as a whole. For both these considerations, the cause(s) and magnitude of soil variability must be understood before taxonomic or cartographic units can be adequately defined or pedogenic processes elucidated.

When comparing data of samples collected from several sampling entities (pedons, field plots, mapping-unit delineations, landscape elements, etc.), some assessment of random versus systematic variability must be made. The magnitude of sampling and laboratory errors must be established, if the probability of two observations being significantly different from each other is to be determined. The rationale holds independent of the magnitude of the differences. A common question is: "How many observations are necessary to estimate the mean of a given property within specified confidence limits?" The response depends on the magnitude of variability within the population for the parameter in question and the probability level placed on the confidence limits. In other words, what is the probability that the number of observations made will be sufficient to yield mean estimates within the desired limits? Hence, whether quantifying pedogenesis, designing mapping-unit legends for soil surveys, determining crop responses to a given set of management systems, or identifying soil property-plant growth responses, a knowledge of soil variability is fundamental.

The magnitude of spatial variability reported in the literature is difficult to compare because few scientists use comparable sampling schemes or observational intervals (Campbell, 1979). In the absence of on-site information, the mean CV's and ranges given in Figs. 4.8—4.11 for selected morphological, physical and chemical properties may be utilized as general

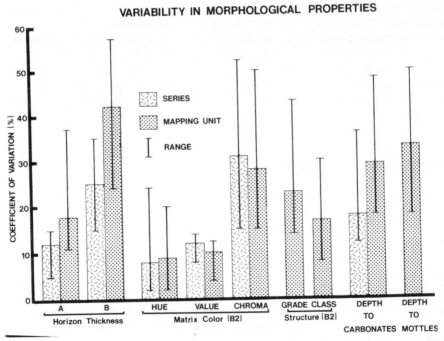

Fig. 4.8. Observed variability among selected morphological properties as a function of landscape units (mapping unit delineations) and respective series concepts (reprinted from fig. 1, Wilding and Drees, 1978, with permission of Soil Science Society of America).

VARIABILITY IN PHYSICAL AND CHEMICAL PROPERTIES

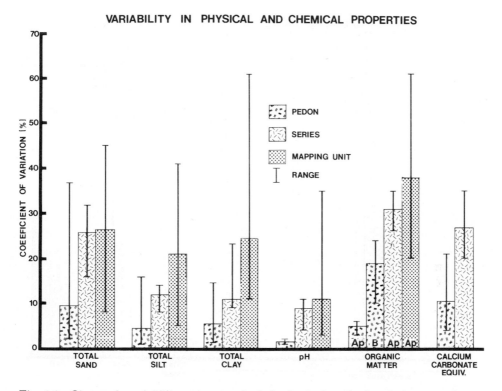

Fig. 4.9. Observed variability among selected physical and chemical properties as a function of pedons, landscape units (mapping unit delineations) and respective series concepts (reprinted from fig. 2, Wilding and Drees, 1978, with permission of Soil Science Society of America).

guides in designing sampling schemes. These illustrations represent a summary of published and unpublished work by the authors and similar work taken from the literature. They represent several hundred pedons over a wide range of soil conditions, parent materials, geography, sampling schemes and nature of units sampled. Much of the data come from temperate regions which have Mollisols and Alfisols developed from loessial or glacio-fluvial deposits. Site-specific variability should be gained for the area in question as soon as plausible because ranges in these *CV* data clearly indicate soil and site specificity.

These data also illustrate that the magnitude of variability generally increases with increasing scale factor from pedons to polypedons to mapping units of a given series to all soils within the survey area (Fig. 4.12). Taxonomic units (pedons and polypedons) are more specific because they have restrictive ranges in differentiating and accessory properties while cartographic units (mapping units) are more inclusive; the latter are land-

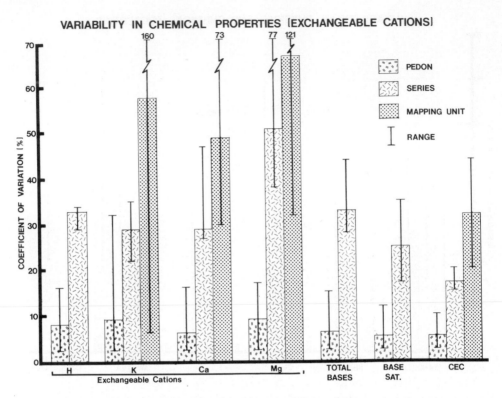

Fig. 4.10. Observed variability among selected cation exchange properties as a function of pedons, landscape units (mapping unit delineations) and respective series concepts (reprinted from fig. 3, Wilding and Drees, 1978, with permission from Soil Science Society of America).

scape counterparts portraying taxonomic units plus any unmappable soil entities as inclusions. Thus, CV's for most properties in mapping units are centered on 25—40%; series concepts (polypedons) are commonly 1/2 to 2/3 of these values, and pedons commonly exhibit CV's of 5—10% or less (Figs. 4.8—4.10). Chemical parameters, especially exchangeable Ca, Mg and K, are extremely variable with mean CV's of 50 to 70% and ranges up to 160% (Fig. 4.10). Spatial variability in physical properties [i.e. Atterberg limits, particle-size distribution, bulk density and water content (Figs. 4.9 and 4.11)] is commonly much less than observed hydraulic conductivities from the same area (Nielson et al., 1973; Babalola, 1978). These workers observed CV's ranging from 50 to 150% for hydraulic conductivity (K); the application of a mean K-value could result in an error of ± 100 orders of magnitude. Schafer (1979) in Montana and McCallister and Hossner (1981) in Texas have recently determined physical and chemical variability in mixed mine-spoil materials. Lithological composition and chemical variability

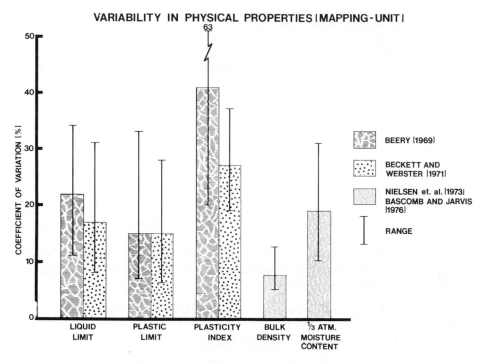

Fig. 4.11. Variability in Atterberg Limits, bulk density and water retention within landscape units (mapping-unit delineations).

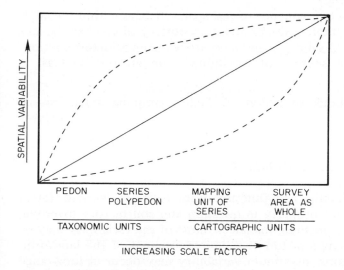

Fig. 4.12. Schematic spatial variability reflecting increasing scale factor (modified from fig. 4, Wilding and Drees, 1978).

(especially water soluble bases, sulfate-S and total-S) are extreme with CV's of 100 to 250% over lateral distances of 10 m or less.

Mausbach et al. (1980), in a variability study of morphologically matched pedons, have observed the following generalized order of spatial variability:

Physical properties $\begin{cases} \text{loess} < \text{glacial drift} < \text{alluvium} \simeq \text{residium} \\ \text{A} \simeq \text{B} < \text{C horizons} \\ \text{no consistent trend among soil orders} \end{cases}$

Chemical properties $\begin{cases} \text{loess} < \text{glacial drift, alluvium and residuum} \\ \text{A} \simeq \text{B} < \text{C horizons (except for pH and sum of} \\ \quad \text{cations)} \\ \text{Vertisols} < \text{Mollisols} \simeq \text{Alfisols} < \text{Entisols} \simeq \\ \quad \text{Inceptisols} \simeq \text{Ultisols} < \text{Spodosols} \end{cases}$

Drees and Wilding (1973), supported by other unpublished work by the authors, suggest the following generalized array of spatial variability for physical, chemical and elemental properties:

Loess < glacial till < glacial outwash $\simeq$ glacial lacustrine $\simeq$ alluvium
Elemental K $\simeq$ Ti $\leqslant$ Zr < Fe $\leqslant$ Ca
No consistent trend among A, B and C horizons

While the magnitude of spatial variability in a landscape body remains constant, our perception of this variability is dependent on the choice of representative sampling units (pedons) and subsequent analyses of these units (Mausbach et al., 1980).

Soil variability is thus a consequence of real space changes within the landscape body, choice of a sampling site or pedon to portray those changes, and systematic or random field sampling and laboratory errors of determination. The magnitude of these sources of variability from greatest to least is proposed as follows:

Landscape body $>>>$ Choice of pedon $>>$ Pedon sampling $>$ Laboratory analyses

SCALE FACTOR AND SPATIAL VARIABILITY

Changes in spatial variability as a function of increasing scale factor (areal extent) depend on the soil property in question and soil factors governing spatial change (Fig. 4.12). In some instances, most of the variability may be over the area encompassing a pedon or a limited segment of the landform. Under other soil conditions, maximum variability may occur at long-range intervals corresponding to mapping units, geomorphic units, or the survey area as a whole. Spatial variability with increasing scale factor may be either linear or curvilinear (Nortcliff, 1978). For example, in Vertisols maximum variability may occur over an area of 1—10 m^2 while in Oxisols or Ultisols maximum variability might be encountered over an area of 100's, 1000's, 10,000's m^2 or larger. This consequence is dependent on both systematic and random spatial change.

Tidball (1976) found the geochemical variability for thirty-one elements in surficial horizons of soils in Missouri was most closely correlated with variation among soil series. No more than 45% and commonly less than 35% of the total variation in these elements was accounted for by differences among soil suborders; variation among soil series was generally larger than variation within areas of a given series. Williams and Rayner (1977) found elemental variability of Ti, Zr, Ca and K to be substantially greater in a soil series sampled from a total area of 6 km^2 than similar work by Drees and Wilding (1973) in a sampling unit of 1—2 m^2.

Schafer (1979) observed that soils developed in mine-spoil materials were more variable than natural soils at a lateral scale of 0—10 m while natural soils were more variable at a scale of >500 m. For example, in natural soils 50—75% of the total variability in soil texture, color, root abundance, A-horizon thickness and depth to carbonates exists at distances >500 m while soils developed from recent mine spoils exhibit comparable variability at a scale of < 10 m. Variation in natural soil properties was correlated with geomorphic variables while soils from mine spoils were dependent on lithologic composition as a function of mining and reclamation methods. Spatial variability in soils from mine spoils is primarily random while systematic variability is dominant in natural soils.

One of the soil properties that exhibits marked short-range spatial variability is hydraulic conductivity. For example, Babalola (1978) observed that CV's for hydraulic conductivity were only slightly greater for a 92 ha field than they were for an 0.3 ha plot of the same soil type. He attributed high local variability to spatial changes in particle-size distribution and bulk density. This is particularly important considering that many of the driving forces governing pedogenesis are dependent on rates and vectors of chemical and water transport. Bouma (Chapter 9) emphasizes the importance of pore-size distribution, pore continuity, and structural attributes of soils to water movement, chemical transformations and consequent leaching potentials. These may vary markedly within a pedon.

Considerably greater short-range spatial variability occurs in soil properties than has been historically recognized. For example, the variability within a single mapping-unit delineation often is greater than among delineations of the same unit (Wilding et al., 1965; McCormack and Wilding, 1969). Variability in parent deposits is such that marked differences may occur over lateral distances of only a few meters or less (Protz et al., 1968; Hock et al., 1973). Variability within a sampling unit (pedon) may be sufficiently great to warrant special sampling considerations to enhance accuracy of mean estimates (Drees and Wilding, 1973; Smeck and Wilding, 1980). Beckett and Webster (1971) suggest that up to half the variability between similar soils occurs within a distance of 1 m. Even micromorphic spatial variation of pore-size distribution, argillans and other microfabric features may be considerable over the distance of only a few millimeters or less (Blevins et al., 1970; Murphy and Banfield, 1978; McKeague et al., 1980). Recognition of this fact has spurred further efforts to document small-scale soil variability in an attempt to identify systematic relationships and to establish probable sampling errors over a wider spectrum of soil conditions.

On a scale approximating that of a sampling site or pedon (an area of 1 m^2), lateral variability in physical and chemical properties within horizons or subhorizons that appear morphologically uniform may still be significant. These changes represent unidentified variation attributed to field sampling and laboratory errors of determination. The precise origin may reflect one or more of the sources identified under the section "Random variation". When interpreting data from several sets of pedons representing different kinds of soils, a measure of sampling and analytical errors must be available before one can make reasonable judgments concerning differences that may exist among soils sampled. Such information bears heavily on soil fertility, soil chemistry, soil mechanics, hydrology, pedogenesis and soil-management considerations. Based on previous work by the authors (Figs. 4.13—4.16), CV's for most physical and chemical properties within pedons average < 10% and range from < 5 to 30%. Ball and Williams (1968) reported CV's of 35—40% for exchangeable K, Ca and Mg. To better understand short-range spatial variability in three-dimension, grid sampling schemes with elevation control are useful (see "Sampling Schemes" section).

PEDOLOGICAL IMPLICATIONS

General order of soil variability

Considering our present base of inference (Figs. 4.8—4.11), the general order of soil variability expected within a natural landscape unit (i.e. mapping-unit delineation of a series) is given in Table 4.2. For all of the most variable properties and some of the moderately variable ones, mean estimates within ± 10% (at a 95% confidence level) are unrealistic because of the impractically large number of observations required (Table 4.1). In this context, a knowledge of spatial variability will permit the pedologist to predict more meaningful confidence limits at appropriate probability levels (i.e. ± 20% of the mean with a confidence level of 70%; Table 4.1).

TABLE 4.2

Variability of soil properties that occur in landscape units of a few hectares, or less, in size

Variability of property	Number of profiles needed *	Property
Least (CV's < 15%)	> 10	Soil color (hue and value) Soil pH Thickness of A horizon Total silt content Plasticity limit
Moderate (CV's 15—35%)	> 10—25	Total sand content Total clay content Cation exchange capacity Base saturation Soil structure (grade and class) Liquid limit Depth to minimum pH Calcium carbonate equivalent
Most (CV's > 35%)	> 25	B2 horizons and solum thickness Soil color (chroma) Depth to mottling Depth of leaching (carbonates) Exchangeable hydrogen, calcium, magnesium and potassium Fine-clay content Organic-matter content Plasticity index Soluble-salt content Hydraulic conductivity water content

* Employing 95% confidence interval and a limit of accuracy ± 10% of mean.

Variation among pedons

The ability to select a pedon representative of the unit to be sampled is critical to verification of soil properties within a soil survey area. Success in this process is dependent on field knowledge of soil property ranges and distributions over the area, the concept of the soil to be sampled, and the precision with which field judgments can estimate differentiating characteristics. Mausbach et al. (1980) concluded from a study of laboratory measured properties in morphologically matched pedons that increased precision of some morphological properties, such as clay, can be gained when field estimates are closely correlated with laboratory measurements. To obtain needed replication without prohibitive costs, they suggest that satellite

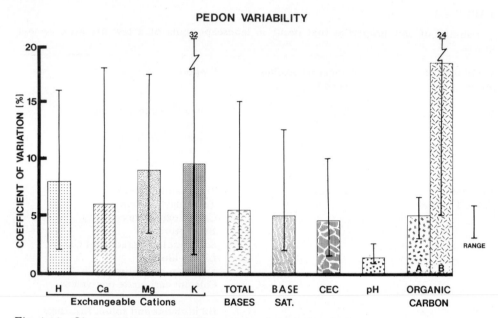

Fig. 4.13. Observed lateral variability among selected chemical properties within horizons of similar morphology for a pedon sampling unit of about 1 m² area (reprinted from fig. 5, Wilding and Drees, 1978, with permission of Soil Science Society of America).

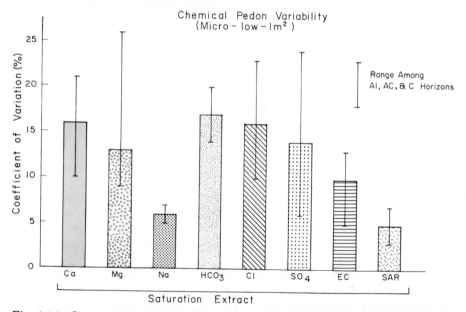

Fig. 4.14. Observed lateral variability of saturation extract parameters within horizons of similar morphology for a pedon sampling unit in Vertisols (about 1 m² area of micro—low gilgai element).

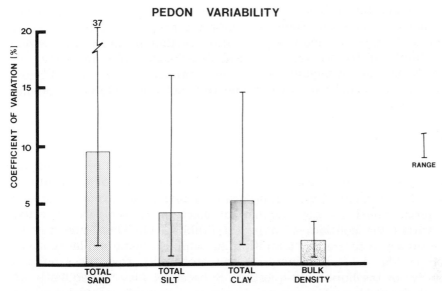

Fig. 4.15. Observed lateral variability of selected particle size and bulk-density properties within horizons of similar morphology for a pedon sampling unit of about 1 m² area (reprinted from fig. 5, Smeck and Wilding, 1980, with permission from Elsevier, The Netherlands).

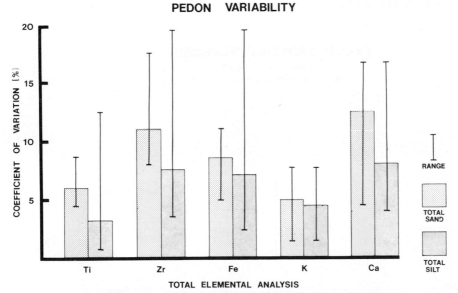

Fig. 4.16. Variability in selected total elemental parameters for particle-size separates sampled within horizons of similar morphology within a pedon sampling unit of about 1 m² area (reprinted from fig. 6, Smeck and Wilding, 1980, with permission from Elsevier, The Netherlands).

samples of important horizons should be collected first to bracket the range of soil concept in question. Then the pedon most representative of the concept may be sampled in detail with confidence that results will be within accepted limits. Thus, to assess vertical distribution of a property, the sampling scheme should include at least one complete pedon plus sufficient additional satellite samples of key horizons to establish acceptable confidence limits of the data.

Variation within pedons

Figures 4.13—4.16 illustrate CV's for commonly measured pedon properties. Considering the relationship between CV and number of observations (Fig. 4.4), the accuracy of estimating property means for given horizons is directly proportional to the number of horizon subsamples collected laterally within the confines of a pedon (Table 4.1). Thus, one way to increase accuracy is to employ a multiple subsample scheme similar to those illustrated in Fig. 4.17; this increases the probability that the sample is representative of the horizon in question. Subsamples may subsequently be composited for analytical purposes, assuming a measure of variance has previously been established to document probable errors for the sampling scheme. Such sampling schemes may not be appropriate for pedons of a cyclic nature, interrupted horizonation, or other kinds of extreme morphological variability.

PEDON SAMPLING SCHEMES
Pedon Area 1-10m^2
Pedon Sampling Interval $^1/_3$ - $^1/_2$m

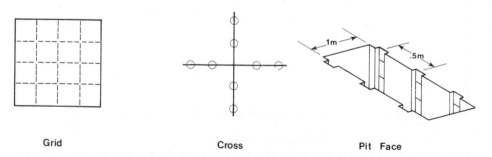

Grid   Cross   Pit Face

Fig. 4.17. Multiple sub-sampling schemes for pedon sampling units (reprinted from fig. 7, Smeck and Wilding, 1980, with permission from Elsevier, The Netherlands).

Employing mean *CV* values for pedon property variation, limit of accuracy as a relative percentage about the mean can be calculated (Table 4.3). Limits about mean estimates can be halved by collecting four horizon subsamples versus one. Advantages of the sampling scheme in increasing the precision of volume factors and quantifying gains and losses accompanying pedogenesis have been considered by Smeck and Wilding (1980). However,

TABLE 4.3

Probable mean errors (values ± relative % of mean with 95% confidence interval) as a function of pedon-sampling method

Property	Probable mean error (%)	
	Normal* sampling (*n* = 1)	Composite* sampling (*n* = 4)
Particle size:		
Sand	19	10
Silt	9	5
Clay	11	6
Organic matter		
Surface	10	5
B horizons	38	19
Bulk density	15	8
pH	3	2
$CaCO_3$ equivalent	21	11
Base saturation	10	5
CEC	10	5
Electrical conductivity	20	10
Exchangeable cations		
H	16	8
K	18	9
Ca	12	6
Mg	18	9
Na	12	6
ESP	14	7
Soluble cations and anions		
Ca	32	16
Mg	26	13
Na	12	6
HCO_3	34	17
Cl	32	16
SO_4	28	14
SAR	10	5

* Normal sampling is defined as one lateral subsample per horizon while composite sampling consists of four lateral subsamples. Composite sampling values assume probable errors not less than errors of laboratory determination.

even the most precise sampling schemes will not identify differences in soil development below 5—10%; these values correspond to analytical errors of property determination.

Pedon variability and Soil Taxonomy

Pedon variability must be appropriately considered in placement of soils in Soil Taxonomy. Class boundaries of the system are rigid, but probable sampling and laboratory errors must be considered in interpreting of the laboratory data in terms of these boundaries. Table 4.4 gives absolute limits

TABLE 4.4

Probable error about selected Soil Taxonomy class boundaries (absolute values with a 95% confidence interval)

Property	Boundary error limits (%)	
	Normal sampling ($n = 1$)	Composite* sampling ($n = 4$)
Particle size		
15% sand	± 2.9	± 1.5
18% clay	± 2.0	± 1.1
35% clay	± 3.9	± 2.1
60% clay	± 6.6	± 3.6
CEC (15 meq/100 g)	± 1.6 meq/100 g	± 0.8 meq/100 g
Base saturation (%)		
35	± 3.5	± 1.8
50	± 5.0	± 2.5
60	± 6.0	± 3.0
75	± 7.5	± 3.8
Organic carbon (%)		
18	± 1.8	± 0.9
12	± 1.2	± 0.6
2.5	± 0.3	± 0.1
0.6	< 0.1	< 0.1
0.2	< 0.1	< 0.1
SAR (13%)	± 1.3	± 0.7
ESP (15%)	± 2.1	± 1.1
Calcium-carbonate equivalent (%)		
15	± 3.2	± 1.7
40	± 8.4	± 4.4
Bulk density (0.95 g/cc)	± 0.14	± 0.08

* Normal sampling is defined as one lateral subsample per horizon while composite sampling consists of four lateral subsamples.

around selected boundaries that correspond to different pedon-sampling schemes (i.e. one or multiple lateral subhorizon sampling). When considering weighted averages of diagnostic horizons, the number of horizons or sub-horizons sampled in a vertical vector that is composited in the weighted value may be considered as approximating multiple subsamples in deter-mining probable errors associated with the weighted mean value. For example, if four Bt subhorizons of an argillic horizon are composited to achieve a weighted clay content, this value may be considered to represent four subsamples for boundary limit probable errors.

It is apparent from Table 4.4 that few properties can be estimated closer than ± 2—3% of the boundary limit even with optimal sampling designs. Under more conventional methods (one lateral subsample), estimates of boundary limits for most properties will not be better than ± 2—6%. Under these constraints, a pedon should not be placed as a variant or taxadjunct of a given series if it exhibits properties that are within specified limits given for class-boundary probable errors. This will avoid misclassification of pedons that meet all other differentiating criteria except for one or two properties that lie within class-limit boundary probable errors.

REFERENCES

Adams, J.A. and Wilde, R.H., 1976a. Variability within a soil mapping unit mapped at the soil type level in the Wanganui district. I. Morphological variation. N.Z. J. Agric. Res., 19:165—176.
Adams, J.A. and Wilde, R.H., 1976b. Variability within a soil mapping unit mapped at the soil type level in the Wanganui district. II. Chemical variation. N.Z. J. Agric. Res., 19:435—442.
Amos, D.F. and Whiteside, E.P., 1975. Mapping accuracy of a contemporary soil survey in an urbanizing area. Soil Sci. Soc. Am. Proc., 39:937—942.
Arnold, R. and Schargel, R., 1978. Importance of geographic soil variability at scales of about 1:25,000 — Venezuelan example. In: Diversity of Soils in the Tropics. SSSA Spec. Publ., 34:45—64.
Babalola, O., 1978. Spatial variability of soil water properties in tropical soils of Nigeria. Soil Sci., 126:269—279.
Ball, D.F., 1976. Site and soils. In: S.B. Chapman (Editor), Methods in Plant Ecology. Blackwell, London.
Ball, D.F. and Williams, W.M., 1968. Variability of soil chemical properties in two uncul-tivated brown earths. J. Soil Sci., 19:379—391.
Ball, D.F., Williams, W.M. and Hornung, M., 1970. Variability of chemical properties in "uniform" soils. Welsh Soils Disc. Group, Rep. 11:31—40.
Bascomb, C.L. and Jarvis, M.G., 1976. Variability in three areas of the Denchworth soil map unit I: Purity of the map unit and property variability within it. J. Soil Sci., 27: 420—437.
Beckett, P.H.T. and Webster, R., 1971. Soil variability: a review. Soils Fert., 34:1—15.
Beery, M.E., 1969. Statistical Summarization of Highway Engineering Data by Soil Mapping Units. M.Sc. Thesis, Ohio State University, Columbus, Ohio.
Belobrov, V.P., 1976. Variation in some chemical and morphological properties of sod-podzolic soils within the boundaries of elementary soil areals and taxonomic groups.

In: V.M. Fridman (Editor), Soil Combinations and their Genesis. Amerind, New Delhi, pp. 147—158.

Berry, B.J.L. and Baker, A.M., 1968. Geographic sampling. In: B.J.L. Berry and D.F. Marble (Editors), Spatial Analysis — A Reader in Statistical Geography. Prentice-Hall, Englewood Cliffs, New Jersey, 3:91—100.

Blevins, R.L., Holowaychuk, N. and Wilding L.P., 1970. Micromorphology of soil fabric at tree—root—soil interface. Soil Sci. Soc. Am. Proc., 34:460—465.

Brewer, R., 1976. Fabric and Mineral Analyses of Soils. Krieger, Huntington, New York, 482 pp.

Burgess, T.M. and Webster, R., 1980a. Optimal interpolation and isarithmic mapping of soil properties. I. The semi-variogram and punctual kriging. J. Soil Sci., 31:315—331.

Burgess, T.M. and Webster, R., 1980b. Optimal interpolation and isarithmic mapping of soil properties. II. Block kriging. J. Soil Sci., 31:333—341.

Campbell, J.B., 1978. Spatial variation of sand content and pH within single contiguous delineations of two soil mapping units. Soil Sci. Soc. Am. J., 42:460—464.

Campbell, J.B., 1979. Spatial variability of soils. Assoc. Am. Geogr., 69:544—556.

Cameron, D.R., 1978. Variability of soil water retention curves and predicted hydraulic conductivities on a small plot. Soil Sci., 126:364—371.

Cassel, D.K. and Bauer, A., 1975. Spatial variability in soils below depth of tillage: bulk density and fifteen atmosphere percentage. Soil Sci. Soc. Am. Proc., 39:247—250.

Cline, M.C., 1944. Principles of soil sampling. Soil Sci., 58:275—288.

Crosson, L.S. and Protz, R., 1974. Quantitative comparison of two closely related soil mapping units. Can. J. Soil Sci., 54:7—14.

Daniels, R.B., Gamble, E.E. and Cady, J.G. 1971. The relation between geomorphology and soil morphology and genesis. Adv. Agron., 23:51—61.

Davis, F.L., 1936. A study of the uniformity of soil types and of the fundamental differences between the different soil series. Alaska Agric. Exp. Stn. Bull., 244:1—153.

Drees, L.R. and Wilding, L.P., 1973. Elemental variability within a sampling unit. Soil Sci. Soc. Am. Proc., 37:82—87.

Dreimanis, A. and Vagners, U.J., 1971. Biomodal distribution of rock and mineral fragments in basal tills. In: R.P. Goldthwait (Editor), Till: A Symposium. Ohio State University Press, Columbus, Ohio, pp. 237—250.

Fridland, V.M., 1976. Soil Combinations and Their Genesis. Amerind, New Delhi, India. pp. 42—47, 147—158, 169—183.

Griffiths, J.C., 1967. Scientific Method in Analysis of Sediments. McGraw-Hill, New York, N.Y., 508 pp.

Hampton, D., Yoder, E.J. and Burr, I.W., 1962. Variability of engineering properties of Brookston and Crosby soils. Highw. Res. Board Proc., 41:621—649.

Harbaugh, J.W. and Merriam, D.F., 1968. Computer Applications in Stratigraphic Analyses. Wiley, New York, N.Y.

Harradine, F.F., 1949. The variability of soil properties in relation to stage of profile development. Soil Sci. Soc. Am. Proc., 14:302—311.

Hock, A.G., Wilding, L.P. and Hall, G.F., 1973. Loess distribution on a Wisconsin-age till plain in southwestern Ohio. Soil Sci. Soc. Am. Proc., 37:732—738.

Huddleston, J.H. and Riecken, E.F., 1973. Local soil—landscape relationships in western Iowa: I. Distributions of selected chemical and physical properties. Soil Sci. Soc. Am. Proc., 37:264—270.

Jacob, W.C. and Klute, A., 1956. Sampling soils for physical and chemical properties. Soil Sci. Soc. Am. Proc., 20: 170—172.

Jenny, H., 1941. Factors of Soil Formation — a System of Quantitative Pedology. McGraw-Hill, New York, N.Y., 281 pp.

Journel, A.G. and Huijbregts, Ch.J., 1978. Mining Geostatistics. Academic Press, London.

Karpachevskii, L.O., 1976. Variation in soil properties depending on the pattern of biogeocenosis. In: V.M. Fridland (Editor), Soil Combinations and their Genesis. Amerind, New Delhi, pp. 179—193.

Kiseleva, N.K., 1976. Variability of exchangeable calcium, magnesium and aluminum in sod-podzolic soils under broad-leaved spruce forest. In: V.M. Fridland (Editor), Soil Combinations and their Genesis. Amerind, New Delhi, pp. 169—178.

Klute, A., 1972. The determination of the hydraulic conductivity and diffusivity of unsaturated soils. Soil Sci., 113:264—276.

Knox, E.G., 1965. Soil individuals and soil classification. Soil Sci. Soc. Am. Proc., 29:79—84.

Lanyon, L.E. and Hall, G.F., 1981. Application of autocorrelation analysis to transect data from a drainage basin in eastern Ohio. Soil Sci. Soc. Am. J., 45:368—373.

Lee, R., Bailey, J.M., Northey, R.D., Barker, P.R. and Gibson, E.J., 1975. Variations in some chemical and physical properties of three related soil types: Dannevirke silt loam, Kriwitea silt loam and Marton silt loam. N.Z. J. Agric. Res., 18:29—36.

Leone, F.C., Nelson, L.S. and Nottingham, R.B., 1961. The folded normal distribution. Technometrics, 3:543—550.

Mausbach, M.J., Brasher, B.R., Yeck, R.D. and Nettleton, W.D., 1980. Variability of measured properties in morphologically matched pedons. Soil Sci. Soc. Am. J., 44:358—363.

McCallister, D.E. and Hossner, L.R., 1981. Spatial variability of selected chemical properties in leveled surface-mined soils. Soil Sci. Soc. Am. J. (in press).

McCormack, D.E. and Wilding L.P., 1969. Variation of soil properties within mapping units of soils with contrasting substrata in northwestern Ohio. Soil Sci. Soc. Am. Proc., 33:587—593.

McIntyre, D.S. and Tanner, C.B., 1959. Abnormally distributed soil physical measurements and nonparametric statistics. Soil Sci., 88:133—137.

McKeague, J.A., Guertin, R.K., Valentine, K.W.G., Belisle, J., Bourbeau, G.A., Howell, A., Michalyna, W., Hopkins, L., Page, F. and Bresson, L.B., 1980. Estimating illuvial clay in soils by micromorphology. Soil Sci., 129:386—388.

Miller, F.P., 1978. Soil survey under pressure: the Maryland experience. J. Soil Water Cons., 33:104—111.

Miller, F.P., Holowaychuk, N. and Wilding, L.P., 1971. Canfield silt loam, a Fragiudalf: II. Micromorphology, physical and chemical properties. Soil Sci. Soc. Am. Proc., 35:324—331.

Miller, F.P., McCormack, D.E. and Talbot, J.R., 1979. Soil surveys: review of data collection methodologies, confidence limits and uses. In: Symposium "The Mechanics of Track Support, Piles, and Geotechnical Data". Trans. Res. Record 733. Trans Res. Board. Natl. Acad. Sci., Washington, D.C., pp. 57—65.

Moormann, F.R. and Kang, B.T., 1978. Microvariability of soils in the tropics and its agronomic implications with special reference to West Africa. In: Diversity of Soils in the Tropics. Soil Sci. Soc. Am., Spec. Publ., 34:29—43.

Murphy, C.P. and Banfield, C.F., 1978. Pore space variability in a sub-surface horizon of two soils. J. Soil Sci., 29:156—166.

Nielson, D.R., Biggar, J.W. and Erh, K.T., 1973. Spatial variability of field-measured soil-water properties. Hilgardia, 42:215—259.

Nortcliff, S., 1978. Soil variability and reconnaissance soil mapping: A statistical study in Norfolk. J. Soil Sci., 29:403—417.

Pomerening, J.A. and Knox, E.G., 1962. Interpolation of Munsell soil color measurements. Soil Sci. Soc. Am. Proc., 26:201—202.

Powell, J.C. and Springer, M.E., 1965. Composition and precision of classification of several mapping units of the Appling, Cecil and Lloyd series in Walton County, Georgia. Soil Sci. Soc. Am. Proc., 29:454—458.

Protz, R., Presant, E.W. and Arnold, R.W., 1968. Establishment of the modal profile and measurement of variability within a soil landform unit. Can. J. Soil Sci., 48:7—19.

Robinson, G.W. and Lloyd, E.W., 1915. On the probable error of sampling in soil surveys. J. Agric. Sci., 7:144—153.

Royle, A.G., 1980. Why geostatistics? In: P.F. Massett-Jones (Editor), Geostatistics. McGraw-Hill, New York, N.Y., pp. 1—13.

Ruhe, R.V., 1975. Geomorphology. Houghton Mifflin, Boston, Mass., 246 pp.

Schafer, W.M., 1979. Variability of mine soils and natural soils in southeastern Montana. Soil Sci. Soc. Am. J., 43:1207—1212.

Schroth, C.L., 1969. Population density functions for nine variables from western Somoa soil profiles. Agron. Abstr., p. 109.

Smeck, N.E. and Wilding, L.P., 1980. Quantitative evaluation of pedon formation in calcareous glacial deposits in Ohio. Geoderma, 24:1—16.

Snedecor, G.W., 1940. Statistical Methods. Iowa State University Press, Ames, Iowa, 485 pp.

Snedecor, G.W. and Cochran, W.G., 1967. Statistical Methods (6th ed.). Iowa State University Press, Ames, Iowa, 593 pp.

Soil Survey Staff, 1975. Soil Taxonomy. A Basic System of Soil Classification for Making and Interpreting Soil Surveys. USDA-SCS Agric. Handbook No. 436. U.S. Govt. Printing Office, Washington, D.C., 754 pp.

Steers, C.A. and Hajek, B.F., 1979. Determination of map unit composition by a random selection of transects. Soil Sci. Soc. Am. J., 43:156—160.

Thornburn, T.H. and Larsen, W.R., 1959. A statistical study of soil sampling. J. Soil Mech. Found. Div., SM5:1—13.

Tidball, R.R., 1976. Chemical variation of soils in Missouri associated with selected levels of the soil classification system. Geol. Surv., Prof. Pap., 954-B. Geochem. Surv. Missouri, U.S. Govt. Printing Office, Washington, D.C., 15 pp.

Van Wambeke, A. and Dudal, R., 1978. Macrovariability of soils of the tropics. In: Diversity of Soils in the Tropics. Soil Sci. Soc. Am., Spec. Publ., 34:13—28.

Vieira, S.R., Nielsen, D.R. and Biggar, J.W., 1981. Spatial variability of field-measured infiltration rate. Soil Sci. Soc. Am. J., 45:1040—1048.

Vznuzdaev, N.A., 1976. Spatial variability of soil moisture and its relation to the pattern of forest biogeocenosis. In: V.M. Fridland (Editor), Soil Combinations and their Genesis. Amerind, New Delhi, pp. 159—168.

Wagenet, R.J. and Jurinak, J.J., 1978. Spatial variability of soluble salt content in a Mancos shale watershed. Soil Sci., 126:342—349.

Webster, R., 1977. Quantitative and Numerical Methods in Soil Classification and Survey. Clarendon, Oxford, 269 pp.

Webster, R. and Burgess, T.M., 1980. Optimal interpolation and isarithmic mapping of soil properties. III. Changing drift and universal kriging. J. Soil Sci., 31:505—524.

Webster, R. and Cuanalo de la C., H.E., 1975. Soil transect correlograms of north Oxfordshire and their interpretation. J. Soil Sci., 26:176—194.

White, E.M., 1966. Validity of the transect method for estimating compositions of soil-map areas. Soil Sci. Soc. Am. Proc., 30:129—130.

Wilding, L.P., 1972. Developing concepts and diagnostic criteria for soil classification. In: Proceedings of a Symposium on Classification of Soils and Sedimentary Rocks. Centre for Resour. Dev., Univ. Guelph, Ontario, CRD Publ. 66.

Wilding, L.P. and Drees, L.R., 1978. Spatial variability: a pedologist's viewpoint. In: Diversity of Soils in the Tropics. Soil Sci. Soc. Am., Spec. Publ., 34:1:1—12.

Wilding, L.P., Jones, R.B. and Schafer, G.M., 1965. Variation of soil morphological properties within Miami, Celina, and Crosby mapping units in west-central Ohio. Soil Sci. Soc. Am. Proc., 29:711—717.

Williams, C. and Rayner, J.H., 1977. Variability in three areas of the Denchworth soil map unit. III. Soil grouping based on chemical composition. J. Soil Sci., 28:180—195.

PEDOLOGY AND GEOMORPHOLOGY

GEORGE F. HALL

INTRODUCTION

The beginning pedologist in first attempts to delineate soils in the field often resorts to a transect or grid approach to determine the boundaries between units. It is only after field experience that the mapper understands the close relationships between soil properties used to make delineations and the micro- and macrochanges in landscape or the geomorphic surfaces of the landscape.

This close relationship should be expected if one considers the definitions of the sciences of pedology and of geomorphology. Pedology [pedon(L) = ground or earth] is the science of the soil, while geomorphology [geo(Gk) = earth; morphos = form] is the science of the shape or form of the earth. Pedology is best defined as the study of the genesis, morphology, distribution and use of soil (Dijkerman, 1974). Geomorphology is the interpretative description of landscapes including an explanation of the history of those landscapes.

In geomorphology the landscape is viewed as an assemblage of landforms which are individually transformed during the process of landscape evolution. Because soils are an integral part of the landforms and the landscape, any study of processes occurring on the landscape has implications for the study of soil processes. Conversely, soil processes are considered by some to be a part of landscape evolution.

Soil for the purpose of this discussion can be thought of in terms of the Soil Taxonomy (Soil Survey Staff, 1975) as a collection of naturally occurring bodies at the surface of the earth that support or are capable of supporting plants. Soil is considered to have formed as a result of the interaction of parent material, climate and living organisms as influenced by relief or topography through time.

Soils form a three-dimensional continuum on the landscape; any study of the soil genesis and distribution requires an understanding of genesis of the landscape. In order to delineate soil boundaries it is necessary to interpret and understand landscapes. In practice, to develop principles of soil—landscape relationships, it is necessary to map soils and geomorphic surfaces independently and then correlate their relationships (Lepsch et al., 1977). It is never permissible, in a new study area, to deduce soils from their landscape position or to deduce geomorphic history from soil properties alone. However, once a soil—geomorphic relationship has been established it is possible to make a number of deductions about soils or geomorphology from a knowledge of the other.

Pedologic studies progressed from the initial parent material biased two-dimensional concept of soil profiles to the somewhat three-dimensional concept emphasized in Simonson's (1959) model of gains, losses, transformations and translocations within the soil system. In practical application, however, this model was too limited. It has become clearer in the past several decades that soils are welded together on a landscape and the processes that occur in the soils of the higher portions of the landscape have an influence on soils that occur in lower parts of the landscape (Ruhe and Walker, 1968; Huggett, 1975). Materials, suspensions and solutions move through and over soil landscapes rather than through only a single soil at a given point on a landscape.

BASIC PRINCIPLES

As noted by Arnold in Chapter 1, soils are very complex natural bodies resulting from the interaction of parent material, vegetation, topography and climate reacting over time. Geomorphic surfaces are also the result of very complex phenomena that are the result of erosion, deposition and tectonic activity at or near the surface of the earth. The resultant soil—landscape interrelationships therefore should be expected to be more complex than either of the two components considered separately.

Prior to any detailed discussion of these relationships a series of definitions is in order. These definitions are not totally accepted by all pedologists or geomorphologists.

Geomorphology: The science that studies the evolution of the earth's surface (Daniels et al., 1971); the science of landforms (Ruhe, 1975); the systematic examination of landforms and their interpretation as records of geologic history (Howell, 1957).

Landforms: Features of the earth that together make up the land surface (Ruhe, 1969); physical, recognizable forms and features produced by natural causes. Taken together landforms make up the surface configuration of the earth (Bates and Jackson, 1980).

Landscape: The portion of the land surface that the eye can comprehend in a single view (Ruhe, 1969).

Geomorphic surface: A portion of the landscape specifically defined in space and time (Ruhe, 1969); a part of the surface of the land that has definite geographic boundaries and is formed by one or more agencies during a given time period (Daniels et al., 1971).

Erosional surface: A land surface shaped by the action of ice, wind and water; usually as the result of running water (Ruhe, 1975); a land surface shaped by the action of erosion and generally applied to level or nearly level surfaces (Bates and Jackson, 1980).

Constructional surface: A land surface owing its character to the process of upbuilding, such as accumulation by deposition (Bates and Jackson, 1980).

GEOMORPHIC SURFACES

A geomorphic surface has been defined earlier as a portion of the land surface specifically defined in time and space (Ruhe, 1969). The surface is a mappable unit that has no size limit and may include a number of land-forms and landscapes. It is usually defined in relation to other geomorphic surfaces and is datable by relative or absolute means. The surface may be erosional or constructional and is often a combination of both.

Although the pedologist in delineating soil boundaries has long understood that the development of distinct soil characteristics (laterite formation, clay pans, caliche, etc.) were related to distinct portions of the landscape, Ruhe (1956) is usually given credit for formally introducing the study of geomorphic surfaces to soil cartography and genesis studies.

Usually more than one geomorphic surface occurs in a given area. When expressed as erosion surfaces they commonly form a series of steps with the age of the surfaces or steps decreasing from higher to lower surfaces. Tectonic activities and variations in bedrock lithology can produce landscape morphologies that are confused with stepped erosion surfaces. Multiple erosion surfaces are most easily identified and correlated in a limited geographic area; however, it has been suggested that correlated stepped surfaces may occur in stable regions throughout the world (Geyl, 1961).

Absolute dating of geomorphic surfaces is usually difficult. It is often easier to get a maximum or relative date. If organic material is buried in a deposit and youthful enough to be within the range of radiocarbon dating, it is possible to obtain an absolute date for the deposit. Most datable material is buried at some depth so that the top portion of the deposit and the geomorphic surface are always younger than the dated material. On active erosional surfaces the geomorphic surface may be much younger than the buried material.

Soil development does not commence until erosion or deposition has reached a steady state. From this assumption it is clear that the soil on a surface is younger than material in which it forms and younger than the surface on which it forms (Ruhe, 1969, p. 165).

In most areas absolute dates of surfaces are not available so dating of erosional surfaces must be relative. Within a given region erosional surfaces can be traced for considerable distances using the basic principle set forth by Trowbridge (1921) and discussed by Ruhe (1975) and Daniels et al. (1971). The principles are most easily applied in tectonically stable areas. These principles state that an erosion surface: (1) is younger than any surface or material that it cuts; (2) is younger than any structure that it bevels; (3) is younger than a formation contributing fragments and fossils to the alluvial deposits on the surface; (4) is the same age as the alluvial deposits that lie on the surface; (5) is the same age or older than the terrestrial deposits that lie on it; (6) is older than a valley cut into and below it; (7) is younger than the erosion remnant above it; (8) is older than or contemporaneous with deposits in the valley below it; (9) is younger than adjacent surfaces occurring at higher levels; and (10) is older than adjacent surfaces occurring at lower levels.

Figures 5.1, 5.2, 5.3 and 5.4 illustrate these and other stratigraphic principles.

The establishment of a relationship between geomorphic surfaces and soils led to testing in a number of geographic areas (Bridges, 1967; Ruhe 1969, 1975; Daniels et al., 1970; Gamble et al., 1970; Parsons et al., 1970; Malo et al., 1974; Parsons and Herriman, 1976; Lepsch et al., 1977; Gile et al., 1981; Peterson, 1981).

In North Carolina, Gamble et al. (1970) worked with soils on surfaces that ranged in age from Pliocene to Holocene. The soils on the oldest surface were relatively uniform as a result of uniformity of the parent material and

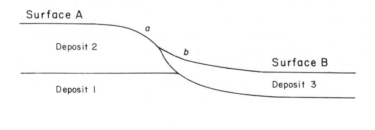

Fig. 5.1. Depositional sequences (after Daniels et al., 1971). Deposit *1* is older than deposit *2* because of the law of superposition: unless overturned a younger bed overlies an older bed in a sedimentary sequence. Deposit *3* is younger than deposits *1* and *2*. The basal surface of deposit *3* represents an erosion surface cut prior to or at the time of emplacement of deposit *3*. An erosion surface is younger than any structure that it bevels. Surface *A* is younger than deposits *1* and *2*. Surface *B* is younger than surface *A* because it bevels the deposits underlying surface *A* and surface *B* cuts surface *A*. Portion *a* of surface *B* is the erosional element and portion *b* is the depositional element. Many surfaces have both an erosional and depositional component. Without datable material no absolute ages can be assigned to the various surfaces and deposits.

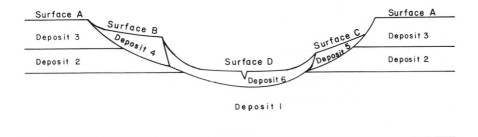

Fig. 5.2. Relationship of surfaces and deposits using stratigraphic criteria (after Daniels et al., 1971). Deposit *4* is emplaced on a surface that bevels deposits *2* and *3* and cuts surface *A*, therefore, deposit *4* is younger than deposit *3* and surface *A*. Surface *B* cuts surface *A* so is younger than surface *A*. Surface *C* is younger than surface *B* because it is at a lower level. Surface *D* is younger than surfaces *B* and *C* because it cuts these two surfaces. Deposit *6* is younger than deposits *1* and *2* because it bevels those deposits.

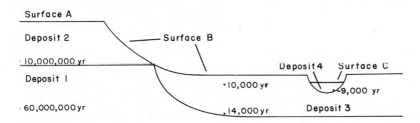

Fig. 5.3. Relationships of surfaces using stratigraphy and isotopic dating (after Daniels et al., 1971). Through the use of isotopic dating and fossil identification it is possible to assign dates to deposits and surfaces. In this example, it is known that the ages of deposits *1* and *2* are 60,000,000 and 10,000,000 yrs, respectively. The erosional portion of surface *B* we can assign it an age of less than 10,000,000 yrs. A radiocarbon date of 14,000 yrs from the base of deposit *3* establishes that the deposit is less than that age. A radiocarbon date from material just below surface *B* is 10,000 yrs. Thus we can see from the relationship that the erosion and deposition phases of the surface are less than 10,000 yrs. The dating of material in deposit *4* which fills a surface cut into and below surface *B* establishes that surface *B* erosion and deposition occurred between 10,000 and 9000 yrs. Surface *C* is less than 9000 yrs but from the information given a more precise date cannot be established.

influence of soil processes over millions of years. The soils of the backslope surfaces were more variable as a result of truncation of the weathering zone. In the same region, Daniels et al. (1970) showed that soil changes across the upper and middle Coastal Plains were related to geomorphic surfaces. Solum thickness and plinthite and gibbsite content increased from the youngest to the oldest surface. This relationship was complicated by water-table regimes and was not linear.

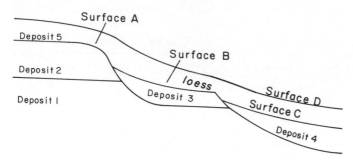

Fig. 5.4. Depositional landscapes (after Daniels et al., 1971). Relative ages of surfaces *A—C* are the same as discussed in Fig. 5.3. Deposit *5* (loess in this example) has been added to the entire landscape as a relatively uniform blanket. It has a tendency to homogenize the landscape. Although the surficial expression of each of the buried surfaces is still present, surface *D* has a single age.

Lepsch et al. (1977) studied the geomorphic surface—soil relationship in tropical Brazil and determined that in general different surfaces had different soils but that more than one soil could be found on a given geomorphic surface.

In the midwest United States, Malo et al. (1974) found that landscape position dictated the magnitude of the geomorphic processes of erosion and sedimentation which in turn affected the soils and their properties. They concluded that their hillslope model provided a framework for evaluating the interaction of pedogenic and geomorphic processes; the hillslope soils represented a continuum and thus soil properties could be treated as continuous rather than discrete variables.

In the Willamette Valley of Oregon, seven geomorphic surfaces and associated soils were mapped by Parsons et al. (1970). The surfaces, traced visually throughout the valley, ranged in age from Pleistocene to Holocene. Although the soils showed a trend of increasing development on successively older geomorphic surfaces, not all the soils in a given geomorphic delineation exhibited the same degree of profile development. They attributed this difference in development to more recent pedisediment on some parts of the surface. They concluded that more detailed geomorphic mapping would have separated these different soils. In the Upper Rogue River Valley of Oregon, Parsons and Herriman (1976) identified six geomorphic surfaces. Ages of the soil—geomorphic surfaces were similar to those in the Willamette Valley. They noted that similar soil—geomorphic surface relationships had been observed in other parts of the western United States and in New Zealand. From their study it was concluded that the sequence of surfaces provided either an absolute or relative means of evaluating soil development.

Ruhe (1956) studied soils on three-stepped geomorphic surfaces in western Iowa. The age of the surfaces ranged from an estimated several hundred thousand years to 6800 yrs. The mineral weathering and soil development on the surfaces were in accord with the anticipated weathering and development trends based on the age of the surfaces.

In the SCS Desert Project area near Las Cruces, New Mexico fifteen geomorphic surfaces and associated soils were mapped as part of an integrated study of geology, geomorphology and soils (Ruhe, 1967; Hawley, 1975; Gile and Grossman, 1979). Detailed geologic—geomorphic and soil—geomorphic relationships were described by Gile et al. (1981). Surfaces range from Early Pleistocene to Holocene and have been dated using tephrochronology, vertebrate paleontology, radiometric methods. The Holocene climate in the Rio Grande Valley and adjacent intermontane basins ranges from arid to semi-arid (Gile, 1975, 1977); but the Pleistocene surfaces and soils (relict, buried, exhumed) reflect complex geomorphic histories involving both climate—vegetation changes and tectonism. An important aspect of Desert Project research concerned genesis of argillic, cambic and calcic horizons of soils associated with both relict and buried surfaces.

SOIL-LANDSCAPE RELATIONSHIPS

Soil landscape

Each soil occupies space and is described in three dimensions. It has definable boundaries and can be mapped. Thus, soils are emplaced upon landforms and landscapes. The geographic distribution of soils on landscapes is the soil landscape (Ruhe, 1975). Different surface and subsurface processes occur on different parts of the landscape. In order to communicate it is necessary to accept some uniformity in landscape terminology.

A number of attempts have been made to identify and define the parts of the landscape in both profile and areal distribution. One of the early attempts was by Wood (1942) in which he segmented the slope profile into four units: waxing slope, free face, debris slope and pediment (Fig. 5.5). Ruhe (1960) modified and renamed the various segments suggested by Wood (1942) and after some further modification has identified five elements in a "fully developed hillslope": summit, shoulder, backslope, footslope and toeslope (Fig. 5.5). In his discussion of hillslopes, Ruhe describes the geometric relationships and some of the surficial geomorphic processes that are ongoing or have caused the slope to evolve. He does not, however, give details about the contemporary processes occurring in the surface mantle, of which the soil constitutes a part.

A somewhat different approach was taken by Conacher and Dalrymple (1977) in an attempt to characterize the landsurface. Their approach was to use the catena concept and define the slope as a three-dimensional unit extending from the summit to the valley floor. In their landscape-catena model they identified and defined landscape units according to responses

124

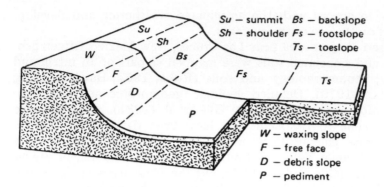

Fig. 5.5. Hillslope elements (after Ruhe, 1975). Foreground from Wood (1942) and background from Ruhe (1960).

to contemporary pedogeomorphic processes. In their definition they were particularly interested in the interactions among soil materials and mobilization, translocation and redeposition of this entity by water and gravity. Their final model consisted of nine landsurface units which are defined in terms of responses to pedomorphic processes operating on a natural landscape unit.

Catena

The catena as presented by Milne (1936a, b) considered the interlocking of soils on a landscape. The word itself is derived from the latin word for chain. The concept of catena has been modified (Bushnell, 1942) and is now used almost interchangeably with toposequence by many, particularly in the United States. Toposequence presently carries with it a morphologic connotation; a change in colors, predominantly a change in grayness, that is related to relative elevation and thus to changes in hydrology. Catena on the other hand carries with it a process-response connotation. The soils of a catena differ not only in morphology but are considered to differ as a result of erosion, transport and deposition of surficial material as well as leaching, translocation and deposition of chemical and particulate constitutents in the soil.

Milne (1936a, b) used the term catena as a mapping unit to describe a regular repetition of soils on a landscape. He considered two types of catenas. In one where the parent rock was uniform; the differences in soils in the catena were the result of differences in drainage and differences due to lateral movement of materials both at the surface and in the subsurface. In the other there was more than one type of parent rock that influenced soil genesis. Discussions in this paper will be limited to the single-material concept.

The original concept of the catena which involved processes causing differentiation along hillslopes as well as processes causing vertical differentiation of soil horizons has been used by many, particularly those outside the United States, to study soil genesis (Greene, 1945, 1947; Dan and Yaalon, 1964; Dan et al., 1968; Huggett, 1975, 1976).

Limiting the catena to a sequence of soils that differ only in hydrologic characteristics ignores the often subtle erosional and sedimentological processes that are constantly occurring on most landscapes. The morphology and processes of each member of the catena is related to every other member of that catena. The members of the catena are continuously adjusting to the environmental changes of the given landscape (Dan and Yaalon, 1964).

Processes in a catena

Recognition of the catena as a basic landscape unit by Milne (1936a) and as a soil or landscape unit by many others has led to the study of the interrelationship of the soils that occur in a catena. Morison et al. (1948) draw a parallel between the processes in a soil profile and the processes in a soil catena. They regarded them both as containing eluvial, colluvial and illuvial portions. Since that time many other workers have studied the movement of materials, both surface and subsurface, on the landscape and the influence of these movements on soil properties (Dan and Yaalon, 1964; Walker and Ruhe, 1968; Smeck and Runge, 1971).

Huggett (1975) and Conacher and Dalrymple (1977) considered the catena to be a two-dimensional concept and stressed that the processes that operated on the landscape were three-dimensional in nature. Huggett defined the boundaries on his soil landscape as the drainage divide, the surface of the land and the base of the soil profile. Conacher and Dalrymple identified their landsurface catena as extending from the center of the interfluve to the stream channel bed and from the base of the soil to the soil—air interface.

Basic to the discussion is the assumption that there exist on the landscape flowlines of material both at the surface and in the subsurface. These flowlines run straight only where the material is uniform and where contour lines are parallel. Wherever curvature occurs in the contour, the flowlines converge or diverge. Contours that are concave downslope lead to convergent flowlines and convex contours lead to divergent flowlines. On the landscape, flow tends to converge in the coves (headslopes) and diverge on the end of spurs (noseslopes).

On most landscapes the movement of water is the primary cause of material movement on slopes. Water movement and distribution on slopes is the principal reason for differences in soils on the landscape. Although overland flow is the most obvious and often dramatic process of water distribution, it is now evident that water movement in the soil horizons below the surface is more important than overland flow in soils of the humid region.

126

Subsurface lateral flow may be either saturated or unsaturated with saturated flow being dominant in concave positions near the base of the slope or where flowlines converge as the result of changes in contour (Kirkby and Chorley, 1967; Anderson and Burt, 1978).

Most soils are assumed to be anisotropic. The anisotropy is the result of non-uniform deposition of materials, processes related to profile development, or the result of an increase in density with depth in uniform materials. Zaslavsky and Rogowski (1969) demonstrated that anisotropy accentuated soil profile and catena development through the influence on the flow of infiltrating water. In soils that lack uniform permeability there is a tendency for the water to flow laterally downslope. There is a tendency for hydraulic conductivity to decrease with depth in the soil. Bear et al. (1968) determined that the hydraulic conductivity vertically downward through a soil profile is always smaller than the hydraulic conductivity parallel to the layers. Again, once the water enters the soil it has a tendency to move downslope.

Slopes have complex curvatures both laterally and vertically. Possible combinations were illustrated and discussed by Troeh (1964). Huggett (1975) used these combinations to illustrate various flow patterns (Fig. 5.6).

Although not using the term catena, Huddleston and Riecken (1973) considered the soils they studied as part of the soil—landscape system and that the soils on the backslope surface were influenced by the processes of erosion and deposition that took place on that slope. The importance of horizontal movement of substances and the genetic interrelationship of soils

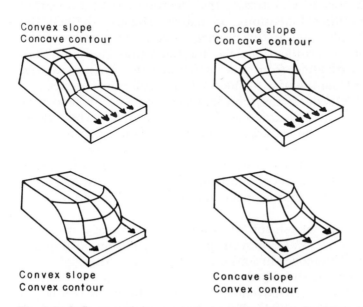

Fig. 5.6. Influence of slope curvature on flowlines (after Huggett, 1975).

on a landscape was also stressed by Fridland (1972). He believed it was erroneous to draw conclusions about soil genesis from the study of a single profile. Fridland used the term "soil cover pattern" for his landscape association of soils and considered each pattern a part of an infinite chain that was interrelated.

Basic to the catena concept is the movement and distribution of water on slopes. Precipitation on the land surface can follow three major pathways: overland flow, throughflow (interflow) and deep percolation. The amount of moisture following these various pathways is governed by a complex set of interrelated factors. These factors include amount and duration of rainfall, topographic characteristics, permeability of the soil, underlying material, vegetative cover and physical condition of the surface of the soil.

A major portion of the precipitation leaves the landscape as throughflow along the surface of less permeable subsurface horizons or bedrock or in root channels or dessication cracks. Whipkey (1969) showed that under forested conditions very little of the moisture traveled as overland flow. Most of it moved as throughflow; passing laterally above a less permeable zone that was 90 cm below the surface.

In a field study to confirm some of the theoretical aspects of flow, Huggett (1976) evaluated the lateral translocation in Tertfordshire, England. He concluded that: (1) silt and clay as well as elemental iron, silicon, manganese and aluminum were translocated laterally and contributed significantly to soil development; (2) convergent throughflow in the cove positions resulted in greater movement of soil plasma in that position than in the nose positions where the throughflow pattern was divergent; (3) throughflow of soil plasma and amorphous colloids decreased with depth in the soil; and (4) the process of lateral translocation might be wave-like. Miller et al. (1971) found that 50% of the January—June precipitation ended up as subsurface runoff (throughflow) above a fragipan. In a single month with low transpiration (February), 80% of the precipitation moved downslope as subsurface runoff above the fragipan. Deep percolation is a significant pathway only in depressional landscape positions or in coarse, very permeable materials such as gravel, sand, or coarse volcanic deposits.

The chemical interrelationship of soils on the landscape was pointed out by Glazovskaya (1968). He approached soil sequences as a part of geochemical landscape in which the soils at different elevations were united by lateral elemental migration. The resulting series of soils were considered a "geochemical soil catena".

Water movement downslope can take place as either saturated or unsaturated flow. Blume (1968) emphasized the importance of a perched water table connecting the members of the catena during periods of the year. He found that the perched water table influences the structure, ion exchange, pH and mineral mobility.

Yaalon et al. (1972, 1974) studied the mobility sequence of minor elements on a landscape in Israel. They concluded that the catena can be viewed as a chromatographic column with movement along the slope. Manganese, the most mobile of the elements studied, reached the lowest part of the slope where it precipitated as nodules. Titanium and iron were less mobile and were retained at midslope. The amount and distance moved is largely dependent on the rainfall. Under conditions of high rainfall many of the bases are lost from the catena and the soils on the slope are very similar (Hallsworth et al., 1952).

In addition to material moving in solution, there is evidence that lateral translocation of particles in suspension also takes place below the soil surface. Huggett (1976) concluded that translocation of soil plasma was a significant contributor to soil development and had concatenated the soils in a valley basin. Materials that he considered mobile included silt, clay and amorphous hydrous oxides and hydroxides of Al, Fe, Mn and Si. Dalsgaard et al. (1981) considered the occurrence of an albic horizon on a slope to be the result of lateral subsurface removal of clay, fine silt and iron.

Soil processes

The prediction of the occurrence of soils on specific landscape positions has received considerable attention during the past several decades (e.g. Aandahl, 1948; Young, 1963; Furley 1968, 1971; Beckett, 1968; Blume, 1968; Davidson, 1977; Kirkby, 1977; Dalsgaard et al., 1981). The reemphasis of the catena concept has given rise to better predictions of processes that occur on many parts of the landscape (Huggett, 1975, 1976; Conacher and Dalrymple, 1977). In addition to these formal studies, the field-soil scientist mapping in a region develops a soil predictive ability that is not easy to quantify. However, the development of equations or models to predict the occurrence of soils on landscapes is still fraught with problems.

Soils are the product of a complex interaction of chemical and physical processes that themselves are governed by climatic and geomorphic interactions occurring over time. As climate, geology and relief vary from area to area the interactions change and therefore any predictive model must change.

A number of researchers, particularly Conacher and Dalrymple (1977), have attempted to relate processes and soils to landscape position. Following is a brief summary of processes that occur on the five landscape positions (Ruhe, 1960) and some of the soil properties that may result. The summary is most applicable for humid regions.

Summit

Where the summit is greater than 30 m wide, much of the water is retained on the surface. As a result, this position is considered to be the most stable element of the landscape. Water movement in the soil is predominantly vertical except near the transition to the shoulder or on undulations on the summit. In these situations some lateral water movement and accompanying surface and throughflow movement can be expected. Uniform retention of water results in greater uniformity of soils. Overall the soils on broad summits are more poorly drained than on other landscape positions. On narrow summits or near the shoulder position on broad summits the soils are less poorly drained and are less uniform.

As a result of low gradient and thus greater retention of water on this surface, the soil often has less distinct horizonation than on other positions. Solum thickness is a function of the permeability of the material and the amount and frequency of rainfall. Where materials are very permeable the soils have thicker sola than in comparable soils on adjacent landscape elements. On less permeable materials the soils are diagnostically shallower.

Shoulder

Convexity of slope is the rule for shoulder positions. Surface runoff is maximized in this element resulting in a highly erosional and relatively unstable surface. Depending on the degree of slope, lateral movement of surface material (soil creep) may become an important process on this part of the landscape. Lateral subsurface water movement is usually also a very important process in this position. This subsurface movement is not uniform across the slope but is often concentrated in defined flowlines (peroclines) downslope. In zones of concentrated subsurface flow there is an increase in eluviation often resulting in thicker E (albic) horizons. Where seepage nears the surface, concentrations of iron, manganese, or calcium carbonate may appear as concretions. These concentrations are also not uniform across the slope. Presence and depth of reduced zones in the soil are dependent on subsoil permeability and degree of slope. Solum thickness and organic matter content are usually a minimum on this element of the landscape.

Backslope

The dominant process on backslope positions is transportation of material as well as water. This transport takes place both at the surface and in the subsurface. Surface transport of material may be in the form of flow, slump, surface wash, or creep. This landscape position is therefore considered to be relatively unstable.

On backslopes that are relatively smooth, the surface transport is uniform. In the subsurface, non-uniform transmission of water results in variability across the slope as was the case on the shoulder position.

On backslope positions which have mass movement as a predominant mode of material transport the surface is hummocky. Soils both across and downslope range widely morphologically and in physical and chemical composition.

Overall the soils on backslopes have thinner A horizons than on other landscape positions with the exception of the shoulder position. The B horizons may be thicker due to better drainage and have stronger structural development as a result of more wetting and drying cycles. Where there is an argillic horizon developed, it is thicker and there are more continuous cutans on the peds. Where mass movements are dominant, there is marked variability both in the presence and developement of diagnostic horizons.

Footslope

Concavity is characteristic of this landscape position. The concavity results in deposition from upslope of particulate material as well as material carried in solution. The position is therefore dominantly constructional and relatively unstable. Seepage zones are common and water retention is high. Where channels occur on the superjacent backslope small fans are found on the footslope. Mass movements are common in this position as the result of loading and water saturation during part of the year. Burial may be rapid. Bases and organic matter increase in this landscape position as well as concretions and nodules of Mn, Fe and $CaCO_3$.

Soils in footslope positions are commonly very heterogeneous due to mass movement, irregular seepage and non-uniform deposition. Drainage is usually poorer than on higher landscape positions but may range to well drained on the higher portions of the microrelief. A horizon and pedon thickness are both variable but tend to increase downslope. Irregular or discontinuous soil horizons are common in these soils. Paleosols reflecting drastic changes in climate or vegetation can also be identified in these positions.

Toeslope

The toeslope element is unstable as a result of its dominantly constructional nature. Alluvial materials in the toeslope position are derived from up valley and to some extent from superjacent footslope and backslope positions. Soils on the toeslope are highly variable reflecting periodic flooding, abandoned stream channels (oxbows) and multiple sources of materials. On the lower toeslopes, soil development is absent or minimal and the water table may be high. Higher above the stream the soils are better drained and show more characteristics of profile development. A horizons are often thick as a result of frequent thin deposition of sediments from flooding. Paleosols are common on the toeslope.

IMPLICATIONS OF PALEOSOLS

Although paleosols had been recognized for some time (Joffe, 1936), it was not until the early 1940's that emphasis was placed on their importance as indicators of preexisting climates and processes. In 1943, Bryan and Albritton stated that soils provided a promising method for investigating climatic changes through geologic time. Simonson (1941) discussed morphology of buried soils and said that although they had been little studied they "do hold promise as a key to environmental conditions of past geologic ages".

Soil properties reflect the influence of climate through its influence on soil-forming processes. With changes in the processes there are changes in the soil morphology. It had long been assumed that most soil characteristics were in some type of steady-state relationship with the existing environment. However, some researchers believe that a majority of soil characteristics are retained from former pedological evolution having a different environment (Ruellan, 1971). Identification of those soil properties and understanding their genesis can lead to a better interpretation of the geomorphic history of a given landscape (Ruhe, 1970). Identification of relict features that are clearly not in equilibrium with the present environment is subjective and prudence must be observed when interpreting these features. This interpretation presumes a thorough knowledge of pedologic processes; "... one can reconstitute the past only after having acquired a certain detailed knowledge of what is actually taking place at present." (Ruellan, 1971.)

Paleosols are commonly divided into three groups: (1) buried soils; (2) relict soils; and (3) exhumed soils (Ruhe, 1965; Ruhe et al., 1971; Ruellan, 1971). In all cases these soils developed on landscapes in the past. The *buried (fossil) soil* was formed at the earth's surface and subsequently buried. The depth of burial for consideration as a paleosol is a matter of a contention. Suggestions for ranges of depth required vary from a few centimeters below the surface to a depth below biological activity (Ruellan, 1971). A *relict soil* is one formed at the earth's surface and never buried. Distinct characteristics point to its formation in a different pedologic environment. The identification of relict features may be subjective because it is difficult to conclusively recognize pedogenic features that evolved in a different environmental setting. This is particularly true where soils have undergone a long pedologic evolution. The *exhumed paleosol* has been buried at some time and then later exposed at the surface as a result of erosion. Depending on the amount of erosion, an exhumed soil may have the entire solum intact or may have been truncated so that only a portion of the B horizon remains. Gerasimov (1971) adds another kind of paleosol that is comprised of erosion and redeposition products of modern and ancient soils. In order to identify this paleosol some of the properties of the preexisting soils must have been retained. Identification of this reconstituted paleosol would be very difficult.

The most commonly recognized paleosol is one which has been completely buried by allochthonous material. In a stratigraphic section this type of soil clearly marks a break in the depositional episode. Properties of the buried paleosols are commonly used to deduce the climatic and vegetative conditions of the preexisting landscape. Numerous workers who have studied the physical and chemical characteristics of buried soils caution that this type of deduction is fraught with potential errors (Ruhe, 1965, 1975; Gerasimov, 1971; Working Group on the Origin and Nature of Paleosols, 1971). A key principle is that once a soil is buried it undergoes some distinct chemical and physical alterations. Degradation and transformation take place with the resultant loss or change of initial properties and the acquisition of new ones. Unless the soil is buried where oxygen is not available, all or part of the organic matter commonly used to identify the A horizon is lost. Percolating waters rapidly change ionic composition at exchange sites and often raise the pH of the entire profile. Rates and kinds of mineralogical weathering may also be affected in the buried soil so that after a long period of time the paleosol may not be a good indicator of past environments.

In soil genesis it is usually assumed that the presently existing soil is in balance with the present environment. If the environment changes, usually through a change in climate, the soil also changes although the change may be slow. In the relict soil it is possible to identify physical, chemical or morphological features that identify characteristics of the preexisting environment. Yaalon (1971) grouped soil-diagnostic features and horizons in paleosols according to their persistence. In the easily altered group (less than 1000 yrs to reach a steady state) were mollic horizons, slickensides, salic horizons and mottles. The relatively persistent group (generally more than 1000 yrs to reach steady state) included the cambic, umbric, spodic, argillic, histic, calcic and gypsic horizons, and fragipans. Features that he considered persistent or essentially irreversible or self-terminating included the oxic, placic and petrocalcic horizons, plinthite, durinodes and gypsic crusts. Some of these features may occur in more than one group as a result of the specific change or the original parent material.

Changes in the soil after burial leads to another area of concern; positive discrimination of a buried soil from a sedimentary profile with soil-like properties resulting from deposition of weathered sediment. There are several problems associated with the clear identification of a paleosol: (1) the imprecise nature of the definitions of soil, weathering zone and sediment; (2) the susceptibility of many soil features to change after burial; and (3) the similarity between soils and sedimentary deposits following diagenesis (Valentine and Dalrymple, 1976). Most buried paleosols are observed and described in relatively small exposures. While it is important to identify pedologic changes in a vertical section, it is more important for positive identification to be able to trace horizontal variation across the landscape and to confirm the occurrence of a paleocatena (Valentine and Dalrymple, 1975). The paleocatena cannot be the result of sedimentation and postburial change. The recognition of a paleocatena assumes an understanding of soil-landscape relationships on the modern landscape and on acceptance of the principle uniformitarianism in soil science. The acceptance of the principle that the processes that are identified today were occurring on former landscapes is reasonable for Quaternary-age paleosols but may not be true for earlier periods (Valentine and Dalrymple, 1975).

Laboratory work by itself will not provide absolute proof of the existence of paleosols; nor will field work consisting of widely separated stratigraphic descriptions. The recognition depends on detailed field work and laboratory analysis coupled with a recognition of processes that both currently and in the past have led to the development of soils.

Periodic erosion, sedimentation and soil formation have become accepted as fact in the study of soil-landscape relationships. Butler (1958) stated that "the occurrence of buried soils in a depositional zone is evidence that both the depositional rate (and hence the erosion rate) and soil development have been periodic". Documentation of the periodic nature of landscape and soil evolution has been undertaken in many parts of the United States and the world (Butler, 1959; Van Dijk, 1959; Churchward, 1961; Malcahy, 1961; Walker, 1962; Ruhe and Daniels, 1965; Gile and Hawley, 1966; Ruhe and Walker, 1968; Walker and Ruhe, 1968; Kleiss, 1970; Ruhe, 1974, 1975; Leamy, 1975; Laffan and Cutler, 1977).

INFLUENCE OF CLIMATE

The importance of climate in soil genesis and landscape evolution has been accepted for over a century. The relationship of landscape types to the climate was discussed by Davis (1899) and many others before him. Dokuchaev (1883) listed climate as one of the factors that was important to the development of regional soil patterns.

Since that early identification of climate as a factor, it has been basic to the understanding of soil genesis; that different intensities of processes that result from climate—vegetation interaction give rise to distinctive soils. Argillic horizons are indicators of subhumid and humid regions with alternating wet and dry periods. Spodic horizons suggest cool humid climates. Oxic horizons are usually found in high-rainfall and high-temperature zones, and calcic, petrocalcic, gypsic, petrogypsic and duripans occur in soils of the arid regions. These climatic—horizon associations are only a first approximation because the influence of local topography, length of time of exposure as well as other factors complicate the relationship. Details of the processes involved in the climatic—horizon relationship of each soil order are discussed in a companion text (Wilding et al., 1983).

One of the most important complicating factors in studying the results of soil genesis is climatic change. Geologists early in this century recognized that there had been climatic changes particularly since the Pleistocene period (Anderson, 1910). Marbut (1935) in his widely accepted soil-classification scheme placed a great emphasis on what he called the normal or fully developed soil. His concept that there was a steady progression of soil changes as the soil "matures" suggests that he considered the climate factor as constant over the time of soil development.

Climatic change since Pleistocene is now an accepted fact. Pedologists, geologists and climatologists are each actively studying the kinds and magnitudes of climatic changes that have taken place. Many lines of evidence are used to study these changes including: pollen analysis, tree rings, fossils, deep sea cores, radiocarbon and other isotopic dating methods, historic records, paleosols and landscape features.

In order for a climatic change to impact on a soil or landscape feature, the change must have continued long enough to bring about observable differences. However, the impact of the change must not have been for so long so as to alter all the older soil and landscape properties. The greatest impact of climatic change can be expected at the interface between two climatic or soil regions. In these tension areas very small changes in precipitation or temperature may have a dramatic effect on the soil or landscape properties. An area where these changes have been studied in detail is at the interface of the arid and semi-arid zone of the southwest United States (Gile, 1975, 1977). The tension zone between the subhumid prairie and humid forest in the midwest has also been a well-documented area.

One of the most widespread and distinctive contributors to landscape changes was Pleistocene glaciation. The features associated with this climatic event include loess and till deposits, remnants of pluvial and glacial lakes and outwash valleys and terraces (Flint, 1976). The greatest effect of the glaciation was recorded near the ice margins in the northern United States and in the western mountainous areas where mountain glaciation modified and produced landforms in the mountains and footslopes.

Periglacial processes caused significant change in the landforms near the glacial border. The periglacial phenomena have left thin sheets of colluvium in eastern North America and western Europe (Flint, 1976). Frost (ice) wedges and pingos are two of the most common indicators (Black, 1964, 1976; Everett et al., 1971). These features are associated primarily with the late Wisconsin glaciation because earlier ones, if originally present, have been largely obliterated by landscape and soil processes. Some of the early work suggested that the area influenced by periglacial activity extended about 10 km beyond the glacial border (Denny, 1956). Many workers reported ice wedges far beyond this limit but Péwé (1973) and Black (1976) question some of these identifications. Many processes have been attributed to low-temperature activities. Creep, gelifluction, sorting and terraces formation have all been attributed to periodic cold climates (Benedict, 1976; Reger and Péwé, 1976). Thickness of the rubble and material moved range from less than a meter to more than 10 m (Denny, 1956; Daugherty et al., 1975; Reger and Péwé, 1976).

The most significant post-Pleistocene climatic change, termed the Hypsithermal, peaked in the midwest United States about 7000 yrs B.P. and terminated 4000—6000 yrs B.P.; earlier in the east and later in the west (Wright, 1976). It is estimated that in some areas temperature was 2°C higher and precipitation 400 mm lower than present. The magnitude of these changes is in agreement with European findings (Davis et al., 1980). The most significant effects of the climatic change were changes in vegetation. In the midwest the prairie—forest border shifted eastward (McAndrews, 1967; Wright, 1976). In New England there was a shift of the tree line and a change in the forest community associated with the Hypsithermal (Davis et al., 1980). In the southwestern United States it has been proposed that complex erosion—sedimentation processes were dominant during the Late Pleistocene and Holocene as a result of a warmer and drier climate, and associated vegetative changes. This shift in climate and vegetative cover also resulted in valley aggradation and eolian deposition over much of the region (Haynes, 1968; Hawley et al., 1976). The presence and impact of postglacial climatic change in the southwest has been discussed by Martin and Mehringer (1965), Van Devender and Spaulding (1979) and Wells (1979).

In the climatic tension zone of the southwest, cyclic erosion patterns prior to settlement were suggested by Bryan (1940). Leopold (1976) related this cutting to changes in intensity of storms rather than to changes in total rainfall. He suggested that the erosion of the late 19th and early 20th century has now been replaced by a period of filling that is correlated with a worldwide cooling trend.

Slope instability is often related to climatic changes. The instability causes erosion and sedimentation modification in the landforms. Using pollen analysis, radiocarbon dating and sediment analysis it is possible in a closed depression to determine actual amounts of sediment transport and the time of transport. In a study of two closed basins in glacial drift in northern Iowa, Walker and Ruhe (1968) determined that erosion had removed 0.5 and 1.62 m from the slopes in the period between 8000 and 3000 yrs B.P. This erosion removed the entire soil profile that had been developed under postglacial forest vegetation. From their data they were able to develop prediction equations for sediment and soil distribution patterns. In a similar study on an open landscape system, Ruhe and Daniels (1965) evaluated two western Iowa watersheds developed in loess. In one watershed they determined that a minimum of 0.95 m was removed between 6800 and 125 yrs ago. The second watershed had a minimum of 1.22 m removed between 1800 and 250 yrs ago. In both cases the thickness of material removed was greater than the thickness of the soil profile. As in the case for the closed system hillslope, models were constructed for this open watershed.

CONCLUSIONS

Geomorphology plays a major role in the processes that dictate the distribution of soils on the landscape. Conversely, pedologic processes can be considered an integral part of landscape evolution. The relationship between geomorphic surfaces and soils has been tested and found useful in many parts of the United States. The hillslope model has proven to be a good framework for testing the interaction of pedogenic and geomorphic processes. To adequately utilize the model for field predictions it is neccessary to visualize the landscape in terms of the soil catena. The morphology and processes of each member of the catena is related to every other member of that catena. Concatenation of soils on the landscape is the result of lateral surface and subsurface movement of materials.

Recognition of the interrelationship of soils on the landscape dictates that the pedologist be able to identify and describe various landscape segments. The five units of the erosional slope model: summit, shoulder, backslope, footslope and toeslope, have proven to be useful for identifying landscape positions in many parts of the United States. More detailed segmenting of the landscape may be useful in some studies.

Paleosols are useful as indicators of environmental as well as landscape changes. An understanding of environmental changes, particularly climatic, since Pleistocene is helpful in relating processes to soil morphology.

There is no clear boundary between the processes in geomorphology and those in pedology. Therefore interdisciplinary studies are required in order to explain many geomorphic and pedologic features.

REFERENCES

Aandahl, A.R., 1948. The characterization of slope positions and their influence on the total nitrogen content of a few virgin soils of western Iowa. Soil Sci. Soc. Am. Proc., 13: 449—454.
Anderson, J.G., 1910. Die Veränderungen des Klimas seit dem Maximum der letzten Eiszeit. 1st Int. Geological Congress, Stockholm.
Anderson, M.G. and Burt, T.P., 1978. Experimental investigations concerning the topographic control of soil water movement on hillslopes. Z. Geomorphol., Suppl., 29: 52—63.
Bates, R.L. and Jackson, J.A., 1980. Glossary of Geology (2nd ed.). American Geological Institute, 749 pp.
Bear, J., Zaslavsky, D. and Irmay, S., 1968. Physical Principles of Water Percolation and Seepage. UNESCO, Paris, 456 pp.
Beckett, P.H.T., 1968. Soil formation and slope development. Z. Geomorphol., 12: 1—24.
Benedict, J.B., 1976. Frost creep and gelifluction features: A review. Quat. Res., 6: 55—76.
Black, R.F., 1964. Periglacial studies in the United States 1959—1963. Biul. Peryglacjalny, 14: 5—29.
Black, R.F., 1976. Periglacial features indicative of permafrost: Ice and soil wedges. Quat. Res., 6: 3—26.
Blume, H., 1968. Die pedogenetische Deutung einer Catena durch die Untersuchung der Bodendynamik. Trans. 9th. Int. Congress Soil. Sci., Adelaide, 4: 441—449.
Bridges, E.M., 1967. Geomorphology and soils in Britain. Soils Fertil., 30: 317—320.
Bryan, K., 1940. Erosion in the valleys of the Southwest. N. M. Quat., 10: 227—232.
Bryan, K. and Albritton Jr., C.C., 1943. Soil phenomena as evidence of climatic changes. Am. J. Sci., 241: 469—490.

Bushnell, T.M., 1942. Some aspects of the soil catena concept. Soil Sci. Soc. Am. Proc., 7: 466—476.

Butler, B.E., 1959. Periodic phenomena in landscapes as a basis for soil studies. CSIRO Aust. Soil Publ., 14, 20 pp.

Churchward, H.M., 1961. Soil studies at Swan Hill, Victoria, Australia. I. Soil layering. J. Soil Sci., 12: 73—86.

Conacher, A.J. and Dalrymple, J.B., 1977. The nine unit landsurface model: An approach to pedogeomorphic research. Geoderma, 18: 1—154.

Dalrymple, J.B., Blong, R.J., and Conacher, A.J., 1968. An hypothetical nine unit land-surface model. Z. Geomorphol., 12: 60—76.

Dalsgaard, K., Basstrup, E. and Bunting, B.T., 1981. The influence of topography on the development of Alfisols on calcareous clay till in Denmark. Catena, 8: 111—116.

Dan, J. and Yaalon, D.H., 1964. The application of the catena concept in studies of pedogenesis in Mediterranean and desert fringe regions. Trans. 8th Int. Congress Soil Sci., Bucharest, pp. 751—758.

Dan, J., Yaalon, D.H. and Koyumdjisky, H., 1968. Catenary soil relationships in Israel. 1. The Netanga catena on coastal dunes of the Sharon. Geoderma, 2: 95—120.

Daniels, R.B., Gamble, E.E. and Cady, J.G., 1970. Some relationships among Coastal Plain soils and geomorphic surfaces in North Carolina. Soil. Sci. Soc. Am. Proc., 34: 648—653.

Daniels, R.B., Gamble, E.E. and Cady, J.G., 1971. The relation between geomorphology and soil morphology and genesis. Adv. Agron., 23: 51—88.

Daugherty, L.A., Hanna, W.E. and Arnold, R.W., 1975. Geomorphology of a glaciated first-order valley in south central New York. Soil Sci. Soc. Am. Proc., 39: 710—716.

Davidson, D.A., 1977. The subdivision of a slope profile on the basis of soil properties: A case study from Mid-Wales. Earth Surface Processes, 2: 55—61.

Davis, M.B., Spear, R.W. and Shane, L.C.K., 1980. Holocene climate of New England. Quat. Res., 14: 240—250.

Davis, W.M., 1899. The geographical cycle. Geogr. J., 14: 481—504.

Denny, C.S., 1956. Surficial geology and geomorphology of Potter County, Pennsylvania. Geol. Surv. Prof. Pap. 288, U.S. Govt. Printing Office, Washington, D.C., 72 pp.

Dijkerman, J.C., 1974. Pedology as a science: The role of data, models, and theories in the study of natural systems. Geoderma, 11: 73—93.

Dokuchaev, V.V., 1883. Russian Chernozem. In: Collected Writings, Vol. 3. Israel Progr. Sci. Trans., Jerusalem 1967.

Everett, K.R., Hall, G.F. and Wilding, L.P., 1971. Wisconsin age cryoturbation features in central Ohio. Geol. Soc. Am. Bull., 82: 1407—1410.

Flint, R.F., 1976. Physical evidence of Quaternary climatic change. Quat. Res., 6: 519—528.

Fridland, V.M., 1972. The soil-cover pattern: Problems and methods of investigation. In: V.M. Fridland (Editor), Soil Combinations and their Genesis. Amerind, New Delhi, pp. 1—31.

Furley, P.A., 1968. Soil formation and slope development: 2. The relationship between soil formation and gradient angle in the Oxford area. Z. Geomorphol., 12: 25—42.

Furley, P.A., 1971. Relationships between slope form and soil properties developed over chalk parent materials. In: D. Brunsden (Editor), Slopes, Form and Process. I.B.G., Spec. Publ., 3: 141—163.

Gamble, E.E., Daniels, R.B. and Nettleton, W.D., 1970. Geomorphic surfaces and soils in the Black Creek Valley, Johnston County, North Carolina. Soil Sci. Soc. Am. Proc., 34: 276—281.

Gerasimov, I.P., 1971. Nature and originality of paleosols. In: D.H. Yaalon (Editor), Paleopedology: Origin, Nature, and Dating of Paleosols. Israel University Press, Jerusalem, pp. 15—27.

Geyl, W.F., 1961. Morphometric analysis and the worldwide occurrences of stepped erosion surfaces. J. Geol., 69: 388—411.

138

Gile, L.H., 1975. Holocene soils and soil—geomorphic relations in an arid region of southern New Mexico. Quat. Res., 5: 321—360.

Gile, L.H., 1977. Holocene soils and soil—geomorphic relations in a semi-arid region of southern New Mexico. Quat. Res., 7: 112—132.

Gile, L.H. and Grossman, R.B., 1979. The Desert Project Soil Monograph. Soil Conservation Serive, U.S. Dept. Agric., 984 pp. (NTIS Publ. No. PB80-135304, U.S. Dept. Commerce, Springfield, VA 22161).

Gile, L.H. and Hawley, J.W., 1966. Periodic sedimentation and soil formation on an alluvial-fan piedmont of southern New Mexico. Soil Sci. Soc. Am. Proc., 30: 261—268.

Gile, L.H., Hawley, J.W. and Grossman, R.B., 1981. Soils and Geomorphology in the Basin and Range area of Southern New Mexico — Guidebook to the Desert Project. N. M. Bur. Mines Miner, Resour., Mem. 39, 222 pp.

Glazovskaya, M.A., 1968. Geochemical landscapes and types of geochemical soil sequences. Trans. 9th Int. Congress Soil. Sci., Adelaide, 4: 303—312.

Greene, H., 1945. Classification and use of tropical soils. Soil Sci. Soc. Am. Proc., 10: 392—396.

Greene, H., 1947. Soil formation and water movement in the tropics. Soils Fertil., 10: 253—256.

Hallsworth, E.G., Costin, A.B., Gibbons, F.R. and Robertson, G.K., 1952. Studies in pedogenesis in New South Wales, II. The chocolate soils. J. Soil Sci., 3: 103—124.

Hawley, J.W., 1975. Quaternary History of Dona Ana County Region, South-central New Mexico. Geol. Soc. 26th Field Conf. Guidebook, pp. 139—150.

Hawley, J.W., Bachman, G.O. and Manley, K., 1976. Quaternary stratigraphy in the Basin and Range and Great Plains province, New Mexico and western Texas. In: W.C. Mahaney (Editor), Quaternary Stratigraphy of North America. Dowden, Hutchinson and Ross, Stroudsburg, Penn., pp. 235—274.

Haynes Jr., C.V., 1968. Geochronology of the late Quaternary alluvium. In: R.B. Morrison and H.E. Wright, Jr. (Editors), Means of Correlation of Quaternary Successions. Univ. of Utah Press, Salt Lake City, Utah, pp. 591—631.

Howell, J.V., 1957. Glossary of Geology and Related Sciences. Am. Geogr. Inst., 325 pp.

Huddleston, J.H. and Riecken, F.F., 1973. Local soil—landscape relationships in western Iowa. I. Distribution of selected chemical and physical properties. Soil Sci. Soc. Am. Proc., 37: 264—270.

Huggett, R.J., 1975. Soil landscape systems: A model of soil genesis. Geoderma, 13: 1—22.

Huggett, R.J., 1976. Lateral translocation of soil plasm through a small valley basin in the Northaw Great Wood, Hertforshire. Earth Surface Processes, 1: 99—109.

Joffe, J.S., 1936. Pedology. Rutgers University Press. New Brunswick, N.J., 575 pp.

Kirkby, M.J., 1977. Soil development models as a component of slope models. Earth Surface Processes, 2: 203—230.

Kirkby, M.J. and Chorley, R.J., 1967. Throughflow, overland flow and erosion. Bull. Int. Assoc. Sci. Hydrol., 12: 5—21.

Kleiss, H.J., 1970. Hillslope sedimentation and soil formation in northeastern Iowa. Soil Soc. Am. Proc., 34: 287—290.

Laffan, M.D. and Cutler, E.J.B., 1977. Landscapes, soils, and erosion of a small catchment on the Wither Hills, Marlborough. I. Landscape periodicity, slope deposits, and soil pattern. N. Z. J. Sci. 20: 37—48.

Leamy, M.L., 1975. Paleosol identification and soil stratigraphy in South Island, New Zealand. Geoderma, 13: 53—60.

Leopold, L.B., 1976. Reversal of erosion cycle and climatic change. Quat. Res., 6: 557—562.

Lepsch, I.F., Buol, S.W. and Daniels, R.B., 1977. Soil—landscape relations in Occidental Plateau of Sao Paulo, Brazil: I. Geomorphic surfaces and mapping units. Soil Sci. Soc. Am. J., 41: 104—109.

Malo, D.D., Worcester, B.K., Cassal, D.K. and Matzdorf, K.D., 1974. Soil—landscape relationships in a closed drainage system. Soil Sci. Soc. Am. Proc., 38: 813—818.

Marbut, C.F., 1935. Soils of the United States. U.S. Dept. Agric., Atlas of American Agriculture, U.S. Govt. Printing Office, Washington, D.C., 98 pp.

Martin, P.S. and Mehringer Jr., P.J., 1965. Pleistocene pollen analysis and biogeography of the southwest. In: H.E. Wright, Jr. and D.G. Frey (Editors), The Quaternary of the United States. Princeton Univ. Press, Princeton, N.J., pp. 433—451.

McAndrews, J.H., 1967. Pollen analysis and vegetational history of the Itasia region, Minnesota, In: E.J. Cushing and H.E. Wright, Jr. (Editors), Quaternary Paleoecology. Yale Press, New Haven, Conn., pp. 219—236.

Miller, F.P., Holowaychuk, N. and Wilding, L.P., 1971. Canfield silt loam, a Fragiudalf: I. Macromorphological, physical, and chemical properties. Soil Sci. Soc. Am. Proc., 35: 319—324.

Milne, G., 1936a. A Provisional Soil Map of East Africa. East African Agriculture Research Station, Amani Memoirs, Tanganyika Territory, 34 pp.

Milne, G., 1936b. Normal erosion as a factor in soil profile development. Nature, 138: p. 548.

Morison, C.G.T., Hoyle, A.C. and Hope-Simpson, J.F., 1948. Tropical soil — vegetation catenas and mosaics. J. Ecol., 36: 1—84.

Mulcahy, M.J., 1961. Soil distribution in relation to landscape development. Z. Geomorphol., 5: 211—225.

Parsons, R.B., Balster, C.A. and Ness, A.O., 1970. Soil development and geomorphic surfaces, Willamette Valley, Oregon. Soil Sci. Soc. Am. Proc., 34: 485—491.

Parsons, R.B. and Herriman, R.C., 1976. Geomorphic surfaces and soil development in the Upper Rogue River Valley, Oregon. Soil Sci. Soc. Am. J., 40: 933—938.

Peterson, F.F., 1981. Landforms of the Basin and Range province defined for soil survey. Univ. of Nevada, Agric. Experiment Station, Techn. Bull., 28, 52 pp.

Péwé, T.L., 1973. Ice wedge casts and past permafrost distribution in North America. Geoforum, 15: 15—26.

Reger, R.D. and Péwé, T.L., 1976. Cryoplanation terraces: Indicators of a permafrost environment. Quat. Res., 6: 99—109.

Ruellan, A., 1971. The history of soils: Some problems of definition and interpretation. In: D.H. Yaalon (Editor), Paleopedology: Origin, Nature and Dating of Paleosols. Israel University Press, Jersusalem, pp. 3—13.

Ruhe, R.V., 1956. Geomorphic surfaces and the nature of soils. Soil Sci., 82: 441—455.

Ruhe, R.V., 1960. Elements of the soil landscape. Trans. 7th Int. Congress Soil Sci., Madison, Wisc., 4: 165—170.

Ruhe, R.V., 1965. Quaternary paleopedology. In: H.E. Wright and D.G. Frey (Editors), The Quaternary of the United States. Princeton University Press, Princeton, N.J., pp. 755—764.

Ruhe, R.V., 1967. Geomorphic surfaces and surficial deposits in southern New Mexico. N. M. Bur. Mines Miner. Resour., Mem. 18, 65 pp.

Ruhe, R.V., 1969. Quaternary Landscapes in Iowa. Iowa State Univ. Press. Ames, Iowa, 255 pp.

Ruhe, R.V., 1970. Soils, paleosols, and environment. In: W. Dort and J.K. Jones (Editors), Pleistocene and Recent Environments of the Central Great Plains. University of Kansas Press, Lawrence, Kans., pp. 37—52.

Ruhe, R.V., 1974. Holocene environments and soil geomorphology in midwestern United States. Quat. Res., 4: 487—495.

Ruhe, R.V., 1975. Geomorphology. Houghton Mifflin, Boston, 246 pp.

Ruhe, R.V. and Daniels, R.B., 1965. Landscape erosion — geologic and historic. J. Soil Water Conserv., 20: 52—57.

Ruhe, R.V. and Walker P.H., 1968. Hillslope models and soil formation, I. Open systems. Trans. 9th Int. Congress Soil Sci., Adelaide, pp. 551—560.

Ruhe, R.V., Miller, G.A. and Vreeken, W.J., 1971. Paleosols, loess sedimentation and soil

140

stratigraphy. In: D.H. Yaalon (Editor), Paleopedology: Origin, Nature, and Dating of Paleosols. Israel University Press, Jerusalem, pp. 41—60.

Simonson, R.W., 1941. Studies of buried soils formed from till in Iowa. Soil Sci. Soc. Am. Proc., 6: 373—381.

Simonson, R.W., 1959. Outline of a generalized theory of soil genesis. Soil Sci. Soc. Am. Proc., 23: 152—156.

Smeck, N.E. and Runge, E.C.A., 1971. Phosphorus availability and redistribution in relation to profile development in an Illinois landscape segment. Soil Sci. Soc. Am. Proc., 35: 952—959.

Soil Survey Staff, 1975. Soil taxonomy: a Basic System of Soil Classification for Making and Interpreting Soil Surveys. Agric. Handbook No. 436. U.S. Govt. Printing Office, Washington, D.C., 754 pp.

Troeh, F.R., 1964. Landform parameters correlated to soil drainage. Soil Sci. Soc. Am. Proc., 28: 808—812.

Trowbridge, A.C., 1921. The erosional history of the driftless area. Univ. of Iowa, Studies in Nat. Hist., 9: 7—127.

Valentine, K.W.G. and Dalrymple, J.B., 1975. The identification, lateral variation and chronology of two buried paleocatenas at Woodhall Spa and West Runton, England. Quat. Res., 5: 551—590.

Valentine, K.W.G. and Dalrymple, J.B., 1976. Quaternary buried paleosols: a critical review. Quat. Res., 6: 209—222.

Van Devender, T.R. and Spaulding, W.G., 1979. Development of vegetation and climate in the southwestern United States. Science, 204: 701—710.

Van Dijk, D.C., 1959. Soil features in relation to erosional history in the vicinity of Canberra. CSIRO Soil Publ., 13, 41 pp.

Walker, P.H., 1962. Terrace chronology and soil formation on the south coast of N.S.W. J. Soil Sci., 13: 178—186.

Walker, P.H., 1966. Postglacial environments in relation to landscape and soils on the Cary drift, Iowa. Iowa Agric. Exper. Stat., Res. Bull., 549: 838—875.

Walker, P.H. and Ruhe, R.V., 1968. Hillslope models and soil formation. II. Closed systems. Trans. 9th Int. Congress Soil Sci., Adelaide, pp. 561—568.

Wells, P.V., 1979. An equable glaciopluvial in the West; pleniglacial evidence for increased precipitation on a gradient from the Great Basin to the Sonoran and Chihuahuan Deserts. Quat. Res., 12: 311—325.

Whipkey, R.Z., 1969. Storm runoff from forested catchments by subsurface routes. Int. Assoc. Sci. Hydrol., 85: 773—779.

Wilding, L.P., Smeck, N.E. and Hall, G.F., 1983. Pedogenesis and Soil Taxonomy. II. The Soil Orders. Elsevier, Amsterdam.

Wood, A., 1942. The development of hillside slopes. Geol. Assoc. Proc., 53: 128—138.

Working Group on the Origin and Nature of Paleosols, 1971. Criteria for the recognition and classification of paleosols. In: D.H. Yaalon (Editor), Paleopedology: Origin, Nature, and Dating of Paleosols. Israel University Press, Jerusalem, pp. 153—158.

Wright, H.E., 1976. The dynamic nature of Holocene vegetation. Quat. Res., 6: 581—596.

Yaalon, D.H., 1971. Soil-forming processes in time and space. In: D.H. Yaalon (Editor), Paleopedology: Origin, Nature and Dating of Paleosols. Israel University Press, Jerusalem, pp. 29—39.

Yaalon, D.H., Jungreis, Ch. and Koyumdjisky, H., 1972. Distribution and reorganization of manganese in three catenas of Mediterranean soils. Geoderma, 7: 71—78.

Yaalon, D.H., Brenner, I. and Koyumdjisky, H., 1974. Weathering and mobility sequence of minor elements on a basaltic pedomorphic surface, Galilee, Israel. Geoderma, 12: 233—244.

Young, A., 1963. Deductive Models of Slope Evolution. (Neue Beitrage zur internationalen Hangforschung.) Vandenhoeck and Ruprecht, Göttingen.

Zaslavsky, D. and Rogowski, A. 1969. Hydrologic and morphologic implications of anisotropy and infiltration in soil profile development. Soil Sci. Soc. Am. Proc., 33: 594—599.

COMPOSITION AND SOIL GENESIS

B.L. ALLEN and D.S. FANNING

INTRODUCTION

The mineral components of many soils are inherited almost exclusively from the parent material, but in others they have developed mostly in situ during the course of weathering and pedogenesis. In the majority of soils the composition is a result of both inheritance and authigenic formation. In the succeeding discussion, primary minerals will be understood to mean those formed at high temperatures in igneous and metamorphic rocks, and secondary minerals will refer to those formed at lower temperatures in sedimentary rocks and soils (Jackson, 1964). Primary minerals may have been subjected to one or more sedimentary cycles or have been components of previously existing soils.

The proportion of secondary (authigenic) versus inherited (allogenic) minerals varies greatly among soils. Almost all the clay has developed in situ in some soils, but in others most of it is inherited. Soil sand and silt may consist entirely of primary minerals, but a significant portion of even these fractions, e.g. metallic oxides and carbonates, may be of authigenic origin.

MINERAL COMPONENTS

Silicates and oxides of silicon

Silicates and the oxides of silicon make up by far the major part of the inorganic solids in most soils. The basic structural unit of silicates is the tetrahedron in which a cation (T) ion is coordinated with four oxygens, e.g. SiO_4^{4-}. A classification of the silicates is outlined in Table 6.1. Among the nesosilicates, composed of independent tetrahedra, the weatherability and conversely persistence in soils, varies widely. For example, olivine, an essential mineral of basalt, is usually present only in soils derived from highly basic crystalline rocks that have been subjected only to low weathering intensities. Conversely, zircon, some garnets (depending upon composition) and sphene tend to persist for long periods in soil environments. Tourmaline is by far the most common cyclosilicate (silicates in which the tetrahedra are linked to form hexagonal rings) in soils (Table 6.1). It is ubiquitous as a resistant

TABLE 6.1

Classification of silicates

Silicate class	Arrangement of tetrahedra[a]	Structural group	T:O[b] ratio	Examples	Structural formula[c]
Nesosilicates		Independent Tetrahedra	1:4	Olivine Zircon Garnet Sphene Epidote	$(Mg,Fe)_2SiO_4$ $ZrSiO_4$ $R_3^{2+}R_2^{3+}(SiO_4)_3$[d] $CaTi(SiO_4)O$ $Ca_2(Al,Fe)_3(SiO_4)_3(OH)$
Sorosilicates		Double Tetrahedra	2:7	Hemimorphite	$Zn_4(Si_2O_7)(OH)_2H_2O$
Cyclosilicates		Hexagonal rings of Tetrahedra	1:3	Tourmaline	$Na(Mg,Fe)_3Al_6BO_3Si_6O_{18}$
Inosilicates		Continuous single Tetrahedral chains	1:3	*Pyroxenes:* Augite Hypersthene	$Ca(Mg,Fe,Al)[(Si,Al)]_2O_6]$ $(Mg,Fe)_2(Si_2O_6)$
Inosilicates		Continuous double Tetrahedral chains	4:11	*Amphibole:* Hornblende Actinolite	$Ca_2Na(Mg,Fe)_4(Al,Si)_8O_{22}(OH,F)_2$ $Ca_2(Mg,Fe)_5Si_8O_{22}(OH)_2$

143

				Formulas
Phyllosilicates	Continuous Tetrahedral Sheets	2:5	Pyrophyllite	$Al_2Si_4O_{10}(OH)_2$
			Talc	$Mg_3Si_4O_{10}(OH)_2$
			Micas:	
			Muscovite	$KAl_2(Si_3Al)O_{10}(OH)_2$
			Illite	$K_xAl_2(Si_{4-x}Al_x)O_{10}(OH)_2$
			Biotite	$K(Mg,Fe)_3(Si_3Al)O_{10}(OH)_2$
			Vermiculite	$(Mg,Fe)_3(Si_{4-x}Al_x)O_{10}(OH)_2$
			Smectite[e]	$(Al_{2-x}Mg_x)Si_4O_{10}(OH)_2^0$
			Kaolinite	$Al_2Si_2O_5(OH)_4$
			Serpentine	$Mg_3Si_2O_5(OH)_4$
Tectosilicates	Three-dimensional Tetrahedral framework	1:2	Quartz	SiO_2
			Opal	$SiO_2 \cdot nH_2O$
			Feldspars:	
			Orthoclase	$KAlSi_3O_8$
			Albite	$NaAlSi_3O_8$
			Anorthite	$CaAl_2Si_2O_8$
			Feldspathoid:	
			Nepheline	$NaAlSiO_4$
			Zeolite:	
			Analcite	$NaAlSi_2O_6 \cdot H_2O$

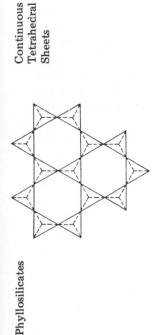

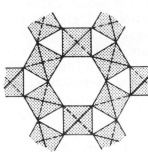

β-quartz projected on 0001

[a] Tectosilicate (β-quartz) arrangement was adapted from Dennen (1960); all other silicate arrangements were adapted from Deer et al. (1963).

[b] T = Tetrahedral cation (Si or Al).

[c] Formulas are only approximate in such minerals as tourmaline, augite and hornblende. Interlayer cations and water in vermiculite and smectite are not listed.

[d] R^{2+} = Mg,Fe,Ca,Mn; R^{3+} = Al,Fe,Cr.

[e] Formula given is for montmorillonite; beidellite and nontronite have significant Al substituting for Si in the tetrahedral position and Fe^{2+} substituting for Al in the octahedral position, respectively. Interlayer cations are not listed.

mineral in sands and silts. Inosilicates are minerals in which the tetrahedra are joined to form either single chains (pyroxenes) or double chains (amphiboles) of indefinite length (Table 6.1). The pyroxenes, augite and hypersthene, are relatively common primary sand- and silt-size minerals in some soils, especially in those influenced by volcanic materials. The amphibole, hornblende, is also of primary origin and significant amounts are often present in sand and silt.

Phyllosilicates occupy a unique role in determination of soil physical and chemical properties because they comprise the clay fraction of most soils. Pyrophyllite and talc, mostly occurring in sands and silts of soils derived directly or indirectly from metamorphic rocks, are rather simple phyllosilicates, in which two sheets of silica tetrahedra are bonded by a single sheet of octahedrally coordinated Al and Mg, respectively. The resulting 2:1 layers are only weakly bound to each other because the structure is electrostatically balanced. Muscovite and biotite are more complex phyllosilicates. Ideally, they differ from pyrophylite and talc in that one-fourth of the tetrahedra have an Al substituting for Si (Table 6.1). The resulting charge is balanced by K in the interlayer (between layers) position. Pyrophyllite and muscovite are considered to be prototypes of dioctahedral phyllosilicates. Talc and biotite occupy a similar role among trioctahedral types. Muscovite is considerably more resistant than biotite to weathering in soils.

Among the phyllosilicates in the clay fraction, illite most closely approximates the macroscopic micas. [Illite is often referred to as "clay mica" or hydrous mica"; it has been referred to variously as "hydromica", "glimmerton", etc. (Fanning and Keramidas, 1977).] It differs from muscovite in that generally less than one-fourth of the tetrahedral positions are occupied by Al. Correspondingly less K is needed to electrostatically balance the charge (Table 6.1). Undoubtedly, there is considerable variation among illites. Most soil illite is inherited from parent sediments; however, some may originate from potassication of expandable 2:1 clays with a high tetrahedral sheet charge (Fanning and Keramidas, 1977).

Vermiculite and chlorite are phyllosilicates that occur in soils ranging from macroscopic to clay-size particles. Dioctahedral vermiculite, apparently resulting from the depotassication of muscovite and/or illite, seems to concentrate in the clay and fine silt fractions; it is rarely observed in $>5\text{-}\mu\text{m}$ discrete particles (Douglas, 1977). Trioctahedral vermiculite seems to be more common in silts and sands (Alexiades et al., 1973; Coffman and Fanning, 1975). It apparently forms by the slow replacement of interlayer K in biotite by hydrated exchangeable cations, but has also been reported as resulting from the weathering of trioctahedral chlorite (Coffman and Fanning, 1975). Both types of vermiculite have limited expandability. The 2:1-layer of chlorite is also similar to that of biotite, but instead of K in the interlayers, there is a charged hydroxide sheet of octahedrally coordinated Al and/or Mg. Primary trioctahedral chlorite, inherited from metamorphic rocks or derivative sediments, seems to be unstable in most soil environments. The widespread occurrence of pedogenic chlorite, or hydroxy interlayered vermiculite (Barnhisel, 1977), suggests that it mostly originates from the incorporation of hydroxy-Al interlayers into expandable mineral structures.

Smectite, the best-known variety of which is montmorillonite, differs considerably from the other 2:1 phyllosilicates. First, most of the charge on the layers arises from substitution of Mg for Al in the octahedral sheet (Table 6.1). Second, the amount of water that can be taken into the interlayers appears to be almost unlimited, especially when certain cations such as Na occupy the interlayer exchange sites. Third, it differs (except from vermiculite) in having its layer charge balanced by exchangeable interlayer cations. It occurs almost exclusively in clay-size particles. Probably most of the smectite in a majority of soils is inherited from materials such as volcanic ash and certain marine formations. However, it may be synthesized in selected soil environments.

Kaolinite, a 1:1-type phyllosilicate, contains one silica tetrahedral sheet and one alumina octahedral sheet per layer. Until recently, hydrogen bonds have been considered the principal interlayer force, but Giese (1973) has shown that the OH—O bond is predominantly electrostatic. Little, if any, substitution occurs in either the tetrahedral and octahedral sheets. Kaolinite is ubiquitous in the clay fraction of soils and sometimes occurs in larger crystals. Although some kaolinite may form as a result of processes generally conceded to be geological in nature, for example hydrothermal activity, most by far results from weathering, including pedogenesis. However, it may have formed in one soil or geologic material and then have been subjected to one or more sedimentary cycles, before occurring in a presently existing soil. A trioctahedral analog, serpentine, of which there are three common varieties, crysotile, lizardite and antigorite, is rarely a soil constituent except as a primary mineral in soils derived from the metamorphic rock, serpentinite (Dixon, 1977).

Halloysite, also a 1:1 mineral, is considerably less common than kaolinite. It differs from kaolinite in having less order in the stacking of the layers, and in having water in the interlayers, resulting in a tubular morphology. Most soil halloysite is authigenically formed. It is especially common in relatively immature soils formed in volcanic ash. Sepiolite and palygorskite (attapulgite), for which the group name "hormites" was suggested by Robertson (1962), differ from the other phyllosilicates in that the tetrahedra and octahedra sheets are not continuous. Continuous oxygen planes exist, however, and form the bases for tetrahedra, the apices of which point in opposite directions in alternating bands. The result may be considered a ribbon-like structure. Water and exchangeable cations occur in channels that alternate with the ribbons. Transmission electron microscopy shows both minerals to have a similar fibrous morphology. Sepiolite and palygorskite are relatively rare soil minerals but are being detected with increasing frequency in arid and semi-arid regions of the world. They are apparently mostly inherited from parent sediments, but may be of pedogenic origin, especially in the case of palygorskite.

When the silica tetrahedra are arranged so that all four oxygens of the tetrahedra are shared with other tetrahedra, a three-dimensional framework structure (tectosilicates) is formed (Table 6.1). When all of the tetrahedral positions are occupied by Si, quartz, or a polymorph thereof, results. Quartz owes its ubiquitousness in sands and silts of soils to its occurrence as a common constituent of crystalline rocks and its relative inertness in the weathering environment. It may also occur as an authigenic soil mineral under certain conditions. Among several polymorphs known to mineralogists, tridymite and cristobalite are the only ones of importance in soils. Both have long been considered to have high temperature origins, but they evidently can form at ambient temperatures (Wilding et al., 1977).

When Al^{3+} substitutes for Si^{4+} in minerals, a charge imbalance results. Electrostatic balance is again achieved when cations (Na, K, Ca) are added as in feldspars (Table 6.1). Two polymorphic forms of potash feldspars, orthoclase and microcline, are common constituents of crystalline rocks. They are significant components in soils, especially in those that have not been intensively weathered. Sanidine, another polymorph generally in K-rich, fine-grained igneous rocks, has been reported as a constituent of soils developed in trachytic materials in West Texas (Ratliff and Allen, 1970). It was also detected in soils developed in the tuffaceous Catahoula Formation of South Central Texas and in soils developed in an eolian mantle of South Texas by W.C. Lynn (pers. commun., 1980). The plagioclase feldspars, originating in igneous rocks, constitute a series of six minerals that range from a sodic end member (albite) to a calcic end member (anorthite) (Table 6.1). The six species are arbitrarily defined according to the relative amounts of Na and Ca. The sodic plagioclases are much less susceptible to weathering than the more calcic members and consequently are considerably more common in soils. Because of difficulties in identification, the relative abundance of the plagioclase feldspars is often not recognized.

Feldspathoids, exemplified by nepheline, form in silica-poor igneous rocks. Because of their lack of stability in the weathering zone, they are unlikely to occur in soils except in relatively immature ones associated with feldspathoid-bearing rocks.

Zeolites, tectosilicates of great chemical diversity, generally are found as minerals of late crystallization in seams and cavities of igneous rocks. They also occur as authigenic minerals in deep-sea sediments, sedimentary rocks, tuffs, saline lacustrine deposits and soils. Due to a high amount of substitution of Al for Si in the tetrahedra, the framework charge is high. Exchangeable cations occur in internal channels because of a more "open" structure than in feldspars and feldspathoids. Zeolites are generally unstable in the soil environment except where highly alkaline conditions are obtained (Baldar and Whittig, 1968).

Amorphous silicates, usually referred to as allophane, do not have sufficient crystallinity to give definitive X-ray reflections. Such materials are often predominant in soils derived from volcanic ash. Probably most of the silicon is in tetrahedral coordination and the metallic cations are in octahedral coordination but the degree of organization among these components is low. When order is sufficient to give diffuse X-ray diffraction reflections, the name "imogolite" is often used (Aomine and Miyauchi, 1965). Amorphous materials formed as decomposition products of crystalline components may constitute a significant portion of the clay fraction in some soils (Zelazny and Carlisle, 1971). Because of the difficulty in determining the amount of amorphous soil constituents, even semi-quantitatively, they are probably more common than usually reported.

Opal is a form of silica that is X-ray amorphous. It may be formed, often in soils influenced by volcanic materials, upon aging of silica gels, which, in turn, represent flocculates of soluble silica (Wilding et al., 1977). Opal phytoliths, silica deposited in plant cells, are common constituents of some soils. They seem to be relatively stable in some soil environments (Bartoli and Wilding, 1980). In contrast, volcanic glass is much less stable. It tends to devitrify even under weathering of moderate intensity. But it still remains as a common component in many relatively immature soils or in situations where it is protected from the full force of weathering processes.

Iron oxides

The term "iron oxides" is used here for oxyhydroxides and hydroxides as well as for the true oxides. These minerals, although less abundant than silicates in most soils, are usually obvious where they occur because of their color. They often occur in very small particles, usually only a few tens or hundreds of Angstroms in diameter, and are adsorbed to other mineral particles. Where these substances are absent, soil colors usually arise from uncoated (naked) mineral grains, e.g. E horizons, gleyed horizons and low chroma, high value mottles.

The discussion here draws heavily on the review by Schwertmann and Taylor (1977). They pointed out that much has been and is being learned about the characteristics and modes of formation of the iron-oxide minerals from laboratory synthesis experiments. Goethite ($FeOOH$), the most common iron oxide in soils, is yellowish-brown to dark brown and appears to precipitate from solution, sometimes mediated by organic compounds. Goethite in Oxisols, Ultisols and selected other soils may contain considerable aluminum substituted for iron in the crystal structure. Sometimes more than 30 mole percent of the goethite structure may be $AlOOH$ (Norrish and Taylor, 1961; Bigham et al., 1978; Fitzpatrick, 1978). In other materials, e.g. in geodes where the iron may have come from iron sulfide (pyrite), the amount of Al substitution in goethite appears low (Fitzpatrick, 1978).

The second most prevalent iron oxide in soils is hematite (Fe_2O_3). Hematite normally has a bright red color (5R—2.5YR hues) and has a very strong pigmenting effect on soil materials. Apparently only a small amount mixed into a goethitic matrix can cause the hue to redden appreciably. Hematite apparently requires ferrihydrite (discussed later), as a precursor for its formation (Schwertmann and Taylor, 1977). It appears to be largely confined to better-drained soils in warm-temperate to tropical areas since the rapid decomposition of organic matter seems to be essential to its formation (Schwertmann and Taylor, 1977).

Lepidocrocite (FeOOH), normally orange colored (5YR—7.5YR hues), is quite common in poorly drained soils. It may result from rapid oxidation of Fe^{2+}—Fe^{3+} hydroxy compounds, e.g. "green rust", or when Fe^{2+} in soil solutions is oxidized. Lepidocrocite in soils is metastable relative to goethite; however, the transformation may take place at a very slow rate. Tarzi and Protz (1978) reported lepidocrocite associated with biotite in two well-drained Ontario soils.

Maghemite (Fe_2O_3) also occurs in soils, especially those derived from basic igneous rocks (Schwertmann and Taylor, 1977). It apparently has a reddish-brown color, but a more interesting feature, in view of its relatively rare occurrence, is its magnetic property. In magnetite (Fe_3O_4), one out of every three iron atoms is Fe^{2+}, whereas in the other iron-oxide minerals discussed thus far, nearly all of the iron is Fe^{3+}. Schwertmann and Taylor (1977) have pointed out that most soil maghemites also contain traces of Fe^{2+}. Work by Fitzpatrick (1978) indicates that a broad series of minerals exist between magnetite and maghemite.

Ferrihydrite, for which a formula of $Fe_5HO_8 \cdot H_2O$ was proposed by Towe and Bradley (1967), has only recently been recognized as a mineral species. It is poorly crystalline, or occurs in very fine particles, or both. It formerly was considered amorphous ferric hydroxide, but studies (Towe and Bradley, 1967; Chukhrov et al., 1973) have shown an X-ray diffraction pattern. It is often associated with goethite in bog iron deposits (Schwertmann and Taylor, 1977).

Ferrous compounds occurring in reducing (anerobic) soil environments have been referred to as "green rust" (apparently an $Fe^{2+}Fe^{3+}$ hydroxy compound) and black hydromagnetite [$Fe_3(OH)_8$]. X-ray diffraction patterns and crystal structures have not been reported for these substances.

Iron-oxide minerals containing Fe^{3+} are unstable in reducing environments. Soluble Fe^{2+} may be translocated by leaching or diffusion to another part of the soil where it may oxidize and precipitate to form mottles or concretions, or it may be leached from the profile. Thus Fe-rich micromorphological zones (mottles and concretions) indicate either a more oxidizing environment or one in which oxidation prevails for longer periods than in the associated Fe-depleted zones.

Aluminum oxides

The term "aluminum oxides" is applied here to hydroxides and oxy-hydroxides as well as to true oxides. In soils, the hydroxides [$Al(OH)_3$], especially gibbsite, are the more common minerals. They occur mainly in Oxisols and Ultisols. Other aluminum-hydroxide minerals reported to occur in soils and bauxite deposits are nordstrandite and bayerite, $Al(OH)_3$, (Hsu, 1977). Oxyhydroxides, boehmite and diaspore ($AlOOH$), apparently are also common in bauxites, but are rare in soils (Hsu, 1977). However, diaspore is considered to be the least soluble, thus most stable, of the aluminum hydroxides and oxyhydroxides (Kittrick, 1969; Lindsay, 1979). Apparently chemical kinetics in soils favor the formation of the metastable minerals, particularly gibbsite. Diaspore apparently is mainly in Paleozoic rocks (Kittrick, 1969). A true aluminum oxide [i.e. corundum (Al_2O_3)], considered to be a high-temperature form, occurs only as an inherited mineral in soils.

In developing soil-mineral solution-stability diagrams, amorphous $Al(OH)_3$, which would be more soluble and thus less stable than any of the minerals mentioned, is also often considered (Lindsay, 1979). Moreover, small quantities of "free Al" estimated by treatment with dithionite or other extractants (Blume and Schwertmann, 1969) are apparently associated with iron oxides, silicates and organic matter. Such complexes are found in many soils that do not contain discrete Al-oxide minerals. For example, Jackson (1963, 1964) proposed the "anti-gibbsite" effect, i.e. the tendency for $Al(OH)_3$ sheets to form interlayers in expansible 2:1 phyllosilicates, thereby precluding the formation of discrete gibbsite. This tendency seems to be greatest from pH 4 to 6 (Rich, 1968). The high affinity of aluminum for iron oxides in selected soils is shown by the high degree of aluminum substitution found in some soil goethites (Bigham et al., 1978).

The source of the Al for formation of secondary Al minerals, as well as the Al associated in complexes such as phyllosilicate interlayers, is the weathering of aluminosilicates in an acidic environment. In more highly weathered soils containing low quantities of organic compounds and expansible 2:1 minerals, etc., discrete aluminum-oxide minerals such as gibbsite apparently form as silica is leached out of the system. In contrast to Fe and Mn, aluminum in soils is not reducible to a more soluble, lower oxidation state; consequently, aluminum-oxide minerals are more likely to accumulate in a leaching environment.

Manganese oxides

The term, "manganese oxides", used herein to include oxyhydroxides as well as true oxides, has been discussed in considerable detail by McKenzie (1977). Pyrolusite (MnO_2) is considered to be the most stable manganese-oxide mineral and was the one most commonly mentioned in early soil science literature. However, investigations have shown that a number of other manganese-oxide minerals occur in soils and may be even more extensive than pyrolusite (Taylor et al., 1964; Ross et al., 1976; McKenzie, 1977). Soil occurrences of birnessite, lithiophorite, hollandite, todorokite and psilomelane, as well as pyrolusite, have been reported (Ross et al., 1976). These minerals are often very poorly crystalline. Perhaps related to their poor crystallinity, or perhaps to stabilize their structures, some of these minerals contain significant amounts of such foreign ions as Ba, Ca, K, Na, Li, NH_4, Co, Cu and Ni (McKenzie, 1977). Formulas for the aforementioned minerals, which often vary greatly in composition, are given by McKenzie. The low pH of the zero-point charge of some manganese oxides (Healy et al., 1966) may contribute to their affinity for heavy metals and other elements.

Manganese oxides show an even greater tendency than iron oxides to occur in concretions, possibly because manganese is chemically reduced to relatively soluble Mn^{2+} more readily than Fe^{3+} is reduced to Fe^{2+}. Illustrative of these relationships, Schwertmann and Fanning (1976) found over 80 percent of the dithionite-extractable manganese oxides in some poorly drained soils to occur in concretions, whereas a maximum of only 32 percent of the dithionite-extractable iron oxides occurred in concretions in the same soils.

Manganese-oxide minerals in soils can be detected by their effervescence in hydrogen peroxide. Manganese-rich micromorphological zones that are black, e.g. some concretions, often also contain large amounts of iron oxides. However, iron-rich "brown" concretions in some soils have been shown to be low in manganese oxides (Schwertmann and Fanning, 1976). Thus manganese-oxide minerals appear to have a strong black pigmenting effect. However, since the pigment has a color similar to that of some humidified organic matter, confusion may arise in field identification of these substances.

Carbonates, sulfates, sulphides and chlorides

Alkaline earth carbonates are of great importance in soils because they often comprise a significant part of the soil mass and have considerable influence on soil chemical and physical properties.

Calcite ($CaCO_3$) and dolomite [$CaMg(CO_3)_2$] are the only carbonates to occur in appreciable quantities in soils. They may occur throughout soil profiles or they may be concentrated in lower horizons to form calcic or petrocalcic horizons. Dolomite may be an important allogenic constituent in soils developed in some glacial tills, fluvial sediments derived from dolomitic limestones, or in dolomitic lacustrine deposits. Large amounts of calcite may have been in original parent sediments, or have been added as calcareous dust (Yaalon and Ganor, 1973). In either case the dissolved ions move downward and may precipitate at depth in the soil, particularly in dry (subhumid to arid) climates, to form a distinct zone of carbonate enrichment. Calcite also precipitates in soils at the capillary fringe from shallow groundwater tables if the water contains appreciable calcium bicarbonate.

Gypsum may occur as an authigenic mineral, sometimes in sufficient quantities to be the most common constituent, in soils of arid regions. In many cases it is inherited from gypsiferous parent sediments. Jarosite $[KFe_3(SO_4)_2(OH)_6]$, formed as a result of oxidation of sulfides, has been identified in tidal marsh soils ("cat clays") after drainage; gypsum may also form if sufficient Ca is present. Barite $(BaSO_4)$ has been reported as an authigenic mineral from lower subsoils in Texas (Lynn et al., 1971) and as an inherited mineral in Australian soils (Beattie and Haldane, 1958). Epsomite $(MgSO_4 \cdot 7H_2O)$ and thenardite (Na_2SO_4), along with several hydrated sulfates were reported by Driessen and Schoorl (1973) in surface-soil efflorescences in Turkey. Thernardite was identified in a South Texas Salorthid (Walthall and Allen, 1980). Also, halite $(NaCl)$, as would be expected, is a major constituent in highly saline soils.

Pyrite, FeS_2, is a common constituent of tidal marsh sediments, shales, lignites and occasionally limestones. A polymorph, marcasite, is less common. Both are unstable in an oxidizing soil environment. Extreme acidity often results from their alteration.

Other minerals

Apatite $[Ca_5(F,Cl)(PO_4)_3]$ is an accessory mineral in slightly to moderately weathered soils. It may be inherited from igneous and metamorphic rocks as well as from some limestones. In reality it is a series of minerals depending on the relative amounts of F and Cl (as well as OH). Also some AsO_4 may substitute for PO_4. Primary apatite is very unstable in a leaching environment.

Rutile (TiO_2) is a common accessory mineral in the heavy fraction of sands and silts. A polymorph, anatase, occurs authigenically in significant amounts in some intensively weathered soils (Tamura et al., 1953; Bain, 1976). Ilmenite $(FeTiO_3)$ is a common opaque mineral in the heavy-mineral fraction of selected soils.

MINERAL STABILITY

Various stability series of minerals in the weathering zone have been proposed (Goldich, 1938; Pettijohn, 1941; Dryden and Dryden, 1946; Van der Marel, 1949). Although there is general agreement among the writers cited, considerable discrepancies occur concerning the relative position of some minerals. Jackson et al. (1948, 1952) proposed a weathering sequence of clay-size minerals that has been widely cited in determining relative stages of soil development. Jackson and Sherman (1953) and Jackson (1964) revised the sequence slightly.

TABLE 6.2

Minerals in order of decreasing stability*

Primary	Secondary (authigenic)
Zircon	Anatase
Rutile	Gibbsite
Tourmaline	Hematite (and goethite)
Ilmenite	Kaolinite
Garnet	Pedogenic chlorite (Hydroxy-interlayered vermiculite)
Quartz	Smectite
Epidote	Vermiculite
Sphene	Illite
Muscovite	Halloysite
Microcline	Sepiolite (and palygorskite)
Orthoclase	Allophane (and imogolite)
Sodic plagioclase	Calcite
Calcic plagioclase	Gypsum, pyrite
Hornblende	Halite (and salts of similar solubility)
Chlorite	
Augite	
Biotite	
Serpentine	
Volcanic glass	
Apatite	
Olivine	

*Sand- and silt-size particles are assumed for the primary minerals and clay-size particles for secondary (authigenic) species.

Brewer (1964) has pointed out that much of the variation among stability tables given by various authors has been due to difference in composition, e.g. the plagioclase isomorphous series, and differences in the weathering environment. Size differences can also be a factor.

Based upon the aforementioned investigations, together with many additional studies on selected soils cited in succeeding sections, weathering sequences for primary and secondary minerals are proposed in Table 6.2. Primary minerals are mostly of sand and silt size. Secondary minerals are mostly clay-size particles, but some are often larger, e.g. calcite. Some minerals, e.g. quartz and anatase, may be either of primary or secondary origin.

The soil environment greatly influences mineral stability. Unrestricted drainage, ample precipitation (and time) to at least leach the solum of calcite and more soluble minerals, a predominantly oxidizing environment, and a temperate or warmer climate have been assumed in developing the table. Nevertheless, most weathering trends would be similar if all the conditions were not satisfied (except for the drainage requirement), but they would proceed more slowly.

Volcanic glass, although not a mineral, is listed in Table 6.2 because of its importance as a primary constituent of soil parent materials. Weatherability of the glass is variable, depending on composition; acidic glass may rank higher in the series than shown. There is little agreement among different writers on the position of apatite in stability series. The position assigned in Table 6.2 is based primarily on the short time required to virtually deplete profiles of apatite in New Zealand dune soils (Syers and Walker, 1969). The position of muscovite may be subject to question since it sometimes is listed as being less stable than the potassium feldspars and sodic plagioclase (albite). The most calcic plagioclase (anorthite) would surely be less stable than indicated, but as the percentage of Na increases to produce minerals with a Ca:Na ratio in the labradorite range, stability increases markedly. The stability of garnet likely varies considerably because of marked differences in composition; Fe-rich varieties are less stable than others. Because both epidote and sphene are common in the heavy mineral fraction of many soils they are placed relatively high in the table; however, there is little agreement among authors on their position in stability series. The position of hornblende, chlorite, and augite probably varies in respect to each other. Brown ("basaltic") hornblende is relatively common in some soils, even in those in which their parent sediments have undergone several erosional and depositional cycles.

Although zeolites are synthesized in some soil environments (Baldar and Whittig, 1968), they were not listed among the secondary minerals (Table 6.2) because of lack of data concerning their stability in soils. However, they undoubtedly are very unstable in most pedogenic environments. The position of allophane differs appreciably from that of Jackson (1964). Allophane is intended here to be the amorphous alumino-silicate usually listed as the first detectable product of volcanic glass decomposition. It is not meant to include the X-ray amorphous decomposition products of phyllosilicate weathering which would rank much higher in the series. Halloysite is placed considerably lower (less stable) than it was by Jackson (1964) because it commonly is the first authigenic mineral detectable by X-ray diffraction in soils developing in volcanic ash (Fieldes, 1955; Aomine and Wada, 1962; Wada, 1967; Dudas and Harward, 1975a; Dixon and McKee, 1974) and its lack of persistence as soils mature. The relatively high position of pedogenic chlorite seems justified by its presence, especially in the surface horizons, in many Ultisols and Oxisols.

MINERAL SYNTHESIS AND TRANSFORMATION IN SOIL PROFILES

Mineral synthesis is the formation of authigenic products from either precipitation of solutes out of solution or the polymerization of colloidal components with weak crystallographic organizations. Mineral transformation is the alteration (diagenesis) of a constituent in which significant structural integrity (of the mineral) is retained throughout the process. Products of both synthesis and transformation are generally crystalline, but some(primarily those that are neoformed) may be X-ray amorphous.

The parent materials of soils constitute a wide spectrum that varies from one extreme of crystalline rock residuum having a limited suite of primary minerals to the other of unconsolidated sediments with an extremely heterogenous composition. In the first case, mineral synthesis and transformation can be determined with considerably more confidence, provided that additions from extraneous sources can be precluded, than they can in the second case. Nevertheless, because of the fundamental importance to an essential understanding of soils, and weathering processes and products in general, numerous studies have been undertaken to elucidate such processes in a great variety of materials and in a diversity of conditioning environments. When such an array of materials and environments are considered, results are expectedly often confusing and sometimes apparently conflicting.

A common approach to the problem of mineral transformation and synthesis during pedogenesis has been to study the composition of successively deeper layers and assume that differences reflect pedogenic changes. Such "depth functions" lend themselves to study because weathering intensity has traditionally been considered to be greatest in the surface horizon and to gradually decrease with depth (Jackson et al., 1948). Although the applicability of the depth function has been questioned in some pedogenic environments, especially arid regions (Nikiforoff, 1937), it nevertheless has had wide appeal for soil mineralogists. Soils with pronounced profile development usually also show greater mineralogical differences with depth. Conversely, most soils having restricted profile development due to one or more limiting factors, e.g. landscape age, high water table, etc., are unlikely to exhibit marked mineralogical differentiation among horizons.

The mineralogical record available for study by comparative analysis of soil horizons results from one or more: (1) differences in original materials; (2) translocation; (3) transformation; (4) degradation (decomposition); and (5) synthesis. Whenever possible 1 is eliminated by selecting homogeneous materials, which in itself is often extremely difficult in many pedogenic environments. The relative intensity of processes 2, 3, 4 and 5 is conditioned by climate, especially water movement through the profile, relief (including the depth to a water table), landscape age and the nature of the parent material. Although we attempt to separate the different processes for purposes of study and assignment of relative importance, it must be remembered that more than one process is taking place simultaneously. For example, while in-situ synthesis of some constituents within a specified horizon is proceeding others are being decomposed. Still others are perhaps being altered. To add further complexity to the system, illuviation may be occurring at the same time. The resulting mineralogy reflects the illuviation record superimposing the in-situ changes.

The morphology of some soil orders reflect distinct processes, e.g. Spodosols. Among some other orders, the processes may be much the same but the relative intensity varies greatly. Some Alfisols (Udalfs) have developed as a result of processes much like those that are instrumental in Ultisol (Udult) formation. On the other hand, Alfisols in semi-arid regions (Ustalfs) have formed by processes similar to those prevailing in some Aridisols (Argids).

In light of the preceding discussion it is not surprising that mineralogical transformations in Spodosols are more distinctive than in Alfisols. In some Alfisols, mineralogical changes are much like those in Ultisols but in others they are like those in Aridisols.

Despite the inherent limitations indicated above, a discussion of the mineralogy and changes therein that result from pedogenesis in the different orders is deemed to be a fruitful approach. Changes in orders that are predominantly in humid regions with well-developed profiles (Spodosols, Alfisols, Ultisols and Oxisols) are discussed first. Changes with time are greatest in these orders. Next, the orders (Mollisols, Vertisols, Aridisols and Inceptisols) in which pedogenesis has been less intense, are considered. Lastly, the minimal mineralogical changes of Entisols are discussed.

The ensuing discussion on mineral synthesis and transformation by soil orders is not comprehensive but will serve to illustrate some of the more widespread mineral changes that prevail.

Spodosols

Most of the Spodosols in North America have formed in glacial drift on late Pleistocene or Holocene surfaces in cold humid climates. They have also developed in highly quartzose sands, which are often influenced by fluctuating groundwater in other areas. Their morphology is discussed by McKeague et al. (1983). Mineralogical changes between the albic and spodic horizons of Spodosols are often pronounced despite relatively young geomorphic surfaces and climatic limitations to intensive weathering. Apparently because of the strong acidity and complexing tendency of downward-moving dissolved organic constituents (chelating agents), the strongly eluviated horizons are zones of intense mineral alteration. Although there is little difference between the spodic and underlying substratum in weatherable sand- and silt-size minerals, markedly less of these minerals occur in the albic horizon (Cady, 1960), resulting in a residue of quartz and other resistant minerals.

Translocated and chemically active components in Spodosols consist mostly of poorly crystalline iron and aluminum oxides and Fe—Al—organo complexes. Most of these materials are amorphous to X-rays or nearly so. Schwertmann and Taylor (1977) speculate that ferrihydrite, which is likely transformed to goethite with time, is the first Fe mineral to form in Spodosols because of the abundance of organic matter. Despite the dominant physico-chemical role of the amorphous complexes of the spodic horizon much less is known about their transformation pathways, or indeed their composition, than about the crystalline components.

Regardless of the apparent secondary physico-chemical role of crystalline phyllosilicates in Spodosols, their pedogenic transformation has interested a number of investigators. (And it should be remembered that these minerals may constitute the only active fraction in strongly developed albic horizons.) There is substantial evidence that non-expandable 2:1 phyllosilicates are altered into smectites in the eluviated horizons of Spodosols (Brown and Jackson, 1958; Franzmeier et al., 1963; Ross and Mortland, 1966; Gjems, 1970) or smectite-rich interstratified clay (Brydon et al., 1968). Ross and Mortland reported beidellite to be the smectite variety in their study. The non-expandable precursor minerals (or those of limited expandability) in the spodic horizon have been variously identified as some combination of mica, chlorite, vermiculite or hydroxy-interlayered vermiculite. Gjems (1970) postulated that the smectite in two Spodosols from Yugoslavia had formed at the expense of hydroxy-interlayered species, the dealumination of which was promoted by the strong acidity of the A2 (E) horizons and of illite. Gjems believed the process to be further enhanced by the formation of aluminum—humus complexes and subsequent translocation to the B horizon.

Coen and Arnold (1972) proposed the further possibility of eolian additions of smectite to albic horizons in New York Spodosols and its persistence there in a metastable state. De Coninck et al. (1968) did not detect smectite in either eluviated or spodic horizons in Belgian soils. In their model, illite (or glauconite) was first transformed into intergradient illite—chlorite, which in turn was decomposed to amorphous components. Amorphous alumina was found to accumulate in the spodic horizon.

General phyllosilicate transformational trends in Orthods may be summarized by:

Micas,		vermiculite,		smectite
trioctahedral	→	pedogenic	→	
chlorite		chlorite		

Little information is available on mineralogical transformations in Spodosols other than Orthods. In contrast to studies made on Orthods in cooler climates, Zelazny and Carlisle (1971) did not detect smectite in Florida Haplaquods. They reported that non-crystalline components dominated the clay fraction in both the A1 (Ah) and A2 (E) horizons. An intergrade mineral (presumably pedogenic chlorite), kaolinite, and gibbsite increased with depth, leading the authors to conclude that all were less stable than the amorphous components in the strongly acidic upper horizons.

In light of the findings of Fanning et al. (1973) that Fe is lost from soil profiles under reducing conditions, Aquods would be expected to suffer net losses of Fe. Apparently there is sufficient weathering of silicates to provide the aluminum to form the necessary Al-humic complexes. Holzhey et al. (1975) reported that the aluminum in Bh horizons of North Carolina Aquods, as demonstrated by extraction with pyrophosphate, was mainly associated with organic matter. Lesser amounts were in aluminum-interlayered vermiculite. The horizons were essentially devoid of Fe.

Alfisols

Alfisols have formed in a variety of materials ranging from glacial till and loess to crystalline bedrock and Coastal Plain marine sediments in climates varying from cool humid to hot semi-arid. They are mostly on middle to late Pleistocene surfaces.

The morphology and, by inference, pedogenic processes instrumental in the formation of Alfisols differ considerably from those in Spodosols. Phyllosilicates have accumulated, at least to a considerable extent, by translocation from an overlying ochric epipedon (A and/or E horizons) to form an argillic (Bt) horizon (Rust, 1983), further complicating evaluation of mineralogical trends during pedogenesis.

Studies generally indicate that clay-mineral alteration, and possibly some synthesis, has occurred in better-drained Alfisols (specifically Hapludalfs) on late Pleistocene surfaces in cool humid climates. Since it is well established that more fine clay, which generally contains more smectite, than coarse clay, is translocated during pedogenesis, more smectite is usually identified in the illuviated Bt than in the A and E horizons. Alteration of sand- and silt-size weatherable minerals appears to have been minimal even in the strongly eluviated, and supposedly the most weathered, horizons (Cady, 1960). However, Caldwell and White (1956) reported some evidence of more feldspar weathering in the upper than in the lower horizons in Indiana loessial soils. Moreover, Bronger et al. (1976) reported a 40 percent decrease in feldspars in the solum relative to the parent material in a "rubified earthy braunlehm" (Udalf?) on a middle Pleistocene surface in Germany.

The glacial and periglacial parent sediments of Udalfs are finer textured than those of Spodosols. They have commonly been described as having illite, inherited from the parent material, as the predominant mineral in the clay fraction. Chlorite and other constituents are usually less-prominent components. The nature of the rocks from which glacial drift was derived is likely of considerable importance in determining the clay mineralogy of the drift and subsequent weathering trends. Paleozoic shales are dominated by illite and tend to weather first to vermiculite and then to mixed-layer vermiculite/chlorite, but Mesozoic and Tertiary shales, also predominantly illitic, tend to weather initially into mixed-layer illite/smectite and finally into smectite. Evidence, mostly obtained from studying profile depth trends,

158

indicates that the first sequence is predominant in the Udalfs formed from glacial materials in the United States. However, the non-collapsible 14A mineral, has been variously referred to as chlorite, mixed-layer chlorite/ vermiculite, pedogenic chlorite, and hydroxy-interlayed vermiculite (Martin, 1954; Klages and White, 1957; Johnson et al., 1963; Fanning and Jackson, 1965; Lietzke et al., 1975).

Khangarot et al. (1971) reported an increase in vermiculite in Ap horizons, relative to underlying Bt horizons in Wisconsin-age loess on terraces in Ohio. They also believed expandable clay (defined as having variable expansion beyond 14A upon glycolation) in the Bt, relative to the C horizon, to be pedogenically derived from the illite. Smeck et al. (1968) reported evidence of illite alteration to vermiculite in one Ohio Hapludalf but postulated the authigenic formation of smectite in another Hapludalf formed from similar but older glacial tills. Later, Wilding et al. (1971) speculated that the sequence:

Illite → vermiculite → smectite (montmorillonite)

in soils derived from the more southern tills in Ohio was due to more Ca and Mg because of a higher carbonate status and dolomite-rich tills, lower K-bearing shale lithorelict content, greater chronological age, or a combination of these conditions. Rutledge et al. (1975) ascribed the lower expandable clay content in eluviated horizons than in underlying Bt horizons on Ohio terrace soils to its instability under strongly acidic conditions. Some of the apparent anomalies of smectite occurrence in selected Udalfs may be due to silica activity, the influence of which has been little studied. General mineralogical trends in Udalfs, Aqualfs and associated Aquolls as a function of profile depth and drainage in the eastern Midwest are depicted in Fig. 6.1.

Small amounts of kaolinite occur throughout the sola of most Udalfs, but there does not seem to be a clear consensus as to whether it is mostly inherited or of pedogenic origin. Depth trends are also inconsistent.

Judging from reported results of numerous investigations, the mineralogy and weathering trends with depth of Udalfs containing fragipans (Fragiudalfs) do not differ appreciably from the regionally associated Hapludalfs (Anderson

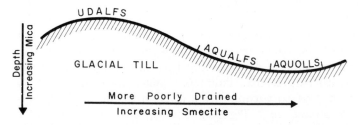

Fig. 6.1. Effects of topographic position and depth on soil mineralogy in selected suborders in the eastern Midwest (L.P. Wilding, pers. commun., 1980).

and White, 1958; Grossman et al., 1959; Peterson et al., 1970; Miller et al., 1971; Lozet and Herbillon, 1971). However, Hutcheson et al. (1959), in a study of soils developed in loess, reported somewhat more smectite and vermiculite in soils containing fragipans than in an associated well-drained soil lacking a fragipan. Ritchie et al. (1974) found considerably more vermiculite and less illite with proximity to the surface in Fragiaqualfs and Ochraqualfs in northeastern Ohio. Some chloritization of expanding components had occurred in selected soils in both great groups in the upper sola but was especially pronounced above the pan in the Fragiaqualfs. Hallmark (1977) found similar mineralogical trends in Fragiaqualfs in the same general area.

Chloritization of biotite may occur prior to active pedogenesis and pedogenic transformation in the phyllosilicates perhaps begins with trioctahedral chlorite. Droste (1956) reported prominent chlorite and vermiculite in unoxidized calcareous tills, respectively, in Ohio.

Coffman and Fanning (1975) found the sequence:

Primary ferruginous trioctahedral chlorite	→	trioctahedral vermiculite	→	kaolinite and iron oxides

to depict the weathering trend in both Hapludalfs and associated soils developed in non-micaceous chloritic metabasalts on the Maryland Piedmont. There was some evidence of "rechloritization" of the vermiculite in surficial horizons due to hydroxy-aluminum interlayering. Most of the feldspars and ferromagnesium minerals were weathered out during pedogenesis.

In contrast, Alexiades et al. (1973) found chlorite, apparently formed as a result of vermiculite chloritization, to remain relatively constant through a Hapludalf profile developed in granite residuum in northern Greece. Mica and authigenic kaolinite were found to increase due to a "residual effect", and smectite to decrease upward in the profile. They explained the smectite decrease as a function of selective translocation of surface bits of mica flakes as they became altered into smectite (and possibly vermiculite). The data suggest that smectite synthesis should not have been precluded since a consistent increase with depth to the R horizon was detected. They explained the enrichment of feldspar and quartz in the sand and silt fractions of the A horizons by the weathering of biotite and trioctahedral vermiculite, leaving a residue of more stable minerals.

Albaqualfs (formerly classified as Planosols) have very strongly developed argillic horizons that greatly deter water movement, resulting in a perched water table in late winter and spring. Whiteside and Marshall (1944), from studies of a Missouri Planosol (Albaqualf?) developed in loess, concluded that some smectite was synthesized in the pan as well as being translocated from the overlying horizons. Kunze and Oakes (1957) found the smectite in the strongly eluviated A horizons of several Planosol (Albaqualf) pedons developed in smectitic marine sediments in Texas to show considerable evidence of smectite degradation relative to both the Bt and C horizons.

Goss and Allen (1968) suggested that conditions were more favorable for smectite synthesis in the lower horizons than in the upper horizons of a Natrustalf and an associated Haplustalf developed in granite residuum in Central Texas. However, they pointed out the possibility of smectite degradation in the upper horizons resulting in a residue of mica and kaolinite, and possibly, of X-ray amorphous products. The smectite increase, even into the C horizon, as detected by X-ray diffraction, was much more pronounced in the Natrustalf than in the Haplustalf. In contrast to the studies of Alexiades et al. (1973), Goss and Allen (1968) found no vermiculite in the clays, but did detect appreciable amounts of it in the coarser fractions.

The limited data available on the mineralogy of dry Alfisols in continental climates (Ustalfs) developed in sedimentary materials indicate little change with time or profile depth. An Aridic Paleustalf, developed in a medium-textured, mineralogically homogeneous eolian mantle on the Texas High Plains, showed little mineralogical variation with depth except for somewhat more (or perhaps better crystallized) smectite in the thick calcic horizons (Kunze et al., 1955; Allen et al., 1972).

Dry Alfisols in Mediterranean climates (Xeralfs in the U.S.) often have opal, or chalcedony-like accumulations in the lower subsoil or substratum (Flach et al., 1969). The secondary silica seems to have been derived from the decomposition of glass, feldspars or ferromagnesian minerals. Baldar and Whittig (1968) reported the authigenic formation of analcime, a zeolite, in the surface horizon of a highly alkaline Natric Haploxeralf in California. Whittig (1959) also suggested the possibility of smectite synthesis, as evidenced by its better crystallinity in the natric horizon of a California Natrixeralf developed in fan alluvium.

Differences in inherited mineralogy in sediments from different source areas may account for some reports of pronounced mineral weathering on apparently rather young geomorphic surfaces. Ahmad et al. (1977) attributed the much greater vermiculite and smectite in the oldest soil (a Haplustalf) on a terrace sequence in subhumid Pakistan to the weathering of chlorite and illite, the dominant phyllosilicates in the less developed soils on younger surfaces. It was not determined whether the much greater content of expanding clay in the Bt versus the Ap horizons of the Haplustalf was due to translocation or to other processes. On the other hand, Sidhu and Gilkes (1977) found little, if any, evidence of alteration of sand, silt or clay minerals in a Natrustalf, associated with Ochrepts, developed in alluvium on the Indo-Gangetic Plain of India.

Ustalfs occur extensively in dry tropical regions of the world, but few definitive studies of pedogenic mineral alteration in such soils have been carried out. Gallez et al. (1975) found the clay in the Paleustalf and Plinthustalf members of a toposequence developed in the basement rock complex of southern Nigeria to be dominated by kaolinite but also to contain significant amounts of crystalline iron oxides. Moderate amounts of smectite in the Haplustalf member suggested a lower weathering intensity, because of impeded drainage, than in the other Ustalfs.

To summarize, the trends in phyllosilicate alteration in Udalfs are dominantly:

Mica, trioctahedral chlorite   →   vermiculite   →   pedogenic chlorite

It is not possible to summarize general trends in other Alfisols because of the diversity of conditioning environments and limited data.

Ultisols

Most Ultisols are considerably more weathered than Alfisols, although their gross morphology is quite similar. The horizonation of some Ultisols is rather subtle, but many have strongly developed morphologies, e.g. thick, sandy albic horizons underlain by even thicker, clayey argillic horizons. Miller (1983) discusses their morphology in more detail. In contrast to Spodosols and most Alfisols, the clays of most Ultisols are either composed mostly of kaolinite or have significant amounts of it. The large amounts of kaolinite are to be expected because: (1) Ultisols are often on older geomorphic surfaces than soils formed in glacial and periglacial materials; and (2) the weathering intensity has been greater due to generally higher mean annual temperatures and greater leaching, resulting in greater H^+ activity. Moreover, many Ultisols on relatively young surfaces such as stream terraces are formed in sediments that have undergone one or more weathering cycles. In addition to kaolinite, significant amounts of pedogenic chlorite in Ultisols has been reported in recent years.

Most studies of Ultisol mineralogy in the United States have been conducted in two broad classes of parent materials: (1) crystalline rock residuum from the Piedmont; and (2) Coastal Plain sediments. In early studies, Alexander et al. (1939) found kaolinite to be the dominant clay mineral in Red-Yellow Podzolic soils (Hapludults?) on the North Carolina Piedmont. Mineral stability trends were not reported, but increased kaolinite and/or gibbsite in the 2—5-μm fraction of the deeper horizons was found in some of the soils studied.

Rich and Obenshain (1955), among the first investigators to observe relatively stable 14 A, 2:1 phyllosilicates in the intensively weathered soils of the southeastern United States, found that a "vermiculite" containing hydroxy-aluminum interlayers increased upwards in a soil (Hapludult?) developed from mica schist in Virginia. They hypothesized that the mixed-layer mineral was even more resistant to weathering than kaolinite. They reported little change in the mica with depth. Rich and Obenshain pointed out that the decreasing pedogenic chlorite and increasing kaolinite with depth suggested stability relationships at variance with the weathering sequence proposed by Jackson et al. (1948).

Increased pedogenic chlorite and decreased kaolinite with proximity to the surface have since been reported in other Piedmont Hapludults, e.g. Bryant and Dixon (1963) and Cook (1973). Bryant and Dixon also found gibbsite to increase with depth and postulated that kaolinite and gibbsite formed directly from the weathering of feldspar and mica in the lower profile as well as from weathering products leached from the upper horizons. McCaleb (1959) also believed that in-situ alteration of feldspar, possibly through a halloysite stage, in Udults of the North Carolina Piedmont accounted for most of the kaolinite throughout the profile, including the C horizon. McCaleb concluded that muscovite and biotite altered through a vermiculite intermediate to kaolinite.

Soil parent materials on the Atlantic and Gulf Coastal Plains differ appreciably from those of the Piedmont, yet mineralogical trends with pedogenesis seem to be remarkably similar. Of course, it should be remembered that much of the parent sediment, at least on the Atlantic segment, was originally derived from the Piedmont. Weed and Nelson (1962) detected a maximum of pedogenic chlorite relative to kaolinite in surface horizons, and a decrease with depth, in Red-Yellow Podzolic soils (Udults) in both Piedmont and Coastal Plain soils of North Carolina. They proposed that mica was the precursor of the mineral.

Soils developed from smectite-bearing Coastal Plain sediments in Mississippi exhibited increasing chloritization upward in the profile in a Paleudult (Nash, 1963) and in Hapludults and Fragiudults on terraces (Nash, 1979). Douglas (1965) reported a similar depth trend for a New Jersey Hapludult, in which the intergradient chlorite—vermiculite was believed to have illite, contained in the parent Quaternary sediments, as its precursor. Fiskell and Perkins (1970), summarizing data from several southeastern states, reported a remarkable similarity in mineralogy of Ultisols. Pedogenic chlorite (chloritized vermiculite) usually increased and kaolinite decreased, with proximity to the surface. Gibbsite was reported as a common clay constituent.

Cady and Daniels (1968) concluded that a general kaolinite increase with depth noted in North Carolina Paleudults on the Coastal Plain was due to its destruction in the upper horizons, the degree of which was strongly influenced by geomorphic surface age. The data indicated that more pedogenic chlorite was present in the Bt horizon than in the E (A2) horizon clay in the Paleudult on the oldest geomorphic surface, whereas the converse was true for the Paleudult on a younger surface. This suggests the eventual destruction of the chlorite. An associated Hapludult on a younger geomorphic surface, apparently reflecting parent sediment composition, showed little mineralogical change with pedogenesis.

Ultisols are apparently very extensive in the humid tropics, but few definitive studies have been made on such soils where the classification is firm. Lepsch and Buol (1974) in a study of a toposequence: Haplorthox (highest in the landscape)—Umbriorthox—Palehumult—Paleudult, in Sao

Paulo state, Brazil, and Sanchez and Buol (1974), studying Paleudults in the upper Amazon Basin, Peru, found kaolinite to be the dominant mineral in the clay in all soils studied. Soils of the Sao Paulo toposequence were developed in surficial deposits derived from nearby sedimentary and basic igneous rocks and those in the Amazon Basin from unconsolidated sedimentary materials. Gibbsite, suggested as an indicator of weathering intensity, decreased, along with chloritized vermiculite from the uppermost to the lowest member of the toposequence. An opposite trend was found for combined mica and vermiculite. In the Amazon Basin study, the investigators reported that smectite increased appreciably in an associated Tropaquept and Tropaqualf, relative to the Paleudult, indicating that the soils with restricted drainage (aquic great groups) were considerably less weathered. In neither study were significant mineralogical changes with profile depth apparent.

Martini and Marcias (1974) reported kaolinite to be the dominant mineral in soils of Costa Rica described as Palehumults. Trace to moderate amounts of chlorite were detected in some pedons, but were not found in others.

Kantor and Schwertmann (1974) found that a catena of kaolinitic Humults on middle and upper slopes and associated smectitic Vertisols in depressions in Kenya were all developed from similar basic igneous rocks. The increased smectite with depth in some of the Humults suggested its formation in situ as the first weathering product and its subsequent decomposition (alteration?), due to lowering of Si and Mg concentration in solution, as weathering advanced. Moreover, they proposed the formation of small quantities of pedogenic illite due to K fixation in some of the Humults. Smectite persisted in the depressions but showed some evidence of alteration to kaolinite in the upper horizons.

Little information is available on phyllosilicate transformations in Aquults. It would seem that weatherable primary minerals would more likely be preserved than in soils in a free-leaching environment. Nevertheless, weathering may be intense when the water table drops. Fanning et al. (1973) clearly showed that the poorly drained Aquult member of a drainage catena in Maryland had suffered marked net losses of free Fe (dithionite extractable) due to reduction and subsequent removal. On the other hand, free Fe had not been removed to an appreciable extent from the somewhat better drained Aquult member, but instead had become concentrated into mottles. These observations emphasize the problem of "weatherable minerals", i.e. an Fe-bearing mineral may be less stable in a reducing than in an oxidizing environment.

To summarize, weatherable primary minerals and 2:1 phyllosilicates, except for pedogenic chlorite, tend to decrease markedly with pedogenic intensity in Ultisols. Pedogenic chlorite is remarkably stable, even more so than kaolinite. The former, along with gibbsite, are the dominant minerals in the clays of some Ultisols in an advanced weathering stage.

Oxisols

Oxisols, considered to be the most-weathered of all soils, are mainly in tropical areas or, when present outside the tropics, are believed to be relics of a past tropical weathering regime. Present climate ranges from arid to extremely wet.

Morphology of modal Oxisols, differing appreciably from most soils in humid temperate climates, do not exhibit evidence of silicate clay translocation (Van Wambeke et al., 1983). Eswaran (1972) described degraded, Fe-enriched cutans in oxic horizons as relics from a former argillic horizon stage. Nevertheless, concepts of zones of eluviation and illuviation are, for the most part, inapplicable.

Many tropical areas formerly thought to be dominated by Oxisols have been found to have mainly Ultisols, or Inceptisols, or both. The requirements of Soil Taxonomy (Soil Survey Staff, 1975) that Oxisols cannot have sufficient clay translocation to meet the requirements of an argillic horizon on the one hand, or of a cation-exchange capacity of enough magnitude to qualify as a cambic horizon on the other, has greatly restricted their geographical range. As a result, mineralogical data on soils firmly classified as Oxisols are limited.

The clay fraction of Oxisols is dominated by: (a) 1:1 phyllosilicates; (b) oxides of Fe and/or Al, or mixtures of a and b. Pedogenic chlorite has been identified as a common secondary component in recent years.

In an early study from Hawaii, Tamura et al. (1953) characterized soils, which apparently are mostly now classified as Oxisols, as dominantly kaolinitic and oxidic. They assigned the soils to weathering stage 10 (Jackson et al., 1948; Jackson and Sherman, 1953) and postulated that kaolinite decomposed, thereby effecting an increase in gibbsite as silica was leached with increased weathering intensity.

Despite the long-prevailing theory that silica is mobilized and lost from the soil profile under intensive weathering in tropical climates, Eswaran (1972) reported micromorphological evidence of increased pedogenic quartz (or cristobalite) crystallaria down to weathered bedrock in Orthox (as well as in some associated Ultisols) derived from basalts in Nicaragua. Based upon studies of soils from Nicaragua and Madagascar, Eswaran and De Coninck (1971), proposed that the immobilization of silica to form sand- and silt-size quartz, in contrast to clay-size silica minerals, would not mitigate against the formation of gibbsite in the clay fraction in tropical soils derived from basalt. They found that halloysite decreased markedly, relative to that in associated Ultisols, and that some gibbsite had formed, apparently as a result of desilication of 1:1 phyllosilicates, in the well-drained Oxisols. Furthermore, increased goethite and hematite, versus amorphous iron oxides, were reported in the Oxisols compared to the Ultisols.

Le Roux (1973) concluded that clays of two Oxisols (Orthox) from South

Africa contained mostly kaolinite, aluminous chlorite and amorphous components. However, gibbsite was included in the latter since it was determined by selective dissolution analysis. In a soil derived from dolerite (equivalent to "diabase" as used in the United States), X-ray data suggested somewhat better crystallinity of the chlorite and slightly lower amounts of kaolinite with proximity to the surface. Although illite was not detected by X-ray diffraction in a soil derived from mixed dolerite-shale colluvium, the K_2O content indicated that small amounts were still present in the solum. An associated soil developed from shales, but situated on steep young surfaces and classified as an Umbrept, contained appreciably more mica throughout the solum.

Lepsch and Buol (1974) found two Orthox from Brazil, developed in surficial deposits of mixed sedimentary-basic igneous rock origin, to show

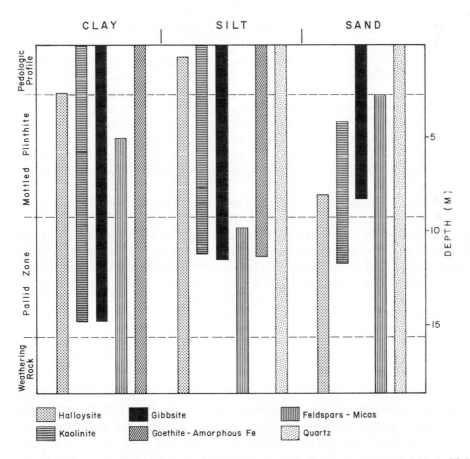

Fig. 6.2. Mineral occurrence by size fraction in weathering zones on granite in Malaysia. (After Eswaran and Wong Chaw Bin, 1978a, b, c.)

little change in the dominantly kaolinitic and gibbsitic mineralogy to a depth of more than 4 m. More gibbsite and less mica and pedogenic chlorite were present than in associated Ultisols.

The results of a very detailed study by Eswaran and Wong Chaw Bin (1978a, b, c) of a deep weathering profile in a Malaysian granite are summarized in Fig. 6.2. They concluded that each secondary mineral is the product of the specific micro-environment characteristic of the weathering zone. The weathering zone in the soil, classified as an Orthox, was separated into the pedologic profile (0– 275 cm), mottled plinthite (275—950 cm), pallid layer (950- 1600 cm), and weathered coherent rock (1600—1900 cm) (Fig. 6.1). Halloysite, apparently formed directly from feldspar as indicated by scanning electron microscopy, was the only secondary silicate mineral in the weathered rock zone. Kaolinite and gibbsite first appeared in the pallid zone, but halloysite remained the predominant secondary mineral; feldspar decreased relative to the amount in the weathered rock. Kaolinite became the dominant secondary mineral at the top of the mottled zone. Halloysite and feldspar disappeared in the pedologic profile (at about 2 m) as a component of the clay and sand fractions, respectively, whereas gibbsite became a significant component in all three size fractions in this zone. Quartz and iron oxides increased upwards in the sand and clay, respectively. Both increased with proximity to the surface in the silt fraction. Eswaran and Wong Chaw Bin (1978a, b, c) reported that biotite was altered to halloysite in the weathered rock and pallid zones, but weathered to a mixture of kaolinite and goethite in the mottled zone. They further concluded that gibbsite formed both pseudomorphically from feldspar and by direct precipitation.

In summary, transformational trends are much the same in Oxisols as in Ultisols. It is a matter of intensity rather than kind.

Possible pathways for phyllosilicate mineral transformations for well-developed soils of humid regions (Spodosols, Alfisols, Ultisols and Oxisols) are presented in Fig. 6.3. Many of the same transformations undoubtedly occur in selected suborders, such as Udolls, Umbrepts and Tropepts, of other orders. Unrestricted drainage is assumed in most cases; however, silication (+Si) is unlikely to be of significance except under the influence of a rising water table.

Mollisols

Mollisols generally occur in drier climates than Spodosols, Alfisols, Ultisols and Oxisols; however, many exceptions can be cited. Ustalfs and Xeralfs are drier than many Mollisols and, of course, Aquolls are naturally wet. Moreover, Mollisols are often intimately associated with Alfisols in the prairie– forest transition zone and in drainage catenas (Fig. 6.1). Since the presence of a mollic epipedon is the one feature essential to placement in the

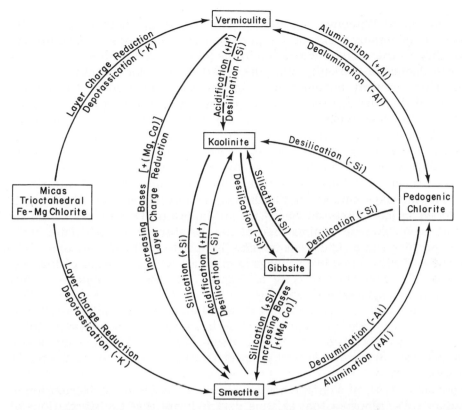

Fig. 6.3. Possible transformational paths among selected minerals. "Alumination" and "dealumination" refer to gain and loss of interlayer Al in 2:1 phyllosilicates. Suggested causes of layer-charge reduction have included: (1) oxidation of Fe^{2+} to Fe^{3+}; (2) formation of OH's by protonation of structural oxygens; and (3) exchange of Si for structural Al in the tetrahedral sheet.

order (Fenton, 1983) mineralogy, as well as profile morphology, is extremely diverse. However, 2:1 phyllosilicates invariably are predominant among the Mollisols of the continental United States and Canada. Mollisols having kaolinitic mineralogy have, however, been reported from Hawaii (Soil Survey Staff, 1979, unpubl.); similar soils likely occur in other tropical areas.

Beavers et al. (1955) reported that Illinois Mollisols (mostly Argiudolls) developed in loess and glacial till were predominantly smectitic and illitic, respectively. Chlorite* was found to be more common in the till-derived soils. Differences in parent-material mineralogy were attributed to sediment-source variations; the loess from a western source was considerably more smectitic

---

*Chlorite inherited from loess and till is likely a trioctahedral type, thus is susceptible to weathering. It should not be confused with pedogenic chlorite.

than the till of Wisconsin age derived from more northern sources. Little change in mineralogy, except for possible slight decreases in smectite with proximity to the surface, was noted in the loess-derived profiles. In contrast, chlorite decreased markedly, illite decreased slightly and smectite increased appreciably upward in the profile in the till-derived soils. The authors recognized that the increased smectite in the upper profile could be partially due to a thin loess mantle; however, they believed their data strongly suggested a weathering of chlorite through a "mixed layer" stage to smectite. Johnson and Beavers (1959) presented data indicating considerable weathering of feldspar in the A horizons of the same loess-derived soils.

Arneman et al. (1958) found little evidence of mineralogical differences, including the clays, among soils of a drainage catena (Hapludolls—Haplaquolls) developed in late Wisconsin glacial till in Minnesota. Differences within the profiles were likewise minimal except for the absence of carbonates in the upper profiles and a significant increase in apatite in the C horizons. Millet and Drew (1963) found little change in mineralogy as a result of pedogenesis in Arguidolls developed directly in Kansan till, and in sediments derived therefrom, in southeastern Nebraska.

St. Arnaud and Mortland (1963) reported an increase in illite, ascribed to "illitization" (K fixation), and a decrease in smectite with proximity to the surface in all members of a till-derived Mollisol—Alfisol sequence in Saskatchewan. Some evidence of chlorite weathering upwards in the profile was also reported.

Kodama (1979), in a comprehensive review of clay-mineral distribution in Canadian soils, reported that existing data indicate that transformations of phyllosilicate clays have been minimal in the Chernozemic soils (Mollisols) of the Prairie provinces. Slight increases in expansible minerals of the surface horizons are suggested in data from a few pedons.

To summarize, existing data suggest minimal mineralogical change as a result of pedogenesis in Mollisols derived from loess. Apparently, there is a tendency for non-expanding 2:1 phyllosilicates to weather into smectite in till-derived soils, compared to those developed in loess, perhaps due to more chlorite, illite or mixed-layer clays in the parent sediment. There are two probable reasons for the lack of pedogenic phyllosilicate alteration in loess- and till-derived Mollisols as contrasted to that observed in Alfisols: (1) the mean weathering intensity is somewhat lower; and (2) the grass vegetation is less effective than forests in causing such changes.

Despite the concept of Mollisols being centered on the dark soils developed in glacial till and loess in cool climates under tall grass, Mollisols develop residually from consolidated rock as well as from other unconsolidated sediments in a variety of climates. Wilkinson and Gray (1954) concluded that little change occurred in the clay mineralogy of two Reddish Prairie soils (Paleustolls), one developed from Pennsylvanian shales and the other from Permian Red Beds in Oklahoma, as a result of pedogenesis. Jarvis et al.

(1959) found changes in silicate clay mineralogy in Brunizems (Argiudolls? and Paleudolls?) from southeastern Kansas developed in residuum and colluvium derived from sandstone, shale and limestone to be limited. The changes consisted mostly of: (1) the formation of interstratified (mixed-layer) types from vermiculite in pedons having slow internal draignage; and (2) the alteration of vermiculite to smectite in some well-drained pedons.

Aquolls associated with Aqualfs and Udalfs in drainage catenas in the eastern Midwest (Fig. 6.2) are commonly more smectitic than the better drained soils. The smectite may have been formed in situ, selectively alluviated since it is usually concentrated in the fine clay, or both processes may have been operative.

Inceptisols

Inceptisols have been subject to pedogenic processes ranging from weakly to moderately intensive. A cambic horizon is usually present but is not mandatory. Moreover, other diagnostic horizons, e.g. a fragipan, may be present. The epipedon is nearly always ochric or umbric. Foss et al. (1983) have discussed the morphological requirements of Inceptisols in considerable detail.

The mineralogy of Inceptisols generally reflects their relative immaturity. Weatherable minerals are always present unless the parent material per se is composed of minerals of an advanced weathering stage, e.g. kaolinitic Tropepts. Most Inceptisols show few detectable changes in clay mineralogy as a result of pedogenesis. Conversely, practically all the clay may be of secondary origin as in the case of Andepts. There may have been a pronounced loss of such components as gypsum and more soluble minerals. On the other hand, sulfates may be synthesized in some environments, e.g. Sulfaquepts. Considering the variety of materials from which Inceptisols form and the differences in dominant pedogenic processes, their mineralogies are predictably diverse.

The mineralogy of Andepts, distinguished by an exchange complex dominated by amorphous material (Soil Survey Staff, 1975), has been studied much more than that of other Inceptisols. Such interest has been due to: (1) their distinctive physico-chemical properties; and (2) the opportunities presented for studying relatively rapid mineral synthesis and transformation. Most Andepts have formed either directly or indirectly from predominantly pyroclastic materials, but a limited number have formed from consolidated extrusives. Most of the ejecta is of andesitic composition but it may range from rhyolitic to basaltic (Birrell and Fieldes, 1952; Fieldes, 1966).

The Andepts have such unusual physico-chemical properties that an additional order, Andisols, has been recently proposed for them (G.D. Smith, unpubl.).

Tamura et al. (1953) reported that soils classified as Hydrol Humic

Latosols (Hydrandepts) were dominated by allophane (amorphous alumino-silicates) and gibbsite. The authors apparently thought that the characteristic mineralogy resulted from decomposition of phyllosilicates and leaching of the released silica; consequently, they assigned the soils to a relatively advanced weathering stage. They found the clay in a Low Humic Latosol (Humitropept?) to consist mostly of kaolinite and hematite.

Considerably later, Wada and Wada (1976) reported that non-crystalline hydrous iron and aluminum oxides were the principal constituents, and that allophane was a minor component, of the Hydrandept clays studied by Tamura et al. (1953). They concluded that the mineralogy was a result of strong desilication in a perhumid climate. Both a Humitropept, derived from mixed old alluvium and volcanic ash, and a Torrox, formed from basalt residuum, were found to have a clay mineralogy dominated by kaolinite, hematite and goethite. The Tropept and Torrox formed in increasingly drier climates. The authors did not consider differences in geomorphic surface age in their study.

In contrast to the study of Tamura et al. (1953), Fieldes (1955) considered that allophane "B" (a mixture of discrete silica and alumina stabilized by colloidal humus) was the first synthesized product of rhyolitic and andesitic ash weathering in New Zealand. He defined allophane A as randomly combined silica and alumina. Fields envisaged the sequence:

Allophane A → allophane AB → allophane B → metahalloysite → kaolinite

as occurring during pedogenesis. Evidence of such a sequence was cited in: (1) progressively older land-surface soils; and (2) a series of buried soils derived from increasingly older ash falls.

Later, Fieldes (1966) reported that allophane was the principal product and that all primary minerals plus glass decreased during weathering of basalt scoria in New Zealand.

Aomine and Yoshinaga (1955) determined that allophane was by far the most common clay mineral in Ando (Andept) soils of Japan. They described "hair-like" particles, which were later to be called "imogolite" (Yoshinaga and Aomine, 1962), in some of the soils.

Aomine and Wada (1962) postulated a weathering sequence of primary minerals:

volcanic glass > andesine—labradorite > hypersthene—augite > magnetite

and the formation of allophane first and then hydrated halloysite from volcanic glass and feldspar. Direct products of the weathering of the hypersthene—augite could not be determined but chemical analyses showed a remarkable loss of bases and a suggestion of desilication.

Miyauchi and Aomine (1964) have questioned the existence of allophane "B" in volcanic ash soils in Japan. Instead Aomine and Miyauchi (1965) proposed the sequence:

allophane → imogolite A → imogolite B

Imogolite A and B gave diffuse X-ray diffraction spacings of 13 and 18A, respectively.

Wada (1967) proposed that the weathering direction of ash to form imogolite or hydrated halloysite was primarily determined by the relative proportions of Si and Al available in the system. But major environmental conditions seemed to differ little for their formation. The development of low-grade order in imogolite was interpreted in terms of a prototypic 2:1-layer structure. Glassy material seemed to favor imogolite formation. The formation of a gibbsite-like sheet and subsequent additions of silica tetrahedra was the apparent initiation of hydrated halloysite formation.

Besoain (1969) reported a transition from the allophane "AB" of Fieldes (1955) in older ashes in Chilean Andosols (Andepts). A similar transition was noted with depth in younger ash falls that buried older falls. Only allophane was detected by Espinoza et al. (1975) in Chilean Dystrandepts developed in late Pleistocene ashes.

Dudas and Harward (1975a, b) proposed the weathering sequence:

volcanic glass → allophane → hydrated halloysite

in Oregon Andepts. The origin of 2:1 phyllosilicates was ascribed to detrital processes and to incorporation of materials from underlying paleosols. They discounted the in-situ origin of smectite in internal channels of pumiceous particles as proposed earlier by Chichester et al. (1969) in the same ash deposit.

Cortes and Franzmeier (1972) reported a much greater variety of clay-size minerals in Colombian Andepts than reported in similar soils by most other investigators. Smectite, vermiculite and an intergradient chlorite were identified in addition to allophane, imogolite and halloysite. The authors proposed the formation of vermiculite from mica deposited with the ash and the possibility of its alteration to the chlorite intergrade by incorporation of hydroxy interlayers. Origin of the smectite could not be readily explained, but the authors thought in-situ formation, similar to that proposed by Chichester (1969), most likely. Deposition of the smectite, or its precursor, as an original constituent of the ash was offered as a less likely alternative. Admixing from underlying paleosols was discounted because of the thickness of the ash deposit and the kaolinitic nature of the paleosol.

Mineralogical investigations of Inceptisols other than Andepts have been much less common. Most Inceptisols do not show appreciable mineral alteration as a result of pedogenesis. For example, Brown et al. (1973) found no detectable differences with profile depth, or among profiles, in Inceptisols developed in Mississippi River alluvium. Mineralogy was highly mixed, reflecting various source areas. Nevertheless, if the necessary pedogenesis has occurred for soils to develop Inceptisol characteristics, then some mineral alteration has likely occurred.

Mineralogical changes as a result of pedogenesis in some Inceptisols other than Andepts have been well documented. Jha and Cline (1963) reported increased evidence of mica weathering to vermiculite in a New York Sol Brun Acide (Fragiochrept?). Incipient chloritization was indicated in the fine silt and coarse clay. The marked clay increase in the fragipan relative to an overlying E horizon, was explained by the authors as due to differential destruction rates rather than to translocation. Degradational processes are perhaps of more importance in determining the mineralogy of Inceptisols in humid regions than is commonly recognized.

Krebs and Tedrow (1957) found that illite had been partially altered to vermiculite and that appreciable weathering of magnetite had occurred, especially in the A horizon, to release iron oxides in an Acid Brown Forest Soil (Ochrept?). McCracken et al. (1962) presented evidence that chlorite present in the parent materials, mostly pre-Cambrian clastic sedimentary rocks, of Sol Brun Acides (Dystrochrepts) had been altered to vermiculite and intergradient chlorite-vermiculite during pedogenesis in the North Carolina Great Smoky Mountains. Feldspars, abundant in the parent rock, were barely detectable in the B horizons. The authors postulated that kaolinite and gibbsite had formed at the expense of the feldspars. Franzmeier et al. (1969) reported that vermiculite increased, whereas mica and/or intergradient mica-vermiculite decreased with proximity to the surface in Dystrochrepts, developed in acid siltstones and shales, of the Cumberland Plateau in Tennessee and Kentucky.

Losche et al. (1970) found that an intergradient vermiculite-chlorite was abundant in a Dystrochrept formed from biotite gneiss in the southern Appalachian Mountains of North Carolina. Presumably the biotite was the precursor of the mineral. Gibbsite and kaolinite, apparently formed from the weathering products of feldspar and phyllosilicates, were also relatively abundant. The investigators concluded that the vermiculite-chlorite and kaolinite were the most stable minerals in the prevailing pedogenic environment. The mineralogy of the Dystrochrepts did not differ appreciably from associated Udults in either the study by Losche et al. (1970) or by Franzmeier et al. (1969).

Mineral synthesis and transformations in some Aquepts, mostly those developed in tidal marsh sediments, are unique. Sulfides, mainly pyrite (FeS_2), present in the parent sediment are oxidized to form jarosite $[K(Fe)_3(OH)_6(SO_4)_2]$; gypsum may also form if sufficient Ca is present (Fanning, 1978). Usually such soils are extremely acidic, often having a sulfuric horizon (Soil Survey Staff, 1975).

Entisols

Evidence of mineral synthesis and alteration are minimal in Entisols. But some changes relative to the parent material have surely occurred, but most of them are not detectable by ordinary field and laboratory methods. As is the case in any other type of pedogenic activity, subtle changes begin to take place from the time a sediment is deposited or when a material is exposed.

To illustrate this concept we may consider an Entisol sequence on crystalline rocks:

(Orthent) → Inceptisol (Ochrept) → Ultisol (Udult)

The mineral fraction of the Entisol would likely consist mostly of comminuted primary minerals (small amounts of eolian-derived clay and silt will likely be present). However, some mineral alteration, e.g. "vermiculitization" of biotite, would probably have begun. In fact, such processes as kaolinization of feldspars may have been initiated. But since the ochric epipedon is the only diagnostic horizon present, the soil would still be an Entisol. With increasing pedogenesis a cambic horizon develops and the soil becomes an Ochrept. Primary mineral alteration may have progressed along similar pathways as in the Orthent but to a greater degree. But synthesis of phyllosilicate clay may also be appreciable by the time this stage is reached. By the time the soil becomes an Udult few weatherable minerals remain and phyllosilicate clay transformation may be marked, e.g. "chloritization" of 2:1 clays.

One more example will further illustrate the concept. Consider a sequence in an aridic environment, developing in calcareous sediments:

Entisols (Torriorthent) → Aridisol a (Camborthid) → Aridisol b (Calciorthid)

As in the humid environment, a cambic horizon develops with increasing pedogenesis and a Camborthid results. (Redistribution of carbonates may be discernable but have not occurred to the extent of forming a calcic horizon.) When a calcic horizon develops the soil is classified as a Calciorthid. The process of $CaCO_3$ redistribution begins in most cases before the Camborthid develops. The same process ($CaCO_3$ redistribution) occurs, but in markedly different degrees in all three taxons.

Although a considerable number of morphological and chemical studies have been made on soils that meet the requirements of Entisols few mineralogical studies have been reported. Syers and Walker (1969) reported that carbonates were leached from Psamments? developed in beach sands in <500 yrs and that acid-extractable Ca phosphate (apatite) decreased appreciably, especially in the upper profile, in the same time span. Selected Torripsamments in southern New Mexico were found to exhibit slight carbonate redistribution (Gile and Grossman, 1979). Carlisle and Zelazny (1974) showed pedogenic chlorite to increase and kaolinite and gibbsite to decrease, presumably by dissolution in Florida Quartzippsamments, with proximity to the surface. The authors did not speculate on the source of the pedogenic chlorite. (Neither mica nor vermiculite without Al interlayers was detected deeper in the profiles.)

Reduction of iron oxides and sulfates occurs in selected aqueous

TABLE 6.3

Mineral composition and transformation by suborders of soil taxonomy

Suborder	Mineralogy	Transformational trends
Aridisols		
Argids	Mixed*, montmorillonitic[†]	Slow rates because of dryness Montmorillonite to mixed-layer types
Orthids	Mixed*, carbonatic[†], montmorillonitic[†], gypsic	Slow rates because of dryness Dissolution of carbonates and gypsum Montmorillonite to mixed-layer types Precipitation of gypsum, halite, epsomite, thenardite, etc. in Salorthids
Alfisols		
Aqualfs	Mixed*, montmorillonitic[†], siliceous[†], illitic[†], carbonatic	Slow rates in phyllosilicates because of wetness Reduction of Fe oxides resulting in net loss and/or redistribution of Fe
Boralfs	Mixed*, montmorillonitic[†], illitic	Illite to vermiculite and/or montmorillonite
Udalfs	Mixed*, siliceous[†], montmorillonitic, illitic, vermiculitic, kaolinitic	Illite to vermiculite and/or pedogenic chlorite Trioctahedral chlorite to vermiculite Feldspar weathering Silt-size mica to vermiculite
Ustalfs	Mixed*, montmorillonitic[†], siliceous[†], carbonatic	Slow rates because of dryness Dissolution of carbonates Montmorillonite synthesis in lower profile
Xeralfs	Mixed*, montmorillonitic[†], kaolinitic, serpentinitic, vermiculitic	Serpentine and vermiculite to smectite (nontronite) Mica to vermiculite Phyllosilicates to kaolinite Glass and primary silicates to opal and chalcedony
Entisols[+]		
Aquents	Mixed*, montmorillonitic[†], siliceous	Slow rates because of wetness
Arents	Mixed*	Minimal because of youthfulness
Fluvents	Mixed*, montmorillonitic[†], siliceous[†], carbonatic	Dissolution of carbonates
Orthents	Mixed*, montmorillonitic[†], carbonatic[†], siliceous	Dissolution of carbonates and gypsum
Psamments	Mixed*, siliceous[†], carbonatic	Dissolution of carbonates and apatite Dissolution of gibbsite (in severe weathering environments)

TABLE 6.3 (*continued*)

Suborder	Mineralogy	Transformational trends
Histosols [§]		
Fibrists	Mixed, siliceous	Minimal because of wetness
Folists	No mineralogy families	
Hemists	Mixed, coprogenous	Minimal because of wetness
		Precipitation of Fe sulfides
Saprists	Mixed*, siliceous[†], montmorillonitic, marly, coprogenous, diatomaceous	Minimal because of wetness
Inceptisols		
Aquepts	Mixed*, montmorillonitic[†], "allophanic"[†], siliceous[†], illitic, kaolinitic, carbonatic, oxidic, illitic, halloysitic, micaceous	Slow rates in phyllosilicates because of wetness
		Reduction of Fe oxides resulting in net loss and/or redistribution of Fe
		Oxidation of Fe sulfides to jarosite
Andepts	Allophane	Glass to allophane
		Allophane to imogolite and halloysite
		Feldspar to halloysite
Ochrepts	Mixed*, siliceous[†], carbonatic[†], montmorillonitic[†], micaceous, serpentinitic, oxidic	Mica to vermiculite and vermiculite-chlorite
		Feldspars to kaolinite and gibbsite
		Serpentine to smectite (nontronite)
Plaggepts	Not identified in U.S.	Information lacking
Tropepts	Mixed*, kaolinitic[†], montmorillonitic, oxidic	2:1 phyllosilicates to kaolinite and oxides
Umbrepts	Mixed*, siliceous	Information lacking
Mollisols		
Albolls	Montmorillonitic*, mixed[†]	Information lacking
Aquolls	Mixed*, montmorillonitic[†], carbonatic[†], siliceous, illitic	Slow rates in phyllosilicates because of wetness
		Synthesis of montmorillonite
		Reduction of Fe oxides resulting in loss of Fe
Borolls	Mixed*, montmorillonitic[†], carbonatic[†], illitic, siliceous	Illite to mixed-layer types or montmorillonite
		Dissolution of carbonates
Rendolls	Carbonatic*, mixed[†]	Dissolution of carbonates
Udolls	Mixed*, montmorillonitic[†], carbonatic, illitic, siliceous	Illite and chlorite to mixed-layer types or smectite
		Dissolution of carbonates
Ustolls	Mixed*, montmorillonitic[†], carbonatic[†], kaolinitic	Slow rates because of dryness
		Dissolution of carbonates
		Serpentine to smectite
Xerolls	Mixed*, montmorillonitic[†], carbonatic, micaceous, serpentinitic, vermiculitic	Dissolution of carbonates
		Mica to vermiculite
		Serpentine to smectite

TABLE 6.3 (*continued*)

Suborder	Mineralogy	Transformational trends
Oxisols		
Aquox	Not identified in U.S.	Slow rates in phyllosilicates because of wetness
		Reduction of Fe oxides resulting in net loss of Fe
Humox	Ferritic*, oxidic[†]	Minimal potential for change
Orthox	Oxidic*, kaolinitic[†], ferritic	Kaolinite to gibbsite
Torrox	Kaolinitic	Slow rates because of dryness
Ustox	Kaolinitic	Slow rates because of dryness
Spodosols		
Aquods	Mixed*, siliceous[†]	Slow rates in phyllosilicates because of wetness
		Reduction of Fe oxides resulting in net loss of Fe
Ferrods	Not identified in U.S.	Information lacking
Humods	Siliceous	Minimal potential for transformation
Orthods	Mixed*, siliceous	Non-expanding and partially expanding 2:1 phyllosilicates to smectite
		Decrease in weatherable minerals in eluviated horizons
Ultisols		
Aquults	Mixed*, siliceous[†], kaolinitic	Slow rates in phyllosilicates because of wetness
		Reduction of Fe oxides resulting in net loss of Fe
Humults	Mixed*, kaolinitic[†], oxidic	2:1 phyllosilicates to kaolinite and oxides
Udults	Mixed*, kaolinitic[†], siliceous[†], oxidic, illitic, glauconite, micaceous	Illite, mica, glauconite and smectite to vermiculite, pedogenic chlorite, kaolinite and oxides
Ustults	Mixed*, oxidic[†]	Information lacking
Xerults	Mixed*, kaolinitic[†]	Information lacking
Vertisols		
Torrerts	Montmorillonitic	Slow rates because of dryness
		Dissolution of carbonates
Uderts	Montmorillonitic*, mixed	Probable degradation of 2:1 phyllosilicates to mixed-layer types
Usterts	Montmorillonitic*, mixed[†]	Slow rates because of dryness
		Dissolution of carbonates
Xererts	Montmorillonitic	Slow rates because of dryness
		Dissolution of carbonates

TABLE 6.3 (*continued*)

*Most common mineralogy class within suborder when more than one class is listed.

†Common mineralogy class(es) within suborder. Other listed classes are less extensive. In the case of Aquepts "allophanic" mineralogy is not listed, but the mineralogy is understood to be dominated by allophane in Andaquepts.

⁺Little mineralogical alteration except for some loss of carbonates and gypsum, because of geomorphic surface age. Moreover, wetness in Aquents and siliceous mineralogy in many Fluvents and Psamments is an additional deterrent to alteration.

§Mineralogy is not used in the classification of Histosols except in "terric" and "limnic" subgroups. (Terric subgroups have a mineral layer ⩾30 cm thick with an upper boundary below the surface tier within the control section. Limnic subgroups have materials ⩾5 cm thick in the control section, composed mostly of inorganic precipitates or deposits produced by the activity of aquatic organisms.) Although not minerals in a strict sense "coprogenous", "diatomaceous", and "marly" classes are used to describe mineralogy classes in limnic subgroups.

depositional environments. This process, although important to pedology, should perhaps be more properly considered a geological process. However, when these materials are drained, or when deeply buried sediments are exposed as in strip mining, oxidation proceeds rapidly. Jarosite and earlier such materials usually become exceedingly acidic unless sufficient $CaCO_3$ is present to counter the acidity. If jarosite mottles are formed and the pH falls below 3.5 (in the drained materials) a sulfuric horizon (Soil Survey Staff, 1975) is recognized. The soil is then classed as an Inceptisol. Obviously the changes are initiated while the soil is still an Entisol en route to becoming an Inceptisol.

Aridisols

The composition of parent materials varies greatly and only minimal alteration of parent sediments in many soils has taken place. Their phyllosilicate mineralogy is dominantly a mixture of non-expanding and expanding 2:1 species, but those in which smectite predominates are relatively common (Table 6.3). Strongly kaolinitic Aridisols in the U.S. are very rare, but as more soils in the arid tropics are studied, an increasing number of kaolinitic ones will perhaps be reported. Many weatherable minerals, especially feldspars, remain in the sands and silts. The mineralogy of some Orthids is dominated by carbonates. Many Aridisols, e.g. Camborthids, show little development and meet only the minimum requirements of a diagnostic subsurface horizon. Conversely, some Aridisols, primarily those on late mid-Pleistocene or older geomorphic surfaces, have strongly developed morphologies, e.g. thick argillic and petrocalcic horizons (Paleargids). Nettleton and Peterson (1983) discuss Aridisol morphology in detail.

Concentrations of carbonates, gypsum, more soluble salts and secondary silica minerals reflect the more obvious mineralogical changes during pedogenesis of most Aridisols. Some of these changes are mostly due to redistribution of constituents within the profile or even eolian additions from extraneous sources. As pointed out by Simonson (1959), similar pedogenic processes obtain in both arid and humid regions, but they may differ markedly in degree. Changes in silicate mineralogy may, therefore, be expected, but often not to the degree that can be readily detected. Nevertheless, the evidence is convincing that, at least in the Aridisols of the United States, the clay mineralogy developed in sedimentary materials is mostly inherited and changes have been minimal during pedogenesis. Assuming that these observations are valid, it is difficult to explain the similarity of soils developed in crystalline rock residuum, although not studied extensively, to associated soils developed in sedimentary materials. The distinct possibility of eolian additions of clays cannot be discounted and may account for the ubiquitous occurrence, although usually in minor amounts, of kaolinite in Aridisols overlying crystalline rocks. The kaolinite was perhaps a product of a more intensive weathering regime and may have gone through one or more cycles of erosion and sedimentation before deposition in its present pedogenic environment. However, distinct differences in profile morphology of soils developed in residuum of different rock types, e.g. limestone versus granite, in the same general area is an argument against most of the clay being wind deposited.

Detailed investigations have not borne out the early assumption that the clays of desertic soils was dominated by expanding clay types. Brown and Drosdoff (1940) recognized the dominance of a mixed layer, "composite mineral of montmorillonite and hydrous mica", with lesser amounts of "kaolin family" minerals, in two soils (Argids?) from the California Mojave Desert. Apparently no differences in the clay mineralogy with depth in either soil, one developed in fan alluvium and the other in granitic residuum, could be detected. It should be recalled that a popular theory existed at the time suggesting that the more clayey subsoils relative to surface horizons were a result of clay development in situ because of their better moisture status (Nikiforoff, 1937).

Buol and Yesilsoy (1964) reported that illite and kaolinite dominated the clay of the upper profile and smectite, coinciding with a lithologic discontinuity, was most common in the lower profile of an Argid from Arizona. They reported that halloysite was common throughout the profile, an apparently rare observation for Aridisol clays. Mineralogy changes resulting from pedogenesis were not observed. The results reported by Smith and Buol (1968) on Arizona Haplargids suggest mineralogical changes, i.e. more smectite with depth, regardless of the presence of lithologic discontinuities. The increased smectite was found in deeper horizons containing free $CaCO_3$.

Nettleton et al. (1973) concluded that micaceous 10A minerals have formed in the surface horizons from 2:1 phyllosilicates of variable expansibility of many dry-region soils, including those with aridic moisture regimes, in the southwestern United States. The release of K^+ and NH_4^+ during plant decomposition and their subsequent fixation by phyllosilicate structures were believed to be responsible for the process. Considerably earlier, Buehrer et al. (1948) suggested that Arizona surface soils contained more illite than subsoils in their respective profiles as reflected by K_2O contents of the "colloidal fraction".

Calcareous Orthids (Calciorthids and Camborthids) would not be expected to show mineralogy changes with pedogenesis even to the degree occurring in Argids. Nevertheless, Mahjoory (1975) reported that clay mica (illite), based primarily on K_2O determinations, decreased with depth in calcareous Orthids, apparently developed on alluvial plains, in Iran. All pedons studied contained appreciable vermiculite which seemed to be partly instratified with the clay mica. On the other hand, Gal et al. (1974) concluded that the mineralogy of Israeli desert soils, some of which would likely have sufficient development to be classed as Aridisols, was mainly inherited from parent sediments. Considerable unpublished data obtained on a number of Orthids from the southwestern U.S. generally support the conclusions of Gal et al.

Extreme translocation of clay, often referred to as "solonization", is apparently caused by high Na activity and occurs in selected subhumid, semiarid, and arid region soils. Solodization (dealkalization) may follow solonization if Na, or Mg, or both, are replaced by H. Such intense pedogenic processes would be expected to result in appreciable mineral alteration; however, few studies have been made of such changes in arid regions. Klages and Southard (1968) concluded that the smectite in Natrargids (intergrading to Borolls), developed from smectite-rich glacial till in northeastern Montana, had suffered alteration to mixed-layer minerals. Clays from the soils, subject to varying degrees of solonization, apparently contained the most highly ordered smectite in the C horizons and exhibited progressively more interstratification (with illite) with proximity to the surface.

There is a real hazard in deducing pedogenic mineralogical changes from profile depth trends in all soils, but probably even more so in Aridisols, because of eolian additions. Undoubtedly, such additions occur, but there is disagreement among earth scientists as to the extent of the deposition in various parts of the world. The results of wind erosion and deposition are obvious in much of the arid western U.S., but much of it has occurred since man initiated agriculture and domestic grazing, mostly within the last hundred years. Also, eolian processes were especially active at times in the Quaternary. Nevertheless, evidence indicates that some mineral alteration, especially of the more weatherable components, such as the 2:1 clay-size phyllosilicates, has taken place.

As indicated in the foregoing discussion, most clay minerals in Aridisols are the same as those present in soils from more humid regions, although perhaps differing in relative amounts and transformation trends. Such does not seem to be the case with the acicular clay minerals, i.e. palygorskite (attapulgite) and sepiolite. They seem to be present almost exclusively in

Aridisols (and associated Entisols) and in calcareous horizons of soils from semi-arid climates. Pedogenic occurrences of acicular clays have been reported with increasing frequency from dry regions within the last two decades (Muir, 1951; Yaalon, 1955; Barshad et al., 1956; Van den Heuvel, 1966; Al-Rawi et al., 1969; Millot et al., 1969; McLean et al., 1972; Singer and Amiel, 1974; Eswaran and Barzanji, 1974; Aba-Husayn and Sayegh, 1977; Abtahi, 1977; Bigham et al., 1980). There has been considerable controversy concerning their origin. Van den Heuvel (1966) believed both minerals to be of authigenic origin in petrocalcic horizons in southern New Mexico. Millot et al. (1969), Singer and Amiel (1974), Eswaran and Barzanji (1974) and Abtahi (1977) studying soils from North Africa, Israel, Iraq and Iran, respectively, concluded that palygorskite was of pedogenic origin. Muir (1951) in Syria and Aba-Husayn and Sayegh (1977) in Saudi Arabia, believed that palygorskite was inherited from limestone and local alluvium derived from Mio-Pliocene beds, respectively. McLean et al. (1972) explained the occurrence of both sepiolite and palygorskite in selected calcareous soils of West Texas and eastern New Mexico by inheritance from parent sediments derived wholly or in part from lacustrine deposits. Bigham et al. (1980) generally agreed with McLean et al. (1972) on the origin of the acicular clays in West Texas soils and concluded that they are unstable in soil environments, apparently being reduced to an X-ray amorphous state.

Vertisols

Vertisols, occurring almost exclusively in tropical and warm-temperate climates, have unique morphologies. Horizonation is often so weakly expressed that the profile appears to be the same throughout because of "self mixing" resulting from the shrinking and swelling of the clay with drying and wetting. Textural differences in the profile are minimal, therefore horizon differentiation is primarily based upon color, structure, etc. Vertisol morphology and genesis are discussed in detail by Ahmad (1983).

Not surprisingly, Vertisol differentiae, e.g. width and depth of cracks, gilgai microrelief, intersecting slickensides, etc., are often associated with smectitic mineralogy. However, the expression of such differentiating features are dependent not only upon the clay-mineral type but also on the amount of clay. Consequently, some Vertisols are characterized as having mixed instead of the expected smectitic clay mineralogy. Nevertheless, the great majority of Vertisols have significant amounts of smectite minerals.

Vertisols seem to have developed mostly from clayey marine sediments exhibiting various degrees of consolidation, impure limestones, basic crystalline rocks, e.g. basalt, or in alluvium derived from such materials. They have also formed in sediments originating from uplands where smectitic soils predominate. In the soils formed in crystalline rock residuum, the smectite obviously has been synthesized. When formed in other materials, it appears to have been mostly inherited, and concentrated by dissolution of carbonates in the case of the limy materials.

Kunze and Templin (1956) and Nelson et al. (1960) showed that little change in silicate mineralogy had occurred during pedogenesis of Usterts in the Blacklands and Grand Prairie of Texas. They concluded that the predominant smectite was inherited from Cretaceous and early Tertiary parent sediments as evidenced by the near identity of X-ray diffractograms of A and C horizon fine clays. The only detectable mineralogical change taking place as a result of pedogenesis was a decrease in calcite upwards in the profile.

A similar relationship between late Pleistocene parent sediments and resulting Uderts and Usterts on the Coast Prairie of Texas was reported by Kunze et al. (1963).

Ahmad and Jones (1969) presented evidence that the smectite in Carribean Vertisols was inherited from the parent Cenozoic marine sediments. In one soil studied, the zeolites, heulandite and clinoptilolite, were detected in the parent rock silt fraction; however, their absence in the solum was interpreted as an indication of their instability in the soil environment.

In contrast to studies indicating the inheritance of smectite in Vertisols from parent sediments, Johnson et al. (1962) reported convincing evidence that Vertisols developed in north-central and eastern Arizona from basalts (and ejecta of basaltic composition) were dominated by smectite synthesized in situ. No change in clay-mineral composition, except for 0—2.5-cm surface layers, could be detected within the profiles, including transitional layers consisting of clay and weathering rock mixtures between rock and sola. Smectite in the thin surface horizons appeared to be somewhat disordered, or in finer particles, as indicated by broader X-ray diffraction peaks. Although not reporting detailed sand and silt mineralogy, the investigators found minerals characteristic of basalt residuum, i.e. augite, olivine and magnetite, throughout the profiles. The presence of quartz and microcline in the profile was attributed to eolian deposition, or to material interbedded with basalt flows, or both.

Chatterjee and Rathore (1976) reported little evidence of significant mineralogical variation among profiles, or within profiles, of Usterts developed from basalts in India. They considered smectite to be the first mineral synthesized as a product of weathering. These findings are in general agreement with those reported by Kantor and Schwertmann (1974) for Usterts and Uderts in depressions associated with Humults on uplands in Kenya. Although Chatterjee and Rathore (1976) suggested that smectite weathered to produce the small amount of kaolinite present, they believed the equally small content of illite and quartz to be due to eolian deposition.

Fitzpatrick and Le Roux (1977) found Fe-rich smectites to be the first weathering product of dolerites in the Transvaal, South Africa. The smectite persisted, apparently becoming partially chloritized, during pedogenesis of

Vertisols in the downslope position of the toposequence studied. However, the smectite was partially altered to kaolinite/halloysite in the more intensively weathered associated upland Mollisol.

Vertisols sometimes are associated with ustic great groups of Alfisols and Mollisols in semiarid regions and with Aridisols in arid regions. They usually occupy depressions (playas) or broad alluvial plains having minimal runoff. The limited data suggest that the smectite in such Vertisols is inherited. Allen et al. (1972) concluded that most of the silicate clay of Usterts in West Texas depressions was derived by alluviation from surrounding upland soils. They based their conclusion upon the near identity of the mineralogy of both coarse and fine clay to that of the associated uplands. The possibility of some mixing of volcanic ash concurrent with the alluvium deposition was suggested. They postulated that the Vertisol properties were due to the much higher clay content relative to the surrounding soils rather than to significant mineralogical differences. Pronounced differences were noted between the mineralogy of the coarse and fine clay, whereas the former was highly mixed, the latter was dominated by poorly ordered smectite. Slight mineralogical changes with profile depth in the Ustert were inconsistent, suggesting that most of the clay was inherited.

Precipitates of carbonates, or gypsum, or both, may occur in the subsoil, often on slickensided surfaces in Usterts and Torrerts.

SUMMARY AND CONCLUSIONS

The mineralogy and transformational trends of suborders recognized in the United States Soil Taxonomy are given in Table 6.3. The mineralogy listed is that for family classes into which established or tentative series in the United States have been placed (Soil Survey Staff, 1980, unpubl.). When only one series has been recognized in a mineralogy family within a given suborder it has been omitted, except in suborders of limited extent where the one series comprises a significant percentage of the suborder, e.g. oxidic in the Humox suborder.

The trends listed are those that may occur under selected conditions, based on the literature and prevailing soil genesis theories. It should be remembered that some trends may prevail among some taxa of a suborder, whereas in others different trends may obtain. And, of course, more than one transformation may be occurring concomitantly within an individual soil.

The inorganic portion of soils is composed of a mineralogically heterogeneous sand and silt framework into which clay, also of variable mineral composition, is dispersed. Primary minerals, mostly silicates and quartz, dominate the sand and silt of most soils. However, the sands and silts of some soils in the tropics may be composed mainly of aluminum and iron oxides. Also, a few soils in arid and semi-arid regions may contain mostly carbonates (calcite) and/or sulfates (gypsum), in the coarser fractions, especially in the lower horizons. Clays are mostly silicates, specifically phyllosilicates, in soils of temperate areas. Again, some tropical soils and a few in warm temperate regions, have clay fractions composed primarily of iron and aluminum oxides. Carbonates occasionally predominate in the clay fraction of arid and semi-arid regions.

Minerals vary greatly in their stability in the soil environment. They may be so ephemeral that their detection in the solid phase depends on the soil moisture content, e.g. the chlorides and some sulfates. Conversely, they may be sufficiently resistant to persist through many weathering and sedimentation cycles. The rate and pathways that characterize soil-mineralogical transformations are conditioned by the composition of the original material and external factors such as climate.

Taxa of soil-classification systems may be extremely heterogeneous in mineralogy or they may be nearly homogeneous, depending on their categorical level and the criteria chosen to define the taxon. For example, a soil series is apt to be much less heterogeneous in composition than an order in the U.S. Soil Taxonomy. Obviously, when the criteria that are used to define a taxon are either mineralogy per se or properties that covary with mineralogy, that taxon will have a more homogeneous mineralogy than one for which other defining criteria are chosen. Not only does composition vary appreciably within most taxa of the higher categories, e.g. order and suborder, but synthesis and transformation processes exhibit significant diversity. However, some generalizations on the mineralogical character and prevailing processes in the higher taxa can still be made.

Spodosols have mostly mixed and siliceous mineralogies*. Although not comprising a large percentage of the whole soil because of their generally coarse-textured nature, smectite tends to form at the expense of non-expanding phyllosilicates in the eluviated horizons. Alfisols vary greatly, from montmorillonitic to kaolinitic and even carbonatic, in mineralogical composition. Transformation reactions likewise are diverse. Illite tends to be altered to vermiculite and/or pedogenic chlorite in humid climates. Conversely, dissolution (and often subsequent precipitation in the lower profile) and the formation of secondary silica minerals at the expense of primary silicates and volcanic glass are often the only detectable mineralogical changes in dry Alfisols.

Ultisols have variable mineralogies but tend to be mixed, kaolinitic or siliceous. Oxidic classes are important in some suborders. 2:1 phyllosilicates tend to alter to vermiculite (often with appreciable hydroxy aluminum interlayering), pedogenic chlorite, kaolinite and oxides. Oxisols are domin-

---

*The mineralogy classes to which reference is made are those presently recognized in the U.S. Soil Taxonomy.

antly oxidic, ferritic and kaolinitic. Synthesis of sesquioxides and the "transformation" of kaolinite to gibbsite seem to be the principal mineralogical trends. Formation of pedogenic chlorite from expanding 2:1 phyllosilicates also occurs.

Mollisols vary greatly in mineralogy. Mixed and montmorillonitic classes predominate, but the carbonatic class is not uncommon. Non-expanding 2:1 phyllosilicates are altered in some cases to mixed-layer clays or smectite. Smectite (likely montmorillonite) is apparently synthesized in aquic moisture regimes. Inceptisols have extremely diverse mineralogies due to great variation in parent materials and conditions under which they have formed. They are mostly mixed, montmorillonitic, siliceous and carbonatic. However, amorphous aluminosilicates (allophane) are dominant in the Andept suborder and in selected great groups of other suborders. Kaolinitic mineralogy is common in the Tropept suborder. The alteration of volcanic glass to allophane, which in turn is altered to imogolite and/or halloysite, occurs in Andepts. Trends in other suborders include the dissolution of carbonates and the alteration of mica to vermiculite and mixed-layer clays.

The majority of Entisols has a mixed mineralogy that is mostly inherited from the parent material. Montmorillonitic, siliceous and carbonatic mineralogies are also common. Mineralogical transformation is minimal because of profile immaturity. Dissolution of carbonates and gypsum has occurred sparingly. Mineralogy is of much less importance in Histosols than in the other soil orders, but mixed, siliceous and montmorillonitic classes have been recognized. Little information is available on mineral alteration, but it is undoubtedly minimal unless the soils are drained.

Mixed, montmorillonitic and carbonatic mineralogies predominate in Aridisols. Mineral transformation occurs, but at very slow rates compared to most soils because of aridity. Dissolution of carbonates, gypsum and more soluble minerals in the upper layers and subsequent precipitation in the lower horizons constitute the more important mineralogical changes. Evidence also suggests a conversion of smectite clays to mixed-layer types in A horizons. Vertisols have mostly montmorillonitic mineralogy, but mixed classes also occur. A degradation of montmorillonite to mixed-layer types is indicated in some soils.

REFERENCES

Aba-Husayn, M.M. and Sayegh, A.H., 1977. Mineralogy of Al-Hasa desert soils (Saudi Arabia). Clays Clay Miner., 25: 138—147.
Abtahi, A., 1977. Effect of a saline and alkaline ground water on soil genesis in semiarid southern Iran. Soil Sci. Soc. Am. J., 41: 583—588.
Ahmad, N., 1983. Vertisols. In: L.P. Wilding, N.E. Smeck and G.F. Hall (Editors), Pedogenesis and Soil Taxonomy. II. The Soil Orders. Elsevier, Amsterdam.

Ahmad, N. and Jones, R.L., 1969. Genesis, chemical properties, and mineralogy of Caribbean Grumusols. Soil Sci., 107: 166—174.

Ahmad, M., Ryan, J. and Paeth, R.C., 1977. Soil development as a function of time in the Punjab River plains of Pakistan. Soil Sci. Soc. Am. J., 41: 1162—1168.

Alexander, L.T., Hendricks, S.B. and Nelson, R.A., 1939. Minerals present in soil colloids: II. Estimation in some representative soils. Soil Sci., 48: 273—279.

Alexiades, C.A., Polyzopolous, N.A., Koroxenides, N.S. and Axaris, G.S., 1973. High trioctahedral vermiculite content in the sands, silt, and clay fractions of a Gray Brown Podzolic soil in Greece. Soil Sci., 116: 363—375.

Allen, B.L., Harris, B.L., Davis, K.R. and Miller, G.B., 1972. The mineralogy and chemistry of High Plains playa lake soils and sediments. Texas Tech Univ. Water Resour. Center, Publ., 72-4: 72—75.

Al-Rawi, A.H., Jackson, M.L. and Hole, F.D., 1969. Mineralogy of some arid and semi-arid land soils of Iraq. Soil Sci., 107: 480—486.

Anderson, J.U. and White, J.L., 1958. A study of fragipans in some Southern Indiana soils. Soil Sci. Soc. Am. Proc., 22: 450—454.

Aomine, S. and Miyauchi, N., 1965. Imogolite of imogo-layers in Kyushu. Soil Sci. Plant Nutr., 11: 212—219.

Aomine, S. and Wada, K., 1962. Differential weathering of volcanic ash and pumice resulting in formation of hydrated halloysite. Am. Mineral., 47: 1024—1048.

Aomine, S. and Yoshinaga, N., 1955. Clay minerals of some well drained volcanic ash soils of Japan. Soil Sci., 79: 349—358.

Arneman, H.F., Khan, A.D. and McMiller, P.R., 1958. Physical, chemical, and mineralogical properties of related Minnesota prairie soils. Minn. Agric. Exp. St. Techn. Bull., 227.

Bain, D.C., 1976. A titanium-rich soil clay. J. Soil Sci., 27: 68—70.

Baldar, N.A. and Whittig, L.D., 1968. Occurrence and synthesis of soil zeolites. Soil Sci. Soc. Am. Proc., 32: 235—238.

Barnhisel, R.I., 1977. Chlorites and hydroxy interlayered vermiculite and smectite. In: J.B. Dixon and S.B. Weed (Editors), Minerals in Soil Environments. Soil Sci. Soc. Am., Madison, Wisc., pp. 331—356.

Barshad, I., Halevy, E., Gold, H.A. and Hagin, J., 1956. Clay minerals in some limestone soils of Israel. Soil Sci., 81: 423—437.

Bartoli, F. and Wilding, L.P., 1980. Dissolution of biogenic opal as a function of its physical and chemical properties. Soil Sci. Soc. Am. J., 44: 873—878.

Beattie, J.A. and Haldane, A.D., 1958. The occurrence of palygorskite and barytes in certain parna soils of the Murrumbidgee region, New South Wales. Aust. J. Sci., 20: 274—275.

Beavers, A.H., Johns, W.D., Grim, R.E. and Odell, R.T., 1955. Clay minerals in some Illinois soils developed from loess and till under grass vegetation. Clays Clay Miner., 3: 356—372.

Besoain, E., 1969. Clay mineralogy of volcanic ash soils. In: H.E. Fassbender (Coordinator), Panel on Volcanic Ash Soils in Latin America. IAIAS, Turrialba, Costa Rica, pp. B1.1—B1.12.

Bigham, J.M., Golden, D.C., Bowen, L.H., Buol, S.W. and Weed, S.B., 1978. Iron oxide mineralogy of well-drained Ultisols and Oxisols: I. Characterization of iron oxides by Mössbauer spectroscopy, X-ray diffractometry, and selected chemical techniques. Soil Sci. Soc. Am. J., 42: 816—825.

Bigham, J.M., Jaynes, W.F. and Allen, B.L., 1980. Pedogenic degradation of sepiolite and palygorskite on the Texas High Plains. Soil Sci. Am. J., 44: 159—167.

Birrell, K.S. and Fieldes, M., 1952. Allophane in volcanic ash soils. J. Soil Sci., 3: 156—167.

Blume, H.P. and Schwertmann, U., 1969. Genetic evaluation of profile distribution of aluminum, iron, and manganese oxides. Soil Sci. Soc. Am. Proc., 33: 438—444.

Brewer, R., 1964. Fabric and Mineral Analysis of Soils. Wiley, New York, N.Y., 470 pp.

Bronger, A., Kalk, E. and Schroeder, D., 1976. Über Glimmer und Feldspatverwitterung sowie Enstehung und Umwandlung von Tonmineralen in rezenten und fossilen Löss-boden. Geoderma, 16: 21—54 (abstr.).

Brown, D.A., Nash, V.E., Caldwell, A.G., Bartelli, L.J., Carter, R.C. and Carter, O.R., 1973. A monograph of the soils of the southern Mississippi River Valley alluvium. Southern Coop. Ser., Bull., 178.

Brown, D.E. and Jackson, M.L., 1958. Clay mineral distribution in the Hiawatha sandy soils of northern Wisconsin. Clays Clay Miner., 7: 213—266.

Brown, I.C. and Drosdoff, M., 1940. Chemical and physical properties of soils and their colloids developed from granitic materials in the Mojave Desert. J. Agric. Res., 61: 335—352.

Bryant, J.P. and Dixon, J.B., 1963. Clay mineralogy and weathering of a Red-yellow Podsolic soil from quartz-mica schist in the Alabama Piedmont. Clays Clay Miner., 12: 509—521.

Brydon, J.E., Kodama, H. and Ross, G.J., 1968. Mineralogy and weathering of the clays in Orthic Podzols and other podzolic soils in Canada. Ninth Int. Congress Soil Sci. Trans., Adelaide, S.A., III: 41—51.

Buehrer, T.F., Robinson, D.O. and Deming, J.M., 1948. The mineral composition of the colloidal fraction of some southwestern soils in relation to field behavior. Soil Sci. Soc. Am. Proc., 13: 157—165.

Buol, S.W. and Yesilsoy, M.S., 1964. A genesis study of a Mohave sandy loam profile. Soil Sci. Soc. Am. Proc., 28: 254—256.

Cady, J.G., 1960. Mineral occurrence in relation to soil profile differentiation. Seventh Int. Congress Soil Sci. Trans., Madison, Wisc., IV: 418—424.

Cady, J.G. and Daniels, R.B., 1968. Genesis of some very old soils — the Paleudults. Ninth Int. Congress Soil Sci., Trans., IV: 103—112.

Caldwell, R.E. and White, J.L., 1956. A study of the origin and distribution of loess in southern Indiana. Soil Sci. Soc. Am. Proc., 20: 258—263.

Carlisle, V.W. and Zelazny, L.W., 1974. Pedon mineralogy of representative Florida Typic Quartzipsamments. Soil Crop Sci. Fla. Proc., 34: 43—47.

Chatterjee, R.K. and Rathore, G.S., 1976. Clay mineral composition, genesis and classification of some soils developed from basalts in Madhya Pradesh. J. Indian Soc. Soil Sci., 24: 144—157.

Chichester, F.W., Youngberg, C.T. and Harward, M.E., 1969. Clay mineralogy of soils formed on Mazama pumice. Soil Sci. Soc. Am. Proc., 33: 115—120.

Chukhrov, F.V., Zvyagin, B.B., Ermilova, L.P. and Gorshkov, A.I., 1973. New data on iron oxides in the weathering zone. Proc. Int. Clay Conf., 1972, Madrid, 1: 397—404.

Coen, G.M. and Arnold, R.W., 1972. Clay mineral genesis of some New York Spodosols. Soil Sci. Soc. Am. Proc., 36: 342—350.

Coffman, C.B. and Fanning, D.S., 1975. Maryland soils developed in residuum from chloritic metabasalt having high amounts of vermiculite in sand and silt fractions. Soil Sci. Soc. Am. Proc., 39: 723—732.

Cook, M.G., 1973. Compositional variations in three Typic Hapludults containing mica. Soil Sci., 115: 159—169.

Cortes, A. and Franzmeier, D.P., 1972. Climosequence of ash-derived soils in the Central Codillera of Colombia. Soil Sci. Soc. Am. Proc., 36: 653—659.

DeConinck, F., Herbillon, A.J., Tavernier, R. and Fripiat, J.J., 1968. Weathering of clay minerals and formation of amorphous material during the degradation of a Bt horizon and podzolisation in Belgium. Ninth Int. Congress Soil Sci. Trans., Adelaide, S.A., IV: 353—365.

Deer, W.A., Howie, R.A. and Zussman, J., 1963. Rock Forming Minerals. Vol. 4: Frame-work Silicates. Wiley, New York, N.Y., 435 pp.

Dennen, W.H., 1960. Principles of Mineralogy. The Ronald Press, New York, N.Y., 453 pp.

Dixon, J.B., 1977. Kaolinite and serpentine group minerals. In: J.B. Dixon and S.B. Weed (Editors), Minerals in Soil Environments. Soil Sci. Soc. Am., Madison, Wisc., pp. 356—403.

Dixon, J.B. and McKee, T.R., 1974. Spherical halloysite formation in a volcanic soil of Mexico. Trans. Tenth Int. Congress Soil Sci., Moscow, VII: 115—124.

Douglas, L.A., 1965. Clay mineralogy of a Sassafras soil in New Jersey. Soil Sci. Soc. Am. Proc., 29: 163—167.

Douglas, L.A., 1977. Vermiculites. In: J.B. Dixon and S.B. Weed (Editors), Minerals in Soil Environments. Soil Sci. Soc. Am., Madison, Wisc., pp. 259—292.

Driessen, P.M. and Schorl, R., 1973. Mineralogy and morphology of salt efflorescences on saline soils in the Great Konya Basin, Turkey. J. Soil Sci., 24: 436—442.

Droste, J.B., 1956. Alteration by clay minerals by weathering in Wisconsin tills. Bull. Geol. Soc. Am., 67: 911—918.

Dryden, L. and Dryden, C., 1946. Comparative rates of weathering of some common heavy minerals. J. Sediment. Petrol., 16: 91—96.

Dudas, M.J. and Harward, M.E., 1975a. Weathering and authigenic halloysite in soil developed from Mazama ash. Soil Sci. Soc. Am. Proc., 39: 561—566.

Dudas, M.J. and Harward, M.E., 1975b. Inherited and detrital 2:1 type phyllosilicates in soils developed from Mazama ash. Soil Sci. Soc. Am. Proc., 39: 571—577.

Espinoza, W., Rust, R.H. and Adams Jr., R.S., 1975. Characterization of mineral forms in Andepts from Chile. Soil Sci. Soc. Am. Proc., 39: 556—561.

Eswaran, H., 1972. Micromorphological indicators of pedogenesis in some tropical soils derived from basalts from Nicaragua. Geoderma, 7: 15—31.

Eswaran, H. and Barzanji, A.F., 1974. Evidence for the neoformation of attapulgite in some soils of Iraq. Trans. Tenth Int. Congress Soil Sci., Moscow, VII: 154—161.

Eswaran H. and DeConinck, F., 1971. Clay mineral formations in basaltic soils in tropical environments. Pedologie, 21: 181—210.

Eswaran, H. and Wong Chaw Bin, 1978a. A study of a deep weathering profile on granite in peninsular Malaysia: I. Physico-chemical and micromorphological properties. Soil Sci. Soc. Am. J., 42: 144—149.

Eswaran, H. and Wong Chaw Bin, 1978b. A study of a deep weathering profile on granite in peninsular Malaysia: III. Alteration of feldspars. Soil Sci. Soc. Am. J., 42: 154—158. Soc. Am. J., 42: 149—153.

Eswaran, H. and Wong Chaw Bin, 1978c. A study of a deep weathering profile on granite in peninsular Malaysia: III. Alteration of feldspars. Soil Sci. Soc. Am. J., 42: 154—158.

Fanning, D.S., 1978. Soil Morphology, Genesis, Classification and Geography. Dept. of Agronomy, University of Maryland, College Park, MD.

Fanning, D.S. and Jackson, M.L., 1965. Clay mineral weathering in southern Wisconsin soils developed in loess and in shale-derived till. Clays Clay Miner., 13: 175—191.

Fanning, D.S. and Keramidas, V.Z., 1977. Micas. In: J.B. Dixon and S.B. Weed (Editors), Minerals in Soil Environments. Soil Sci. Soc. Am., Madison, Wisc., pp. 195—255.

Fanning, D.S., Hall, R.L. and Foss, J.E., 1973. Soil morphology, water tables, and iron relationships in soils of the Sassafras drainage catena in Maryland, pp. 71—79. In: E. Schlieting and U. Schwertmann (Editors), Pseudogley and Gley. Chemie Verlag, Weinheim, pp. 71—79.

Fenton, T.E., 1983. Mollisols. In: L.P. Wilding, N.E. Smeck and G.F. Hall (Editors), Pedogenesis and Soil Taxonomy. II. The Soil Orders. Elsevier, Amsterdam.

Fieldes, M., 1955. Clay mineralogy of New Zealand soils. II. Allophane and related mineral colloids. N.Z. J. Sci. Techn., 37: 336—350.

Fieldes, M., 1966. The nature of allophane in soils. Part I. Significance of structural randomness in pedogenesis. N.Z. J. Sci., 9: 599—607.

Fiskell, J.G.A. and Perkins, H.F., 1970. Selected Coastal Plain soil properties. Southern

Coop. Ser. Bull., 148.

Fitzpatrick, R.W., 1978. Occurrence and Properties of Iron and Titanium Oxides in Soils along the Eastern Seaboard of South Africa. Ph.D. Diss., University of Natal, South Africa.

Fitzpatrick, R.W. and LeRoux, J., 1977. Mineralogy and chemistry of a Transvaal black clay toposequence. J. Soil Sci., 28: 165—179.

Flach, K.W., Nettleton, W.D., Gile, L.H. and Cady, J.G., 1969. Pedocementation: Induration by silica, carbonates, and sesquioxides in the Quaternary. Soil Sci., 106: 442—453.

Foss, J.E., Moormann, F.R. and Rieger, S., 1983. Inceptisols. In: L.P. Wilding, N.E. Smeck and G.F. Hall (Editors), Pedogenesis and Soil Taxonomy. II. The Soil Orders. Elsevier, Amsterdam.

Franzmeier, D.P., Whiteside, E.P. and Mortland, M.M., 1963. A chronosequence of Podzols in northern Michigan. III. Mineralogy, micromorphology, and net changes occurring during formation. Mich. Agric. Exp. Stn. Q. Bull., 46: 37—57.

Franzmeier, D.P., Pederson, E.J., Longwell, T.J., Byrne, J.G. and Losche, C.K., 1969. Properties of some soils in the Cumberland Plateau as related to slope aspect and elevation. Soil Sci. Soc. Am. Proc., 33: 755—761.

Gal, M., Amiel, A.J. and Ravikovitch, S., 1974. Clay mineral distribution and origin in the soil types of Israel. J. Soil Sci., 25: 79—89.

Gallez, A., Juo, A.S.R., Herbillon, A.J. and Moorman, F.R., 1975. Clay mineralogy of selected soils in southern Nigeria. Soil Sci. Soc. Am. Proc., 39: 577—585.

Giese Jr., R.F., 1973. Interlayer bonding in kaolinite, dickite, and nacrite. Clays Clay Miner., 21: 145—149.

Gile, L.H. and Grossman, R.B., 1979. The Desert Project Soil Monograph. U.S. Govt. Printing Office, Washington, D.C.

Gjems, O., 1970. Mineralogical composition and pedogenic weathering of the clay fraction in Podzol soil profiles in Zalesine, Yugoslavia. Soil Sci., 110: 237—243.

Goldich, S.S., 1938. A study in rock weathering. J. Geol., 46: 17—58.

Goss, D.W. and Allen, B.L., 1968. A genetic study of two soils developed on granite in Llano County, Texas. Soil Sci. Soc. Am. Proc., 32: 409—413.

Grossman, R.B., Stephen, I., Fehrenbacher, J.B., Beavers, A.H. and Parker, J.M., 1959. Fragipan soils of Illinois: II. Mineralogy in reference to parent material uniformity of Hosmer silt loam. Soil Sci. Soc. Am. Proc., 23: 70—73.

Hallmark, C.T., 1977. Effects of Extractable Iron, Aluminium, and Silicon on Strength and Bonding of Fragipans of Trumbull Co., Ohio. Ph.D. Diss., Ohio State Univ. Columbus.

Healy, T.W., Herring, A.P. and Fuerstenau, D.W., 1966. The effect of crystal structure on the surface properties of a series of manganese dioxides. J. Colloid Interface Sci., 21: 435—444.

Holzhey, C.S., Daniels, R.B. and Gamble, E.E., 1975. Thick Bh horizons in the North Carolina Coastal Plain. II. Physical and chemical properties and rates of organic additions from surface sources. Soil Sci. Soc. Am. Proc., 39: 1182—1187.

Hsu, P.H., 1977. Aluminum hydroxides and oxyhydroxides. In: J.B. Dixon and S.B. Weed (Editors), Minerals in Soil Environments. Soil Sci. Soc. Am., Madison, Wisc., pp. 99—143.

Hutcheson Jr., T.B., Lewis, R.J. and Seay, W.A., 1959. Chemical and clay mineralogical properties of certain Memphis catena soils of western Kentucky. Soil Sci. Soc. Am. Proc., 23: 474—478.

Jackson, M.L., 1963. Interlaying of expansible layer silicates in soils by chemical weathering. Clays Clay Miner., 11: 29—46.

Jackson, M.L., 1964. Chemical composition of soils. In: F.E. Bear (Editor), Chemistry of the Soil (2nd ed.). Reinhold, New York, N.Y., pp. 71—141.

Jackson, M.L. and Sherman, G.D., 1953. Chemical weathering of minerals in soils. In: A.C. Norman (Editor), Advances in Agronomy. Academic Press, New York, N.Y., 5: 221—309.

Jackson, M.L., Tyler, S.A., Willis, A.L., Bourbeau, G.A. and Pennington, R.P., 1948. Weathering sequence of clay-size minerals in soils and sediments: I. Fundamental generalizations. J. Phys. Colloid Chem., 52: 1237—1260.

Jackson, M.L., Hseung, Y., Correy, R.B., Evans, E.J. and Van den Heuvel, R.C., 1952. Weathering sequence of clay-size minerals in soils and sediments: II. Chemical weathering of layer silicates. Soil Sci. Soc. Am. Proc., 16: 3—6.

Jarvis, N.L., Ellis Jr., R.L. and Bidwell, O.W., 1959. A chemical and mineralogical characterization of selected Brunizem, Reddish Prairie, Grumusol, and Planosol soils developed in Pre-Pleistocene materials. Soil Sci. Soc. Am. Proc., 23: 234—239.

Jha, P.P. and Cline, M.G., 1963. Morphology and genesis of a Sol Brun Acide with fragipan in uniform silty material. Soil Sci. Soc. Am. Proc., 27: 339—344.

Johnson, L.J., Matelski, R.P. and Engle, C.F., 1963. Clay mineral characterization of modal soil profiles in several Pennsylvania counties. Soil Sci. Soc. Am. Proc., 26: 568—572.

Johnson, P.R. and Beavers, A.H., 1959. A mineralogical characterization of some loess-derived soils in Illinois. Soil Sci. Soc. Am. Proc., 23: 143—146.

Johnson, W.M., Cady, J.G. and James, M.S., 1962. Characteristics of some brown Grumusols of Arizona. Soil Sci. Soc. Am. Proc., 26: 389—393.

Kantor, W. and Schwertmann, U., 1974. Mineralogy and genesis of clays in red-black soil toposequences on basic igneous rocks in Kenya. J. Soil Sci., 25: 67—78.

Khangarot, A.S., Wilding, L.P. and Hall, G.F., 1971. Composition and weathering of loess mantled Wisconsin and Illinoian-age terraces in central Ohio. Soil Sci. Soc. Am. Proc., 35: 621—626.

Kittrick, J.A., 1969. Minerals in the Al_2O_3—SiO_2—H_2O system and a theory of their formation. Clays Clay Miner., 17: 157—167.

Klages, M.G. and Southard, A.R., 1968. Weathering of montmorillonite during formation of a solodic soil and associated soils. Soil Sci., 106: 363—368.

Klages, M.G. and White, J.L., 1957. A chlorite-like mineral in Indiana soils. Soil Sci. Soc. Am. Proc., 21: 16—20.

Kodama, H., 1979. Clay minerals in Canadian soils: Their origin, distribution, and alteration. Can. J. Soil Sci., 59: 37—58.

Krebs, R.D. and Tedrow, J.C.F., 1957. Genesis of three soils derived from Wisconsin till in New Jersey. Soil Sci., 83: 207—218.

Kunze, G.W. and Oaks, H., 1957. Field and laboratory studies of the Lufkin soil, a Planosol. Soil Sci. Soc. Am. Proc., 21: 330—335.

Kunze, G.W. and Templin, E.H., 1956. Houston Black clay, the type Grumusol: II. Mineralogical and chemical characterization. Soil Sci. Soc. Am. Proc., 20: 91—96.

Kunze, G.W., Oaks, H. and Bloodworth, M.E., 1963. Grumusols of the Coast Prairie of Texas. Soil Sci. Soc. Am. Proc., 27: 412—421.

Kunze, G.W., Templin, E.H. and Page, J.B., 1955. The clay mineral composition of representative soils from five geological regions of Texas. Clays Clay Miner., 3: 373—383.

Lepsch, I.F. and Buol, S.W., 1974. Investigations in an Oxisol—Ultisol toposequence in Sao Paulo State, Brazil. Soil Sci. Soc. Am. Proc., 38: 491—496.

Le Roux, J., 1973. Quantitative mineralogical analysis of Natal Oxisols. Soil Sci., 115: 137—144.

Lietzke, D.A., Mortland, M.M. and Whiteside, E.P., 1975. Relationship of geomorphology to origin and distribution of a high charge vermiculite soil clay. Soil Sci. Soc. Am. Proc., 39: 1169—1177.

Lindsay, W.L., 1979. Chemical Equilibria in Soils. Wiley, New York, N.Y., 439 pp.

Losche, C.K., McCracken, R.J. and Davey, C.B., 1970. Soils of steeply sloping landscapes in the southern Appalachian Mountains. Soil Sci. Soc. Am. Proc., 34: 473—478.

Lozet, J.M. and Herbillon, A.J., 1971. Fragipan soils of Condroz (Belgium): mineralogical, chemical and physical aspects in relation with their genesis. Geoderma, 5: 325—343.

Lynn, W.C., Tu, H.Y. and Franzmeier, D.P., 1971. Authigenic barite in soils. Soil Sci. Soc. Am. Proc., 35: 160—161.

Mahjoory, R.A., 1975. Clay mineralogy, physical, and chemical properties of some soils in arid regions of Iran. Soil Sci. Soc. Am. Proc., 39: 1157—1164.

Martin, R.T., 1954. Clay minerals of five New York soil profiles. Soil Sci., 77: 389—399.

Martini, J.A. and Marcias, M., 1974. A study of six "Latosols" from Costa Rica to elucidate the problems of classification, productivity, and management of tropical soils. Soil Sci. Soc. Am. Proc., 38: 644—652.

McCaleb, S.B., 1959. The genesis of the Red-Yellow Podzolic soils. Soil Sci. Soc. Am. Proc., 23: 164—168.

McCracken, R.J., Shanks, R.E. and Clebsch, E.E.C., 1962. Soil morphology and genesis at higher elevations of the Great Smoky Mountains. Soil Sci. Soc. Am. Proc., 26: 384—388.

McKeague, J.A., DeConinck, F. and Franzmeier, D.F., 1983. Spodosols. In: L.P. Wilding, N.E. Smeck and G.F. Hall (Editors), Pedogenesis and Soil Taxonomy. II. The Soil Orders. Elsevier, Amsterdam.

McKenzie, R.M., 1977. Manganese oxides and hydroxides. In: J.B. Dixon and S.B. Weed (Editors), Minerals in Soil Environments. Soil Sci. Soc. Am., Madison, Wisc., pp. 181—193.

McLean, S.A., Allen, B.L. and Craig, J.R., 1972. The occurrence of sepiolite and attapulgite on the southern High Plains. Clays Clay Miner., 20: 143—149.

Miller B.J., 1983. Ultisols. In: L.P. Wilding, N.E. Smeck and G.F. Hall (Editors), Pedogenesis and Soil Taxonomy. II. The Soil Orders. Elsevier, Amsterdam.

Miller, F.P., Wilding, L.P. and Holowaychuk, N., 1971. Canfield silt loam, a Fragiudalf: II. Micromorphology, physical, and chemical properties. Soil Sci. Soc. Am. Proc., 35: 324—331.

Millet, J.I. and Drew, J.V., 1963. Characterization and genesis of Pawnee and Adair soils in southeastern Nebraska. Soil Sci. Soc. Am. Proc., 27: 683—688.

Millot, G., Paquet, H. and Ruellan, A., 1969. Néoformation de l'attapulgite dans les sols a'carapaces calcaires de la Basse Moulouya (Maroc Oriental). Pedologie, 268: 2771—2774.

Miyauchi, N. and Aomine, S., 1964. Does "allophane B" exist in Japanese volcanic ash soils? Soil Sci. Plant Nutr., 10: 199—203.

Muir, A., 1951. Notes on the soils of Syria. J. Soil Sci., 2: 163—183.

Nash, V.E., 1963. Chemical and mineralogical properties of an Orangeburg profile. Soil Sci. Soc. Am. Proc., 27: 688—693.

Nash, V.E., 1979. Mineralogy of soils developed on Pliocene—Pleistocene terraces of the Tombigbee River in Mississippi. Soil Sci. Soc. Am. J., 43: 616—623.

Nelson, L.A., Kunze, G.W. and Godfrey, C.L., 1960. Chemical and mineralogical properties of San Saba clay, A Grumusol. Soil Sci., 89: 122—131.

Nettleton, W.D. and Peterson F.F., 1983. Ardisols. In: L.P. Wilding, N.E. Smeck and G.F. Hall (Editors), Pedogenesis and Soil Taxonomy. II. The Soil Orders. Elsevier, Amsterdam.

Nettleton, W.D., Nelson, R.E. and Flach, K.W., 1973. Formation of mica in surface horizons of dryland soils. Soil Sci. Soc. Am. Proc., 37: 473—478.

Nikiforoff, C.C., 1937. General trends of the desert type of soil formation. Soil Sci., 43: 105—131.

Norrish, K. and Taylor, R.M., 1961. The isomorphous replacement of iron by aluminum in soil goethites. J. Soil Sci., 12: 294—306.

Peterson, G.W., Ranney, R.W., Cunningham, R.L. and Matelski, R.P., 1970. Fragipans in Pennsylvania soils: A statistical study of laboratory data. Soil Sci. Soc. Am. Proc., 34: 719—722.

Pettijohn, J.F., 1941. Persistence of heavy minerals and geologic age. J. Geol., 49: 610—625.

Ratliff, L.F. and Allen, B.L., 1970. The mineralogy and genesis of two soils from Trans-Pecos, Texas. Soil Sci., 110: 268—277.

Rich, C.I., 1968. Hydroxy interlayers in expansible layer silicates. Clays Clay Miner., 16: 15—30.

Rich, C.I. and Obenshain, S.S., 1955. Chemical and clay mineral properties of a Red-yellow Podzolic soil derived from muscovite schist. Soil Sci. Soc. Am. Proc., 19: 334—339.

Ritchie, A., Wilding, L.P., Hall, G.F. and Stahnke, C.R., 1974. Genetic implications of B horizons in Aqualfs of northeastern Ohio. Soil Sci. Soc. Am. Proc., 38: 351—358.

Robertson, R.H.S., 1962. The acceptability of mineral group names. Clay Miner. Bull., 5: 41—43.

Ross, G.J. and Mortland, M.M., 1966. A soil beidellite. Soil Sci. Soc. Am. Proc., 30: 337—343.

Ross Jr., S.J., Franzmeier, D.P. and Roth, C.B., 1976. Mineralogy and chemistry of manganese oxides in some Indiana soils. Soil Sci. Soc. Am. Proc., 40: 137—143.

Rust, R.H., 1983. Altisols. In: L.P. Wilding, N.E. Smeck and G.F. Hall (Editors), Pedogenesis and Soil Taxonomy. II. The Soil Orders. Elsevier, Amsterdam.

Rutledge, E.M., Wilding, L.P., Hall, G.F. and Holowaychuk, N., 1975. Loess in Ohio in relation to several possible source areas: II. Elemental and mineralogical composition. Soil Sci. Soc. Am. Proc., 39: 1133—1139.

Sanchez, P.A. and Buol, S.W., 1974. Properties of some soils of the Upper Amazon Basin of Peru. Soil Sci. Soc. Am. Proc., 38: 117—121.

Schwertmann, U. and Fanning, D.S., 1976. Iron-manganese concretions in hydrosequences of soils in loess in Bavaria. Soil Sci. Soc. Am. Proc., 33: 438—444.

Schwertmann, U. and Taylor, R.M., 1977. Iron oxides. In: J.B. Dixon and S.B. Weed (Editors), Minerals in Soil Environments. Soil Sci. Soc. Am., Madison, Wisc., pp. 145—180.

Sidhu, P.S. and Gilkes, R.J., 1977. Mineralogy of soils developed on alluvium in the Indo-Gangetic Plain (India). Soil Sci. Soc. Am. J., 41: 1194—1201.

Singer, A. and Amiel, A.J., 1974. Characteristics of Nubian Sandstone-derived soils. J. Soil Sci., 25: 310—319.

Simonson, R.W., 1959. Outline of a generalized theory of soil genesis. Soil Sci. Soc. Am. Proc., 23: 152—156.

Smeck, N.E., Wilding, L.P. and Holowaychuk, N., 1968. Genesis of argillic horizons in Celina and Morley soils of western Ohio. Soil Sci. Soc. Am. Proc., 32: 550—556.

Smith, B.R. and Buol, S.W., 1968. Genesis and relative weathering intensity studies in three semiarid soils. Soil Sci. Soc. Am. Proc., 32: 261—265.

Soil Survey Staff, 1975. Soil Taxonomy. A Basic System of Soil Classification for Making and Interpreting Soil Surveys. Agric. Handbook. No. 436. U.S. Govt. Printing Office, Washington, D.C., 754 pp.

Soil Survey Staff, 1980. Classification of Soil Series of the United States, Puerto Rico, and the Virgin Islands. (Unpubl. material.)

St. Arnaud, R.J. and Mortland, M.M., 1963. Characteristics of the clay fractions in a chernozemic to podzolic sequence of soil profiles in Saskatchewan. Can. J. Soil Sci., 43: 336—349.

Syers, J.K. and Walker, T.W., 1969. Phosphorus transformations in a chronosequence of soils developed on wind-blown sand in New Zealand. II. Inorganic phosphorus. J. Soil Sci., 20: 318—324.

Tamura, T., Jackson, M.L. and Sherman, G.D., 1953. Mineral content of Low Humic, Humic and Hydrol Humic Latosols of Hawaii. Soil Sci. Soc. Am. Proc., 17: 343—346.

Tarzi, J.G. and Protz, R., 1978. The occurrence of lepidiocrocite in two well-drained Ontario soils. Aust. J. Soil Res., 2: 235—248.

Taylor, R.M., McKenzie, R.M. and Norrish, K., 1964. The mineralogy and chemistry of manganese in some Australian soils. Aust. J. Soil Res., 2: 235—248.

Towe, K.W. and Bradley, W.F., 1967. Mineralogical constitution of colloidal hydrous ferric oxides. J. Colloid Interface Sci., 24: 384—392.

Van den Heuvel, R.C., 1966. The occurrence of sepiolite and attapulgite in the calcareous zone of a soil near Las Cruces, New Mexico. Clays Clay Miner., 13: 193—207.

Van der Marel, H.W., 1949. Mineralogical composition of a heath podzol profile. Soil Sci., 67: 193—207.

Van Wambeke, A., Eswaran, H., Hesbillon, A.J. and Comerma, J., 1983. Oxisols. In: L.P. Wilding, N.E. Smeck and G.F. Hall (Editors), Pedogenesis and Soil Taxonomy, II. The Soil Orders. Elsevier, Amsterdam.

Wada, K., 1967. A structural scheme of soil allophane. Am. Mineral., 52: 690—708.

Wada, K. and Wada, S., 1976. Clay mineralogy of the B horizons of two Hydrandepts, a Torrox, and a Humitropept in Hawaii. Geoderma, 16: 139—157.

Walthall, P.M. and Allen, B.L., 1980. Mineralogy and genesis of two Texas Salorthids. Agron. Abstr., p. 215.

Weed, S.B. and Nelson, L.A., 1962. Occurrence of chlorite-like intergrade clay minerals in Coastal Plain, Piedmont, and mountain soils of North Carolina. Soil Sci. Soc. Am. Proc., 26: 393—398.

Whiteside, E.P. and Marshall, C.E., 1944. Mineralogical and chemical studies of the Putnam silt loam soil. Mo. Agric. Res. Bull., 386.

Whittig, L.D., 1959. Characteristics and genesis of a Solidized—Solonetz of California. Soil Sci. Soc. Am. Proc., 23: 469—473.

Wilding, L.P., Drees, L.R., Smeck, N.E. and Hall, G.F., 1971. Mineral and elemental composition of Wisconsin-age till deposits in west-central Ohio. In: R.P. Goldthwait (Editor), Till: A symposium. Ohio State Univ. Press, Columbus, Ohio, pp. 290—318.

Wilding, L.P., Smeck, N.E. and Drees, L.R., 1977. Silica in soils: quartz, cristobalite, tridymite, and opal. In: J.B. Dixon and S.B. Weed (Editors), Minerals in Soil Environments. Soil Sci. Soc. Am., Madison, Wisc., pp. 471—552.

Wilkinson, G.E. and Gray, F., 1954. A clay mineralogical study of certain Reddish Prairie soils of Oklahoma, with an estimation of the montmorillonite and illite content. Soil Sci. Soc. Am. Proc., 18: 264—268.

Yaalon, D.H., 1955. Clays and some non-carbonate minerals in limestones and associated soils of Israel. Bull. Res. Council, Israel, Zool., 5B-2: 161—167.

Yaalon, D.H. and Ganor, E., 1973. The influence of dust on soils during the Quaternary. Soil Sci., 116: 146—155.

Yaalon, D.H. and Weider, M., 1976. Pedogenic palygorskite in some arid brown (Calciorthid) soils of Israel. Clays Clay Miner., 11: 73—80.

Yoshinaga, N. and Aomine, S., 1962. Imogolite in some Ando soils. Soil Sci. Plant Nutr., 8: 22—29.

Zelazny, L.W. and Carlisle, V.W., 1971. Mineralogy of Florida Aeric Haplaquods. Soil Crop Sci. Fla. Proc., 31: 161—165.

SOIL BIOLOGY

F.C. UGOLINI and R.L. EDMONDS

INTRODUCTION

Five major factors control soil formation: climate, parent material, topography, time and organisms. This chapter examines the importance of organisms in relation to soil formation and also the cycling of carbon and nitrogen.

Only in recent geological time have terrestrial organisms been so abundant as to influence soil formation. The appearance of life on this 4—5 billion year old planet occurred about 3.2 billion years ago; however, terrestrial plants and animals have been widespread for only the last 350 m.y. (Press and Siever, 1978). Presumably before this time, terrestrial geological substrata were not influenced by living organisms. It can be inferred that during the Carboniferous epoch when the CO_2 concentration in the atmosphere was about 100 times the present (Bidwell, 1974), the biota would have affected the geological substratum and therefore the formation of soil differently and more markedly than at present.

Can soils developed during Pre-Cambrian time be considered legitimate pedological entities even if devoid of organic matter and organisms? We feel the answer is yes. As long ago as 1927, Neustruev (1927) suggested that soil-forming processes occurring under abiotic conditions should be still considered within the realm of pedology. Soil development under abiotic or virtually abiotic conditions is currently occurring in the high barren Arctic and in the ice-free areas of Antarctica and a number of investigators consider this to be a true pedological event (McCraw, 1960; Tedrow and Ugolini, 1966; Tedrow, 1978). In Antarctica, where plant cover is absent and temperatures are well below freezing, ionic migration and weathering of primary and secondary minerals accompanied by iron oxidation and migration occur in xeric and ultraxeric soils (Claridge, 1965; Ugolini and Anderson, 1973; Ugolini, 1977; Ugolini and Jackson, 1982). Chemical weathering is responsible for the reddening of the fine-granular material at the Viking I landing site on Mars, and the formation of glassy droplets and agglutinates on the Moon caused by the impact of micrometeorites are sufficient to refer to these unconsolidated planetary surfaces as soils (Clanton et al., 1974; Huck et al., 1977). On Earth, however, it is indisputable that soil formation proceeds many times faster in the presence of biota than without.

Ours is the only planet in the solar system with abundant, carbon-based life. Besides carbon, the other element most intimately associated with the Earth's biota is nitrogen. Nitrogen, which occurs in the amino acids of all organisms, comprises a vital, unifying link through terrestrial food chains. The primary site of its fixation is in the soil. The dynamics of both nitrogen and carbon in the biosphere begin with the interaction of organisms and the inorganic outer crust of the earth. These interactions play a major role in the formation of soils.

CARBON AND NITROGEN CYCLING

The carbon cycle

Living organisms play an important role in the cycling of carbon through the atmosphere, oceans and lithosphere (Fig. 7.1). Relative amounts of carbon in these major components of the carbon cycle are shown in Table 7.1. The major chemical constituents of the carbon cycle are methane (CH_4), carbon monoxide (CO), carbon dioxide (CO_2) and organic matter (CH_2O). Methane is evolved by decomposition of organic material under anaerobic conditions occurring in rice paddies, swamps, bogs, intestinal fermentation in animals and anoxic marine sediments (Holland, 1978). On reaching the atmosphere methane is oxidized to carbon monoxide (CO). Methane is the major source of CO in the atmosphere, the remainder is mostly produced from the decomposition of organic matter in soils. Garrels et al. (1975) calculated the mean residence time of CO in the atmosphere to be 0.1 yr.

The major source of CO_2 for the atmosphere is the decomposition of organic matter formed by photosynthesis. Residence time for atmospheric CO_2 is 4 yrs (C in atmosphere/atmospheric C flux = $54,600 \times 10^{12}$ moles/ $13,600 \times 10^{12}$ moles yr^{-1}). This short residence time emphasizes the fact that changes in CO_2 release could alter its levels in a relatively short time (Garrels et al., 1975). In addition to the burning of fossil fuels, the approximate 18% increase in atmospheric CO_2 since 1850 may have been the result of deforestation and cultivation of virgin land (Stuiver, 1978).

The nitrogen cycle

The N cycle (Fig. 7.1) is interrelated with the C cycle, although unlike the C on earth, most of the N interfaces with the biosphere. Moreover, whereas the bulk of the carbon is in the sedimentary rocks (Table 7.1), between 30 and 70% of the nitrogen is in the atmosphere (Holland, 1978). Although the complex nitrogen cycle is not well understood (Delwiche, 1970; Garrels et al., 1975; Söderlund and Svensson, 1976), the major known constituents of this cycle are: molecular nitrogen (N_2), ammonia/ammonium

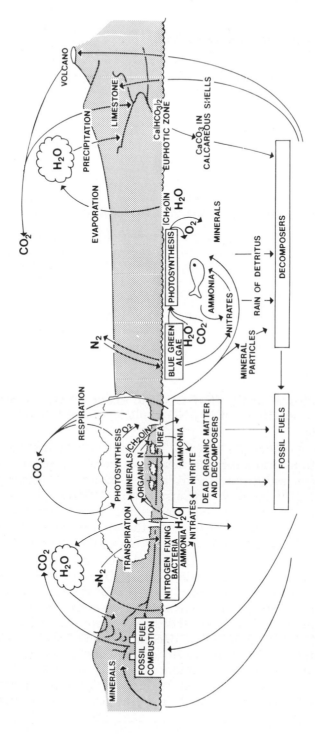

Fig. 7.1. The carbon and nitrogen cycles (modified from Hutchinson, 1970).

TABLE 7.1

Carbon and nitrogen content in major reservoirs

Reservoirs	g ($\times 10^{15}$)	Relative amounts	Source
Carbon			
Atmosphere	655	1	Garrels et al. (1975)
Living and dead organisms	1200	1.8	given in moles of C,
Ocean	39,120	60	changed by the authors
Sedimentary rocks	73,440,000	112,088	into g of C
Nitrogen			
Atmosphere	3,950,000	1	Holland (1978)
Living and dead organisms	772	0.00003	Delwiche and Likens (1977)
Ocean	20,190	0.005	Delwiche and Likens (1977)
Sediments	999,600	0.25	Garrels et al. (1975) given in moles of N, changed by the authors into g of N
Juvenile N	7,000,000	1.77	Holland (1978) (assuming the earth is half degassed)

(NH_3/NH_4^+), nitrous oxide (N_2O), nitric oxide (NO), nitrogen dioxide (NO_2), nitrous acid/nitrite (HNO_2/NO_2^-), nitric acid/nitrate (HNO_3/NO_3^-) and organic nitrogen.

For gaseous molecular N_2 to enter into the cycle, it first has to be fixed. Presently, fixation occurs through natural or industrial processes. Industrial fixation has been estimated at 2.51×10^{12} moles yr^{-1} whereas microbial fixation is 3.1×10^{12} moles yr^{-1} (Garrels et al., 1975).

Nitrous oxide (N_2O) is the second largest reservoir of atmospheric nitrogen, and it is photochemically converted in the stratosphere into NO and N_2. Nitric oxide (NO) is in turn oxidized by ozone to nitrogen dioxide (NO_2). Nitrous oxide and nitric oxide (N_2O and NO) are fixed in internal combustion engines; in addition, nitric oxide (NO) is produced by fossil fuel burning. Subsonic and supersonic planes also produce nitrogen oxides. Bacterial activity in soils and oceans is involved in the process of denitrification whereby nitrates (NO_3^-) or nitrites (NO_2^-) are reduced to N_2O and N_2.

Ammonia (NH_3) is produced via decomposition of organic matter such as urine (Söderlund and Svensson, 1976) on land and in aquatic environments. Garrels et al. (1975) estimated the ammonia (NH_3) content of the atmosphere at 1.83×10^{12} moles with approximate fluxes of 5.4×10^{12} moles yr^{-1} from the land and 2.9×10^{12} moles yr^{-1} from the sea. Volcanic emanations and fossil fuel and wood combustion are other sources of atmospheric ammonia. In the atmosphere, ammonia (NH_3) reacts with water vapor and is hydrolized into ammonium (NH_4^+) and hydroxyl (OH^-) ions. Ammonium, ammonium compounds and gaseous ammonia are returned to the ocean by precipitation and dry deposition. Appreciable amounts of ammonium (NH_4^+) combine with SO_4^{2-} which is deposited in rain as ammonium sulfate. The ammonia or ammonium that is present in the soil is either taken up by plants, adsorbed by the clay or converted to nitrite (NO_2^-) and nitrate (NO_3^-) by chemo-autotrophic bacteria. Nitrate may be taken up by plants, leached or denitrified.

Leached nitrogen together with N in dead organic matter may reach the sediments and eventually become part of the earth's crust. The major imbalances in the nitrogen cycle occur on land on which nitrogen is added by fertilizer, or by biological fixation.

THE IMPORTANCE OF THE MICROBIAL COMPONENT OF ECOSYSTEMS

A considerable amount of carbon on earth exists in and flows through both living and dead organisms. Living organisms can be ecologically classified as producers, consumers or decomposers of organic-C. Photosynthetic plants are producers. They utilize the energy of sunlight to build complex organic molecules. Animals using plants as food are consumers, while micro-organisms and small animals in the soil or on plants decompose organic residues.

Fixed carbon may be eaten by primary consumers (herbivores) who may themselves be eaten by secondary consumers (carnivores). This is the grazing food chain. Dead bodies of producers and primary and secondary consumers enter the detritus food chain in the soil, which is the focus of our attention here. The mineralization of the fixed-C to CO_2 and H_2O is, however, neither immediate nor complete.

Ecosystems vary in their ability for sustaining biomass (Table 7.2). Lowest-standing crops and productivities occur in tundra and desert ecosystems. Highest productivities occur in grassland ecosystems. Highest-standing crops occur in forest ecosystems with the highest in temperate coniferous forests (Table 7.2).

The biomass of primary producers is considerably greater than microbial biomass in the same ecosystem. The biomasses of fungi, bacteria and microfauna from a variety of ecosystems are shown in Table 7.3. The highest biomass would appear to occur in grassland and forest ecosystems, while the lowest occurs in tundra, taiga and desert ecosystems. Generally, fungal biomass is greater than bacterial biomass (Alexander, 1977), particularly in forests, and microfloral biomass is greater than microfaunal biomass. A discussion of the decomposer communities in contrasting biomasses is included in Swift et al. (1979).

TABLE 7.2

Range of standing biomasses and productivities of primary producers in terrestrial ecosystems (Rodin et al., 1975)

Ecosystem type	Standing biomass (kg ha^{-1})	Productivity (kg ha^{-1} yr^{-1})
Tundra	200— 35,000	40— 3500
Desert	1000— 4500	200— 1500
Grassland	20,000— 40,000	3000—46,000
Temperate deciduous forest	90,000—400,000	14,440—21,000
Boreal and temperate coniferous forest	125,000—700,000	4800—12,800
Warm-temperate broadleaf and tropical forest	120,000—450,000	8300—21,000

In the soils of grassland ecosystems, the total microbial component was estimated to be about 15—20% of the total biomass (Richards, 1974). Richards data, however, are hypothetical and he suggests that actual proportions would be slightly lower. For forest ecosystems, the proportion is much smaller, generally believed to be around 1%, but Fogel and Hunt (1979) recently reported a value of 4.4% for a 45 year old Douglas-fir ecosystem, largely due to the inclusion of the mycorrhizal component. An even smaller percentage occurs in taiga ecosystems. Although the microbial biomass is small compared to the ecosystem biomass, the role of the former is dis-

TABLE 7.3

Range of biomasses (kg ha^{-1}) of microflora and microfauna in terrestrial ecosystems

Ecosystem type	Microflora		Microfauna
	Fungi	Bacteria	
Tundra and taiga	20—80 [1]	3—9 [1]	8—36 [2]
Desert	135 [3]	4 [3]	7 [4]
Grassland	4000 [5]	3000 [5]	226 [5]
Temperate deciduous forest	890—1290 [6]	1—265 [6]	83—786 [7]
Boreal and temperate coniferous forest	836—4620 [8]	1—110 [6]	84—282 [6]
Warm-temperate broadleaf and tropical forest	4500 [9]	1100 [9]	84 [10]

[1] Flanagan and Van Cleve (1977); [2] MacLean (1974); [3] Mishutin (1966); [4] U.S. IBP Desert Biome Research Memorandum RM72—1; [5] Richards (1974); [6] Dommergues and Mangenot (1970); [7] MacFayden (1963); [8] Soderstrom (1979); [9] Calculated from Swift et al., (1979); [10] Odum (1970).

proportionally high because of its rapid turnover. The turnover time for the fungal component in a Douglas-fir ecosystem is 1.3 yrs (Fogel and Hunt, 1979). This is five times faster than that for the forest floor. In the taiga ecosystems, it may be even faster (Flanagan and Van Cleve, 1977).

An understanding of microbial processes may help us understand the effects of land-management practices. Management practices which alter the balance of primary producers, decomposers and mycorrhizae could alter the productivity and pool sizes in ecosystems. For example, Fogel and Hunt (1979) have suggested that the temporary reduction in growth height of Douglas-fir on poor sites after thinning might be a result of immobilization of soil N by microbes during decomposition of fine roots and mycorrhizae of culled trees.

DECOMPOSITION PROCESSES AND THE ACCUMULATION OF ORGANIC MATTER IN SOILS

Decomposition processes

The study of organic-matter decomposition in soil is of importance not only because a great deal of the energy captured by photosynthesis is released by this process, but also because nutrients are mineralized or immobilized during the process. This has a large influence on the productivity of the photosynthetic plants. Furthermore, decomposition rates strongly influence organic-matter accumulation and soil formation.

TABLE 7.4

Decomposition constants for litter in various ecosystems throughout the world

Ecosystem type	Range of decomposition constants (k, yr^{-1})	Source
Tundra and taiga	0.1—0.23[1]	Heal and French (1974)
Desert	0.5[1]	Staffeld and Vogt (1974)
Grassland	1.2[1]	Bell (1974)
Temperate deciduous forest	0.37—0.85[1]	Gosz et al. (1973)
Boreal and temperate conifer forest	0.11—0.58[1]	Will (1959) Mikola (1960), Fogel and Cromack (1977), Edmonds (1979)
Warm temperate broadleaf and tropical forest	1.0—4.0[2]	Olson (1963)

[1] Estimated from litter bags.
[2] Estimated from annual litter production/litter accumulation ratios.

A measure of the average rate of decomposition is the fractional loss rate (k) (Jenny et al., 1949; Olson, 1963). The fractional loss-rate concept is useful for comparing litter-decomposition rates in various terrestrial ecosystems. Such a comparison is made in Table 7.4 for leaf litter. In general, the highest k values or highest decomposition rates occur in the ecosystems with the hightest productivities as indicated in Table 7.2. Thus, litter-decomposition rate and primary producer productivity are closely linked.

In general, decomposition is most rapid in well-aerated environments. Most micro-organisms do not function above moisture contents of 30% by volume. At high soil-moisture contents, oxygen becomes limiting and only facultative and obligate anaerobic bacteria can function. Soil fungi and bacteria generally operate between 0° and 65°C with many having an optimum near 25°C. Both fungi and bacteria have optimum growth near neutral pH, but fungi tend to dominate in acid conditions and bacteria tend to tolerate higher pH.

Organic-matter accumulation in soils

Under conditions optimal for microbial activity, organic matter is decomposed so rapidly that accumulation does not occur. Accumulation occurs when: (1) annual production is high; or (2) conditions are not optimal for decomposition such as in areas where precipitation exceeds evaporation, and in coastal areas where the groundwater table is high. However, in marginal environments accumulation can be large despite low vegetative production if decomposition conditions are poor.

Table 7.5 shows some estimates of organic-matter accumulation in soil profiles in various ecosystems in the world. In general, highest accumulations occur in ecosystems where decomposition is inhibited either by lack of oxygen (swamp and marsh) or cold temperatures (tundra and alpine).

TABLE 7.5

Means and ranges of total detritus (kg cm^{-2}) in soil profiles of ecosystems of the world (after Schlesinger, 1977)

Ecosystem type	Mean	Range
Tundra and alpine	21.6	3.7— 49.8
Desert scrub	5.6	3.4— 9.6
Temperate grassland	19.2	13.3— 26.2
Tropical savanna	3.7	0.3— 8.7
Temperate forest	11.8	7.2— 24.0
Woodland and shrubland	6.9	2.4— 13.5
Boreal forest	14.9	5.0— 31.8
Tropical forest	10.4	3.7— 20.5
Swamp and marsh	68.6	38.5—149.8

Generally the average amount of detrital carbon per unit area of soil increases from the tropics to the poles. Although primary productivity and litterfall are high in tropical forests, decomposition is rapid and soil carbon accumulations are less than those in other forest types.

Schlesinger (1977) points out that it is not the amount of detritus that differs so much from ecosystem to ecosystem but the distribution of detrital carbon within soil profiles. In tropical forests and temperate grasslands, most of the carbon is contained in the lower soil horizons. In grasslands this is largely due to the death of roots at depth and it may explain why there is more carbon in the soils in temperate grasslands than in temperate forests.

THE BIOTIC FACTOR IN SOIL FORMATION

The factors of soil formation were first suggested by Dokuchaev, who recognized: climate, vegetation, parent material, relief and the geological age of the land as the essential elements in the formation of soils (Glinka, 1927). Jenny (1941) expressed these factors in a functional form:

S or s = f (cl, o, r, p, t, ...)

where: S = soil; s = any soil property; cl = climate factor; o = organisms or biotic factor; r = topographic factor; p = parent material; t = time factor; and ... = unidentified factors.

However, Jenny did not consider these factors as soil-formers, but as parameters defining the state of a soil system. In addition, Jenny (1941) considered each of the factors individually, allowing each to vary independently while the others are held constant. In the specific case of the biotic factor, the following equation applies:

S or s = f (biotic factor) cl, r, p, t, ...

When the soil, the dependent variable, is qualitatively evaluated as a function of the biotic factor, the equation expresses a biosequence. If expressed quantitatively, it is known as a biofunction (Jenny, 1958). In a biofunction, Jenny allowed only the biotic factor to vary while climate, parent material, relief and time are held constant. On the other hand, in climo-, topo-, litho- and chrono-functions, the biotic factor is allowed to remain constant while the other factors vary. There is an apparent difficulty in holding the biotic factor constant while the climate or time factors vary. This is solved by Jenny (1941, 1958) by defining the biotic factor as the potential vegetation or the incidence of disseminules of species and biotypes arriving at that particular site. In the case of biofunctions, the biotic factor is represented by the actual vegetation growing at the site. Accordingly, the biotic factor can be then considered either as independent or dependent factor (Crocker,

1952; Jenny, 1958). Birkeland (1974) summarized the vegetation—soil relationships and quoted examples that adhere to Jenny's conceptual model of univariant functions. Quantitative solutions of the univariant functions have been reviewed by Yaalon (1975) who points out that, contrary to the progress made in numerical solutions of topo- and climofunctions, biofunctions still remain descriptive even if they have a predictive value. Moreover, unless a code is developed for assigning numerical values to the different bio-assemblages, the quantification of the biotic factor is at the present impossible.

In view of the present state of knowledge of biofunctions, the ensuing discussion deals with the specific effect of plant assemblages or individual species on soil properties and soil formation. Many biochemical processes involving the cycling of different elements occur in soil where the organic compounds exuded by the roots and produced by microbial degradation of organic debris are involved and provide the energy needed in the biological-weathering process. The soil biota consists of: (1) lower plants here including the Monera; (2) higher plants; and (3) animals. Biochemically controlled electron transfers are important in creating and maintaining oxidizing or reducing conditions in soil micro-environments. Histosols form because of excess water in the soil which favors reducing conditions and the accumulation of plant debris.

Lower plants

Fungi, bacteria and algae

It is difficult to isolate the exclusive role of these micro-organisms in the soil system considering their diversity and proportion of the soil biota. However, the microbial participation may be more clearly evaluated in a polar desert ecosystem where the rest of the biotic component is either absent or considerably reduced. It is for this reason that many assessments of the role of micro-organisms in weathering and soil formation have been conducted in polar environments or in the laboratory under controlled conditions.

The fact that bacteria and algae have been detected even in the harshest terrestrial environments lends support to the belief that near-surface weathering at these sites is not exclusively a physical-chemical process, but also a biochemical one (Cameron et al., 1970). For example, in the Antarctic, Friedmann (1978) observed the presence of endolithic blue-green algae as well as other photosynthetic and non-photosynthetic micro-organisms in a number of rock types. Previous work by Friedmann (1971) in hot deserts, Negev (Israel) and Death Valley Desert (California), had also disclosed the presence of endolithic algae. The in-situ observation of algal cells attached to rock particles led Friedmann (1971) to suggest that the endolithic algae in deserts may be capable of solubilizing the surrounding minerals and disintegrating rock through shrinking and swelling of gelatinous algae cell sheaths.

Algae, because of their resistance to desiccation and their ability to grow rapidly when moisture is available, are recognized as important soil organisms in all arid regions (Shields et al., 1957; Cameron, 1963, 1964; Dregne, 1976). In desert soils, algae play a role in forming the desert crust which stabilizes the soil surface against erosion and provide a source of nitrogen since many algae fix atmospheric N (Cameron and Fuller, 1960; Dregne, 1976).

In other cold environments, such as the northwest shore of Lake Ladoga, northwestern Russia, Gromov (1957) found algae, bacteria and fungi present in the early stages of rock weathering. With some exceptions, the microflora of rock surfaces and primitive soils near Lake Ladoga increased with increasing colonization of lichens, mosses and higher plants; similar observations were made by Webley et al. (1963) in northeast Scotland. In lichen-covered basalt, granite and tuff rocks, Krasil'nikov (1949) found the microbial population confined mostly to the top 2 cm and most abundant in the basalt and granite and least in the tuff.

One of the early works quantifying the role of micro-organisms in rock weathering was conducted by Thiel (1927) who subjected a variety of crushed rocks to sterile and non-sterile conditions. A fifty-three percent increase in soluble constituents occurred in the samples contaminated with micro-organisms.

The effectiveness of micro-organisms in decomposing rocks and minerals was also demonstrated by Glazovskaya (1950) in the high elevations of central Tienshan, southwestern Russia. Fungi, bacteria, diatoms, green and blue-green algae were isolated from rocks. Fungi of the genus *Penicillium*, considered the most destructive among the microflora, produced chelating organic acids similar to natural humic components — humic and fulvic acids. Muscovite appeared less resistant to micro-organism weathering than biotite and the latter less than orthoclase. Clay minerals, calcite and amorphous silica were formed as secondary minerals. Vernadeskiy as quoted by Glazovskaya (1950) experimentally demonstrated that diatoms of the genus *Nitzschia* are able to decompose kaolin.

In northeast Scotland, Webley et al. (1963) found that bacteria, actinomycetes and fungi were present in mineralogically weathered rocks but were absent in the unweathered ones. Organic compounds isolated from the weathered rocks were found capable of dissolving calcium and magnesium silicates. Among fungi, the most effective were *Botrytis, Mucor, Penicillium* and *Trichoderma* (Webley et al., 1963). Bacteria producing 2-ketogluconic acid were found to be the most effective in dissolving silicates. 2-ketogluconic acid produced by bacteria can chelate calcium and render silicate and phosphate soluble (Duff and Webley, 1959). An additional study by Webley and Duff (1965) reported that organisms producing 2-ketogluconic acid were not abundant in environments rich in organic matter.

Release of metallic and silicate ions from minerals, rocks and soils by fungal activity is further documented by the work of Henderson and Duff

(1963). Strains of fungi producing citric and/or oxalic acid appear particularly effective in decomposing natural silicates. Both citric and oxalic acids were identified in cultures of *Aspergillus niger* grown on mica flakes. These acids were considered responsible for the mobilization of potassium and other metals and the alteration of mica (Boyle and Voigt, 1973; Boyle et al., 1974). Parfenova (1966) also observed the transformation of biotite into opal in the surface horizon of a podzolic soil in northern Karelia and suggested that micro-organisms such as fungi were responsible for this transformation. *Penicillium simplicissimum*, isolated from the weathered basalt, induced solubilization of Si, Al, Fe and Mg from rock in culture. Fungal attack on rocks also induced alteration of infrared adsorption in the Si—O vibration region (Silverman and Munoz, 1970). Fungal hyphae, in the litter layers of different forest ecosystems, are capable of producing calcium oxalate (Graustein et al., 1977).

Mulder and Van Veen (1968) provided an assessment of microbial transformations of sulfur and phosphorous compounds and a more indepth examination of the transformation of Fe, Mg and Cu. Berthelin (1971) and Berthelin and Dommergues (1972) also examined the effects of microbial products on the solubilization of Mn, Ca, Fe, Mg and Al.

An interesting approach to assess biological transformation of clay-size sediments in simulated aquatic environments was carried out by Wall et al. (1974). These workers used clay-sized sediments suspended in distilled water or in sewage effluents. The clay-size sediments were altered as shown by a decrease in the mica, expansibles and vermiculite and an increase in quartz and chlorite. Solution pH showed a slight increase as did Si, whereas K decreased. They concluded that a high microbial population, a carbonate substratum and anaerobic conditions (unshaken) favor this alteration.

A comprehensive review of microbial transformations of metals: Hg, Cd, Pb, Zn, Fe, Mn, Sb, As, Se and Te has been provided by Summers and Silver (1978). Although these authors do not intentionally focus on soil micro-organisms, the role of the latter is mentioned in considering the individual metal biogeochemistry.

Lichens

The role of lichens in soil formation and plant succession has been emphasized in the classical ecology literature; but this has been challenged by Cooper and Rudolph (1953) and Beschel (1965). The fact remains that "these humble plants occupy the most forbidding environments on earth" (Lamb, 1959) and therefore, even if their role in rock weathering has been overestimated, it is recognized that they do attack rocks and grow where no other plants can. The pedogenic significance of lichens is mostly restricted to unique sites, such as rock faces and surfaces and cliffs. They acquire prominence in harsh and severe environments such as continental Antarctica where mainly algae, lichens and mosses perform biological weathering; and even these organisms are not very abundant. The action of lichens on rock includes both physical disintegration and chemical decomposition. The mechanism of physical weathering involves the penetration of rhizines, bundles of fungal hyphae, into the rock followed by expansion and contraction of the thalli. The penetration of rhizines into the rock is not, as reported by Syers and Iskandar (1973), a random process. Rhizines penetrate mica grains, but not feldspar or quartz crystals in granite. Yarilova (1947) found that hyphae preferentially move and disintegrate plagioclase in syenite, rather than chlorite and feldspars. In limestone the rhizines preferentially penetrate the boundaries of calcitic fossils (Syers, 1964). The mechanical action of crustose lichens on substrates of shale, schist, gneiss, limestone and obsidian was studied by Fry (1927). He found that expansion and contraction of the thalli in response to moisture fluctuations causes the detachment of rock fragments; shale yielded more fragments than gneiss and the latter more than obsidian. Limestone fragmentation by lichen was observed by Syers (1964) whereas Yarilova (1947) showed mechanical weathering on five different minerals by growth of the lichen *Rhizocarpon*. Flaking of rock by lithophilic lichens, *Parmelia* spp., was reported by Polynov (1945) who concluded that the fine earth resting on the top of a coarse-gravel soil profile at the bottom of a granite—gneiss slope was derived from the action of lichens.

Chemical weathering induced by lichens was suggested in the mid-1800's (Syers and Iskandar, 1973). Fry (1922) suggested that the boring action of endolithic lichens on limestone was produced by carbonic acid attacking rocks and dissolving carbonates. Oxalic acid has been recognized as a metabolic product of lichens and is considered important in rock weathering. However, the formation of insoluble calcium oxalate derived from the reaction of calcium with the excreted oxalic acid is considered to be of minor importance in the removal of calcium from rock (Syers and Iskandar, 1973). More important are water soluble, lichen-derived compounds that function as metal-complexing agents. These compounds are generally referred to as lichen acids and found to contain aromatic rings, depside linkages and polar groups such as -OH, -CHO, -COOH (Asahina and Shibata, 1954). Lichens such as *Caloplaca elegans*, *Parmelia conspersa*, *Parmelia stenophylla* and *Umbilicaria arctica* are capable of synthesizing depsidones, whereas DL-usnic acid or D- and L-usnic acids have been found in *Cetraria*, *Cladonia*, *Usnea* and *Ramalina* species (Pauli, 1968). Water extracts of lichens or ground lichen thalli when shaken with water suspensions of minerals and rocks form colored complexes and show that appreciable amounts of Ca, Mg, Fe and Al are complexed by the lichen compounds (Schatz et al., 1956; Schatz, 1963; Iskandar and Syers, 1972). Although these in-vitro experiments provide positive results, it is not known whether the same soluble metal complexes are formed under natural conditions or have sufficient mobility. Recent work by Dawson et al. (in press) has shown that water-soluble lichen compounds such as usnic acid are mobile within the soil profile of an arctic soil.

Extensive documentation exists indicating that lichens can chemically alter mineral substrata. Parfenova and Yarilova (1962) cite examples of mineral synthesis caused by lichens such as: formation of iron oxide and magnetite from olivine; opal from biotite; chlorite from hornblende; sericitization and kaolinite formation from feldspars; and hydromica and kaolinite from mica. Polynov (1953) reports a number of secondary minerals produced by the action of lichens in addition to microcrystalline calcite. Jackson and Keller (1970) found the lichen-covered weathering crust to be enriched in Fe and impoverished in Si, Ti and Ca when compared with the lichen-free weathering crust of recent Hawaiian lava flows.

In addition to causing mineral alterations and synthesis, lichens accumulate nutrient elements. Polynov (1945) established that the amount of elements absorbed by the lichens is never proportional to the elemental composition of the rock. Scarce elements in the rock such as P and S are concentrated in lichen tissue (Polynov, 1945). Because many lichens contain N_2-fixing blue-green algae, they are able to produce their own supply of this element. A peculiar nutritional feature of lichens is their ability to retain high concentrations of heavy metals such as Zn, Cd, Pb, Mn and B.

Lichens established on bare rocks trap atmospheric dust and other debris. Once mixed with the lichen thalli, this dust contributes to the accumulation of fines and to the formation of primitive soils.

Mosses

The invasion of mosses on barren terrain is often viewed as the next stage in plant succession following initial colonization by lichens (Polynov, 1953; Targul'yan, 1959; Parfenova and Yarilova, 1962). Mosses, like lichens, are hardy plants that can live in hostile environments such as polar regions, high mountains and on newly exposed terrain. This stage of biotic succession is characterized by abundant formation of fines from further comminution of the rocks by moss rhizoids that penetrate into cracks and crevices (Parfenova and Yarilova, 1962). An example of moss-caused weathering in northern Caucasus, Russia, cited by Parfenova and Yarilova (1962), shows that fine earth collected under the *Polytrichum* moss contained less plagioclase and chlorite than the original quartz-diorite rock. In addition in the clay fraction, secondary minerals consisting of mica, hydromica and montmorillonite minerals were found. In eastern Siberia, Targul'yan (1959) observed that in the first stages of weathering on moss-lichen tundra, primitive soils have a strong acid reaction, a low base saturation and lower $SiO_2 : Fe_2O_3$ and $SiO_2 : Al_2O_3$ ratios than parent rocks. In continental Antarctica, although mosses represent the highest form of plant life, their distribution is limited to moist and protected microsites. Moss becomes more prominent further north in the Antarctica Peninsula, the Sub-Antarctic Islands, Palmer Archipelago and South Shetland and South Orkney Islands. In the ice-free areas of continental Antarctica, the soils developed under moss cushions (Proto-rankers) offer the possibility of assessing the impact of mosses on soil forma-tion. In Southern Victoria Land, Antarctica, Protorankers have more soluble salts as well as more C, N and organic P than soils without mosses (Ahumics). However, no indication was found that mosses increased iron-release rates or affected the formation of clays (Claridge, 1965; Ugolini, 1977; Ugolini and Jackson, 1982).

Moss grows profusely under climatic conditions more favorable than in Victoria Land, such as those existing in the Antarctica Peninsula and on the Antarctica offshore islands. In the cool maritime climate of these sub-Antarctic regions as well as in the Aleutian Islands of the northern hemisphere, moss tends to accumulate and form thick organic soils. In the South Shet-land Islands, Everett (1976) suggests that the thick moss cover of *Polytrichum* spp. favors the establishment of permafrost; a similar observation was also made on Signy Island (Allen et al., 1967). On Signy Island these authors also found that many of the nutrients stored in the moss residues originated from sea spray, from the guano of nearby bird rookeries, and from the weathering of rocks.

Higher plants

"Pure cultures" of higher plants have been successfully used to examine their effect on weathering of layer silicates. Mortland et al. (1956) showed the alteration of biotite into vermiculite by wheat plants in culture where biotite was the only source of K. Even more striking results were obtained by Spyridakis et al. (1967) who grew conifers and deciduous seedlings in sand culture containing biotite as the only source of potassium. After 12 months, X-ray diffractions revealed that biotite was altered into kaolinite. According to these authors, white cedar (*Thuja occidentalis*) was the most effective in the kaolinization of biotite followed in order of decreasing effectiveness by eastern hemlock (*Tsuga canadensis*), white pine (*Pinus strobus*), white spruce (*Picea glauca*), red oak (*Quercus rubra*) and maple (*Acer saccharum*).

Mid-continental grassland and forest

The most commonly used example for contrasting the effects of different plant communities on soil properties is forest versus prairie under conditions where all the rest of the environmental parameters are kept equal for both plant assemblages. In the United States, the morphological and chemical properties of forest and adjacent prairie soils have been discussed by numer-ous authors, e.g. White (1941), Jenny (1941), Kilburn (1959), McComb and Riecken (1961), Lotspeich et al. (1961), Ruhe (1969), Ugolini and Schlichte (1973), Al-Barrak and Lewis (1978), and summarized by Jenny (1941),

Buol et al. (1973, 1980), and Birkeland (1974). The following tabulation systematizes the morphological and chemical differences of the soils developed under grassland and forest tree species. This information depicts a mid-continent situation in the United States and has been compiled from the following sources: Jenny (1941), White and Riecken (1955), and Buol et al. (1973, 1980).

Morphological properties

O horizons: Prairie soils have thinner organic horizons than the adjacent forest soils.

A1 (Ah) horizon: This horizon is generally thinner and lighter in color under the forest than in the prairie.

A2 (E) horizon: The A2 (E) horizon is absent in the prairie but present in the forest soils.

B horizon: This horizon is generally brighter and redder in the forest than in the prairie.

Clay content: The surface of the prairie soils has higher clay content than the adjacent forest soils. On the other hand, the forest soils have accumulated more clay at depth than the prairie ones.

Chemical properties

pH: Soils developed in the forest are in general more acid than those in the prairie, but exceptions do exist especially when the forest soils are developed under deciduous species.

Organic matter: Prairie and forest soils contain comparable amounts of organic material, but in the prairie soils the organic matter is distributed to greater depths.

Nitrogen: This element follows the same trend as the organic matter; it is mostly concentrated near the surface in forest soils, but it reaches greater depths in the prairie.

C/N ratio: This ratio is wider in the forest than in the prairie.

Base saturation: The prairie soils have higher base status than the forest soils.

In the Midwest, the soils derived under prairie have an ABC sequence and are classified as Mollisols; those under forest have AEBC sequence and are classified as Alfisols.

Maritime humid-temperate forests and prairies

Biosequences in the maritime humid-temperate climate of the Pacific Northwest have been presented by Lotspeich et al. (1961), Broersma (1973), Ugolini and Schlichte (1973) and Ramborger (1980). The example given here comes from the Puget Sound area (Figs. 7.2--7.4). Here the effect of prairie vegetation is constrasted with Douglas-fir on soils derived from late Wisconsin outwash deposits (Ugolini and Schlichte, 1973; Ramborger, 1980).

Morphological properties

Morphology of the horizons in both forest and prairie soils is similar to that reported in the previous example from the mid-west, except no A2 (E) horizons were observed under forest cover.

Clay content: Although weakly expressed there is a trend of clay concentration in the A horizon in the prairie soils and in the B horizon of the forest soils.

Chemical properties

Organic matter, N, C/N ratio of forest and prairie profiles of the Pacific Northwest show trends comparable to those for the mid-continent United States. pH, on the other hand, is acid for both prairie and forest profiles.

Humic/fulvic acid ratios: This ratio rapidly decreases from the A to the B horizon in both soils.

Extractable iron: Pyrophosphate (Fe_p), oxalate (Fe_o) and dithionite (Fe_d)—Fe_d shows a rapid decrease with depth in the forest soils, but a gradual decrease in the prairie soils; both Fe_o and Fe_p display an accumulation in the B horizons of the forest soils, but not in the prairie.

Clay mineralogy

Both forest and prairie soils show similar assemblages. At the surface these assemblages consist of chlorite—vermiculite intergrades, vermiculite and clay-size quartz and feldspars; in the C horizon, chlorite, a small amount of mica and clay-size quartz and feldspars.

In the Pacific Northwest, prairie soils have an ABC profile. Even though the forest soils lack an A2 (E) horizon, they show a more developed B horizon

Fig. 7.2. View of the Wier Prairie, Olympia, Washington. The bordering trees are invading Douglas-fir; Mount Rainier, 4377 m, is in the background.

Fig. 7.3. *Caption on p. 212.*

Fig. 7.4. *Caption on p. 212.*

than the prairie soil. However, both soils are classified as Inceptisols with the prairie soils being Umbrepts and the forest ones Ochrepts.

Leaching and translocation of iron and clay is greater in the forest where the mobile organic compounds depress the pH and chelate and transport the iron from the surface into the B horizon. In the prairie, despite presence of organics capable of complexing iron, these complexes are not as mobile as in the forest soils. Organic matter is more deeply distributed in the prairie than in the forest soils because grasses produce finer, deeper and more easily decomposable root biomass and soil fauna is often more abundant.

Subalpine and alpine areas

The effect of arboreal and herbaceous species growing in close proximity is further evident in the subalpine and alpine areas of the North Cascades, Washington (Bockheim, 1972). On Mt. Baker, soils in the subalpine forest or in the krummholz display albic horizons in contrast with umbric horizons present in the adjacent meadows. Dithionite extractable iron and aluminum increased five times from the A2 (E) to the B2hir (Bs1) horizon in the forest soils, but less than 0.4 times from the A1 (Ah) to the B2h (Bs2) in the meadow soils. Weathering, both physical and chemical, as portrayed by percentage and mineralogy of the clay fraction is more intense under the forest than under the meadow (Bockheim, 1972).

Chronosequences and vegetational changes

Studies assessing the role of time in plant succession and soil development can also provide important information on the effect of different plant communities on soil properties. Crocker and Major (1955) found that changes in soil properties such as the decrease of N were associated with the replacement of alder with spruce in Glacier Bay, Alaska. Ugolini (1968), working in the same area, observed a similar nitrogen trend; in addition, he observed the appearance of an A2 (E) horizon, iron translocation in the B horizon, a rapid drop in pH and an increase in exchangeable acidity coinciding with the dominance of spruce forest. Another chronosequence along raised marine terraces in Glacier Bay, Alaska, showed that the establishment of a western hemlock forest promotes podzolization and fostered the formation of placic horizons. In these Spodosols, the indurated placic horizons were subsequent-

Fig. 7.3 (p. 210). Spanaway soil profile, Andic Xerumbrepts (prairie). The black Ah horizon is 40 cm thick; the B2 (Bw) horizon, black brown, is 18 cm thick (reprinted from Ugolini and Schlichte, 1973, with permission of Williams and Wilkins Co.).

Fig. 7.4 (p. 211). Everett soil profile, Dystric Xerochrepts (forest). The black brown A horizon is 5 cm thick; the B21 (Bw1) and B22 (Bw2), dark brown and brown, respectively, are 45 cm thick (reprinted from Ugolini and Schlichte, 1973, with permission of Williams and Wilkins Co.).

ly instrumental in the formation of a perched water table that favored an aquic regime followed by the invasion of sphagnum moss and the replacement of the well-drained forest with bogs (Ugolini and Mann, 1979).

In a study of forest succession and soil development near the Chena River in interior Alaska, Viereck (1970) found that soil temperature, soil moisture and depth of thawing varied directly as a 15 yr old willow stand succeeded through a 20 yr old white spruce forest to a climax black spruce-sphagnum moss stand. In the early willow and poplar successions, the soil was colder and froze rapidly to a greater depth than in the more advanced stages of succession. On the other hand under the poplar and willow stages, thawing was completed by the end of May, but in the black spruce-sphagnum stage thawing was never completed and permafrost was encountered at a depth of 40—80 cm. Soil-moisture regimes in the willow-white spruce forest ranged from xeric to mesic, but were replaced by hydric regimes in the black spruce-sphagnum stage.

Effects of individual trees

The effect of vegetation cover on soil properties is not limited to the impact of different plant communities. Individual plants, especially trees, can spatially influence the soil. These spatial variations occurring in the proximity of a single tree are more intense near the tree stem and decrease toward the edge of the canopy (Swindale, 1955; Zinke, 1956; Zinke and Crocker, 1962; Gersper and Holowaychuk, 1970a, b, and 1971; Lodhi, 1977; Ramborger, 1980). Perhaps the most dramatic spatial soil changes have been reported in New Zealand where Podzols (Spodosols), with thick eluvial A2 (E) horizons, occur only around each individual Kauri pine (*Agathis australis*) (Swindale, 1955). Zinke (1956, 1962) analyzed soil samples collected along a radial transect from the stem to the edge of the canopy of four arboreal species: Ponderosa pine (*Pinus ponderosa*), Incense cedar (*Libocedrus decurrens*), Douglas-fir (*Pseudotsuga menziesii*) and Shore pine (*Pinus contorta*). He found that pH increased from the bole outward in the case of the pines and cedar, but it decreased in the case of Douglas-fir. Exchangeable bases, cation exchange capacity and N all increased away from the trunk except under the Shore pine where a reverse trend was observed. Gersper and Holowaychuk (1970a, b and 1971) demonstrated that the variations in soil properties observed outward radially from the trunks of beech trees (*Fagus grandifolia*) could be explained on the basis of volume and composition of the percolating water. The soils next to the trunk received considerably more water in the form of stemflow than those further away where the soil is affected by canopy drip. Rainfall intercepted by the tree is funnelled downwards along the trunk as stemflow. The volume of this flow can be as much as five times greater than that in the open (Gersper and Holowaychuk, 1971). The portion of precipitation retained in the canopy reaches the soil via canopy drip. The chemical composition of both stemflow and canopy drip is considerably different from the precipitation in the open. For example, in the *Abies amabilis* zone of western Washington, the pH of the canopy drip is, on the average, one unit lower than the precipitation in the open (Ugolini et al., 1977). Gersper and Holowaychuk (1970a, b and 1971) found for beech trees that the stemflow induces a more vigorous translocation of iron and clay in the profile next to the trunk than the rainfall 2 m away from it. Furthermore, a decrease in total N and C, and an increase in base saturation and pH occurs with increasing distance from the trunk (Gersper and Holowaychuk, 1970a, b and 1971).

Individual tree species in lowland western Washington are responsible for morphological and chemical differences in soils developed under otherwise similar soil-forming factors (Ramborger, 1980). For instance, the A1 (Ah) horizon developed under Oregon white oak (*Quercus garryana*) is darker and thicker near the bole and at the canopy edge than under Douglas-fir (*Pseudotsuga menziesii*). The B2 (Bw2) horizon is thicker under the bole of Douglas-fir than under the oak. There is more organic C, N, exchangeable hydrogen and cation-exchange capacity next to the bole of the Douglas-fir than the oak. The same parameters are, however, higher under the canopy of the oak than the Douglas-fir. Dithionite and pyrophosphate extractable Fe and Al show higher values next to the Douglas-fir bole than the oak; however, the same metals are higher under the canopy of the Oregon white oak than the Douglas-fir. Total exchangeable cations, exchangeable Ca and Mg, pH and the humic/fulvic acid ratio do not exhibit a definite radial trend, but they are higher under the oak and lower under the Douglas-fir.

It is not, however, a universal rule that vegetational differences always induce differentiation in soil properties. In a study conducted in the central Brooks Range, Alaska, soils developed under individual white spruce trees (*Picea glauca*) in the boreal forest were virtually indistinguishable, morphologically and chemically, from those developed under lichen mixed-heath cover in the nearby alpine tundra (Ugolini et al., 1981). Apparently widely different plant assemblages can engender the same soil-forming processes.

Soil evolution and vegetational changes

The soil is often seen as a thermodynamic system (Jenny, 1941, 1958) existing in equilibrium with certain external, soil-forming factors. Changes in these factors cause the soil to move towards a new equilibrium (Nikiforoff, 1959). Soil properties differ in their speed of change in the face of a new set of soil-forming factors (Yaalon, 1971). Resistance to change is termed pedogenic inertia (Bryan and Teakle, 1949). It is apparent therefore that a soil at equilibrium consists of a number of equilibria; one perhaps for each soil property. General or total equilibrium in a soil is an ideal state whose occurrence is very much a function of the response of its different properties to time.

Soil properties that are direct consequences of the biotic factors such as organic matter, nitrogen, pH and types of structure, are altered easily, reaching a new steady state generally in less than 1000 yrs (Yaalon, 1971). Also spodic horizons can be degraded in relatively short time once the native vegetation under which the horizon developed is replaced (Soil Survey Staff, 1960). Pacific silver fir (*Abies amabilis*) and a mountain hemlock (*Tsuga mertensiana*) invading a subalpine meadow in the Cascades of Washington have changed, chemically but not visually, an A1 (Ah) horizon, originally developed under herbaceous species, into an A2 (E) horizon in less than 400 yrs. At this same site, the invading conifers are changing the A2 (E) horizon of a buried profile into a B2 (Bw2) (Singer and Ugolini, 1974). Jungerius (1969) also noted the incipient formation of an A2 (E) horizon at the base of an A1 (Ah) horizon when grassland had been replaced by forest. In an undisturbed oak forest in northern Wisconsin, the replacement of eastern hemlock (*Tsuga canadensis*) with Hill's oak prairie (*Quercus ellipsoidaeis*) and Jack pine prairie (*Pinus banksiana*) after fire caused the original A2 (E) of Podzols (Typic Haplorthod) developed under hemlock to change into an A1 (Ah) (Milfred et al., 1967). On the Keewatin Peninsula, Canada, Sorenson et al. (1971) and Sorenson (1977) reconstructed the arctic tree-line position in the last 6000 yrs on the basis of morphological features expressed by the surficial and buried soils. Expansion of the forest into the tundra, in response to a climatic amelioration, was documented by the occurrence of buried Podzols and spruce macrofossils beyond the present tree-line. The recession of the tree-line, in response to climatic deterioration, was established by the extension of Arctic Brown soils developed in the tundra inside of the present limit of the forest. These changes took place in approximately 1000 yrs.

Animals

Earthworms

In 1896, Charles Darwin stated that worms "have played a more important part in the history of the world than most persons would at first suppose". He reported that in many areas of England a weight of more than 10 tons (10,516 kg) of dry soil per acre (0.405 ha) is digested annually by worms and carried to the surface. Darwin goes on to describe how the soil particles are abraded in the intestines of the worms. He suggests that the earthworms contribute to the earth's denudation by bringing to the surface a thin layer of fine loose soil which is eventually washed by the streams and carried to the ocean (Darwin, 1896). In a sod-podzolized soil kept for two years under grass, Ponomareva (1953) calculated the existence of 1,750,000 earthworms per hectare and 52 metric tons of casts per hectare. These values were higher than those under wheat and rye. According to Evans (1948), an estimated 1—25 tons (0.984—22.68 metric ton) of casts per acre (0.405 ha yr^{-1}) are brought to the surface where they form a stone-free layer. Earthworm burrowing, dragging of leaves into the soil and subsurface mixing result in: the homogenization of the soil surface, creation of voids and formation of soil structure.

Amelioration of structure has been often associated with earthworm activity. On the other hand, other factors, such as organic matter and root, fungal and bacterial metabolites may be partly responsible for the good aggregation qualities of earthworm-rich soils (Hopp, 1946). However, it is noteworthy that decimation of earthworms by extreme pest-control measures causes both deterioration and changes of soil structure (Van de Westeringh, 1971).

Earthworms casts are neutral in reaction, richer in organic matter, higher in electrolytes, exchangeable cations, calcite, Al_2O_3, Fe_2O_3, P_2O_5 and silt and clay, and higher in bacteria, actinomycetes, *Collembola* and *Acarina* than soils from which they were collected (Lunt and Jacobson, 1944; Kollmannsperger, 1952; Joshi and Kelkar, 1952; Ponomareva, 1953; Nye, 1955; Schütz and Felber, 1956; Ryan, 1979. The role of earthworms in the mineralization of N has been studied by numerous authors and reviewed by Heath (1965). Non-available N once ingested by the worms becomes mineralized. Substantial amounts of N are thus made available to plants; some of it being recycled through earthworm biomass.

Although the influence of earthworms on soil structure and fertility is well known, little is known about their role in soil genesis. The best established function of earthworms is the formation of A1 (Ah) horizons (Wittich, 1963; Nielsen and Hole, 1964; Perel et al., 1966) and in the mixing of the horizons. The term "vermisols" was introduced by Buntley and Papendick (1960) to indicate a specific group of grassland soils in South Dakota showing a complex mixing of the subsurface horizons by earthworms. Recent invasion of earthworms in virgin Podzols have altered the A2 (E) horizons into an Ap [sic] Ah by incorporating the litter layer (Langmeid, 1964). Ryan (1979) noted that earthworms influence profiles by mixing the A and B horizons and forming transitional horizons. By promoting good structure and, consequently, good aeration, Ryan (1979) suggested that worms are indirectly responsible for the high chroma of B horizons.

Termites and ants

Termites are polymorphic social insects living in nests (termitaria) of their own construction (Lee and Wood, 1971). The effect of termites on soil formation may be considered with respect to: (1) the development of microrelief; (2) the formation of soil horizons; (3) the chemical and physical properties of termitaria; (4) the development of laterite; and (5) geochemical prospecting (Watson, 1974).

Construction of mounds by termites involves considerable earth-moving activity. Macrotermes mounds occurring in the African savannah may reach a height of about 9 m and a basal diameter of 30 m (Watson, 1974). Smaller mounds are, however, more common. Large mounds of macrotermitinae may harbor a population of several millions with a distribution of less than 10 mounds per hectare. Smaller mounds support smaller populations, several thousand individuals, but their frequency may approach 1000 mounds ha^{-1} (Lee and Wood, 1971). The frequency and height of the mounds are governed by climate, vegetation and soil characteristics. In northern Australia, the distribution of *Amitermes vitiosus* is related to soil texture. Increasing amounts of clay increase the number of mounds as well as their height. High frequencies of termite mounds affect the distribution of effective precipitation by influencing infiltration and runoff. Concentration of carbonates below mounds is explained by the protective influence of the mounds themselves (Lee and Wood, 1971).

Another aspect of the earth-moving activities of termites is the formation of stone-free soils. Nye (1955) recognized a number of horizons formed by faunal activity and weathering in western Africa. Below a surficial horizon developed from earthworm-cast material, a horizon was formed from material transported by termites. This horizon overlays a gravelly horizon which, in turn, is followed by weathered rock. A similar three-layered profile was also reported by Watson (1960) in Rhodesia and by Williams (1968) in Australia. The fine stone-free material carried by the termites from the weathered rock zone has been calculated by Williams (1968) to amount to 6000 m^{3}ha^{-1}. Lee and Wood (1971) recalculated the following rates of accumulation of soil at the surface:

West Africa: 0.025 mm yr^{-1} (from Nye's 1955 data)
Northern Australia: 0.0125 mm yr^{-1} (from Williams' 1968 data)
Northern Australia: 0.10 and 0.02 mm yr^{-1} (Lee and Wood, 1971)

Termite mounds are richer in bases such as Ca, Mg, K and Na than adjacent soils. Lee and Wood (1971) calculated that although the mounds constitute only 2% of the total weight of the soil of the A horizon, the amount of total C, N, P and exchangeable Ca, K, Mg and Na in the mounds was far in excess of that in the A horizon. Calcium carbonate often occurs in large quantities in termite mounds built on non-calcareous soils (Watson, 1974). This anomaly has tentatively been explained as the result of carbonate movement from the groundwater by the termites and the protective influence of the mounds against leaching. Termites are also responsible for storing substantial amounts of organic matter in mounds, subtracting it from circulating in the rest of the ecosystem (Lee and Wood, 1971).

Vesicular laterite consisting of ferruginous masses permeated by anastomising tubes and channels, found in the uplands of Angola, was originally attributed to the deposition of iron oxides in the galleries of abandoned termitaria (Lee and Wood, 1971). Similar formations were reported in the Sudan, Congo, in northeastern Brazil and Vietnam. More critical evaluation of these lateritic structures has revealed that this interpretation is not entirely justified since strictly abiotic processes could explain vesicular laterite (Lee and Wood, 1971). Termites do cause the burial and degradation of laterite crusts and Boyer (1955) suggests that lateritic crusts and gravel are progressively destroyed by the activity of termites that favor a chemical regimen of dissolution of the iron and manganese hydroxides.

Finally, Watson (1974) suggests that termite mounds have potential use for geochemical prospecting. He cites an example in Rhodesia where termite mounds built on Kalahari sand contained an anomalous concentration of Au and Zn. These metals are present together with Pb, Mo and Ag in the basement complexes which underlie the Kalahari sand. According to Watson (1974), termites may have carried the gold from the basement rock through the Kalahari sand from a depth of 27 m!

The effect of ants on soil is somewhat similar to that of termites. Ants, by building mounds, move soil to the surface, disturb the morphology of the pre-existing soils, change the bulk density and alter the particle-size distribution. They also increase the content of organic matter, N, available nutrients and free iron oxides and increase the general biological activity. Salem and Hole (1968) counted 25 mounds of *Formica exsectoides* in an area of 1040 m^2 representing 1.9% of the surface at a site in southern Wisconsin. The mounds averaged 0.37 m in height, had a basal diameter of 1.1 m and a volume of 0.13 m^3. In 2.2 yrs the ants had reworked the soil to a depth of 160 cm and moved to the surface a quantity of soil equivalent to 1.25% of the plow layer or 30,000 kg ha^{-1}. Studies by Baxter and Hole (1967) recorded that the ant, *Formica cinerea*, had reworked the entire soil of an area in Grant County Wisconsin, in 600—1200 yrs. Lyford (1963) observed small, 1 cm high and 7 cm wide mounds built by ants in the Harvard Forest, Massachusetts, and suggested that the upper 35 cm of a Soil Brun Acid (Dystrochrept) had been reworked by the ants. In Australia, the meat ant, *Iridomyrmex purpureus*, was observed to have built 66 nests per 4 hectares involving a total volume of excavated soil of 39,423 cm^3 (Greenslade, 1974).

In the subalpine region of British Columbia, ant activity (*Formica fusca*) strongly influenced the morphological features of the soils (Wiken et al., 1976). The area affected by this activity was about 6—7% amounting to 1150 mounds ha^{-1} and had an estimated volume of excavated material of 54 m^3ha^{-1}. The ant activity extended approximately to 50 cm below the surface. Moderate, medium subangular blocky structure with firm consistency was observed in the B horizon of the active sites; whereas, the ant-free sites had a medium granular structure with friable consistency. The mounds themselves displayed reticulate tabular or ovoid aggregates 5—20 mm thick. Particularly striking was the particle-size segregation introduced by mound-building activity. The dominant texture of the mounds was a clay loam in contrast with a gravelly loam texture of the unmounded soils. The textural differentiation is related to the particle-carrying capacity of the ants. Textural differences caused by ant activity were also emphasized by Stewart (1959) in Australia and Baxter and Hole (1967) in Wisconsin. Nests built by the meat ant (*Iridomyrmex purpureus*) are covered by gravel from 0.2 to 3.75 mm. This lag gravel covering the nests seems to play a role in condensing dew, acting as mulch, and in defending the nest (Greenslade, 1974).

Soil material affected by ant activity appears to be richer in exchangeable ions and organic matter or at least as rich as the surface horizon of adjacent soils (Wiken et al., 1976). An increase in soil organic matter, total N, available K, P, exchangeable bases, bacteria and fungi were reported by Czerwinski et al. (1971) and Petal et al. (1970) for a grassland system affected by ants in Poland.

Wiken et al. (1976) suggested that pedogenesis of areas covered by ant nests is retarded by the reduced leaching existing below ant mounds. Greenslade (1974) concluded that nest construction by the meat ant was of little significance to pedogenesis once the ant population had been established.

Other animals

Activity by small rodents and other mammals is also important in reworking the soil surface, opening galleries and changing the physical and chemical properties of soils. Rodents, amphibians and reptiles are all involved. Pocket gophers have been considered responsible for the construction of Mima mounds, circular or ovoidal shape, 5—30 m in diameter and rising about 0.5—2 m, occurring in many areas of the western United States (Hilgard, 1884; Bretz, 1913; Arkley and Brown, 1954). The involvement of gophers (*Thomomys mazama* Johnson) in the construction of these mounds is still conjectural (Dalquest and Sheffer, 1942) but better explains the pedological characteristics of Mima mounds in western Washington and California than other theories.

Rodents are considered some of the most active animals in inducing pedoturbations. The term "crotovina", derived from the Russian word "krot" meaning a mole, is extensively used for denoting tunnels, passageways and nests of rodents filled with soil (Joffe, 1949). Sukachev, as quoted by Joffe (1949), conducted extensive studies of Russian crotovinas and showed that subsoil material was brought to the surface and dark humus soil was carried into the B horizon. The most common crotovinas occur within 1—1.5 m of the surface and infrequently crotovinas are found at the depth of 3—4 m. Deeper occurrence, 5—7.5 m, is considered evidence of a buried soil. Woodchunks (*Aretomys boboc*), ground squirrels (*Spermophyllus guttatus*), the blind mole rat of Europe (*Spalax typhlus*) and hamsters (*Cricetus frumentarius*) were recognized as different species responsible for crotovinas in Russia. As pointed out by Sukachev and earlier observed by Dokuchaev (Joffe, 1949), the presence of crotovinas in the forest provides evidence for the past northern extension of the prairie. Additional information on the paleo-vegetation can be obtained from the pollen present in the buried humus of crotovinas (Dinesman, 1967). Crotovinas formed by ground squirrel (*Citellus beecheyi*) were observed in California where Borst (1968) estimated that complete mixing of the A and B horizons in Rendzinas (Rendolls), Regosols, (Entisols) and minimal Non-calcic Brown soils (Xeralf or Ochrept) would take about 360 yrs under the influence of these rodents.

Small mammals such as the lemming (*Lagurus lagurus*) and marmots increase the organic-matter content and help desalinization in steppe soils (Khodashova and Dinesman, 1961; Abaturov, 1963).

The Arctic ground squirrel (*Citellus undulatus*) is active on south-facing slopes, but is absent on north-facing slopes in the arctic tundra of the Ruby Range, Yukon Territory. It excavates considerable soil for building dens. Price (1971) calculated that these squirrels could excavate 8 tons (7.25 metric tons) per acre (0.405 ha^{-1}) per year of soils. This activity not only disturbs the soil and creates new surfaces, but also has considerable effect on mass-wasting, solifluction and valley asymmetry (Price, 1971).

In well-drained sites in the Arctic, Ugolini has observed the effect of ground squirrels on soil rejuvenation and profile destruction. This activity is further accentuated by grizzly bears (*Ursus arctos*) that excavate the ground squirrel (*Spermophylus parryii*) dens in search of food. Caribou (*Rangifer tarandus*) trails along migration routes through the Brooks Range, Alaska, criss-cross the landscape. The exposed mineral soil in the trails may be affected by frost action that can induce further deterioration of the vegetative cover and of the soil profile (Brown, 1966).

In alpine and subalpine meadows, marmots (*Marmota* sp.) create mounds and tunnels in the process of building dens, and mice and voles build tunnels and trails under the winter snow pack. Also in alpine regions, the role of pika (*Ochotona princeps*) in the revegetation of talus and scree is important. Herbaceous plants collected by this small rodent and stored in cavities of the chaotically arranged rocks, together with other debris, provide a substratum for plant colonization and soil development.

In the Brooks Range, Alaska, the top of limestone tors are often used by raptorial birds and by mountain sheep as lookout points. The droppings of these animals induce a luxuriant growth of nitrophillic vegetation and acidify and dissolve the limestone substrata. Consequently, unusually acidic soil conditions are found at these lookout sites (Ugolini and Tedrow, 1963).

Large grazing and browsing mammals affect soil properties both directly and indirectly. These herbivores may change the vegetation through selective feeding and cause indirect, plant-mediated effects on the soil. The direct effect of animals on soil is through the action of the hooves on the soil surface. Compaction of soil varies depending on the various species of ungulates or on the weight of individuals. The pressure exerted by the hooves of a sheep (Kerry Hill) is about 800—900 g cm^{-2} and that for cattle (Jersey) between 1280–1460 g cm^{-2} (Spedding, 1971). Steinbrenner (1951) found highly compacted soils in heavily cattle-grazed wood-lots in southern Wisconsin. Federer et al. (1961) detected compaction due to the grazing of dairy cattle to a depth of 8 inches (20.4 cm). On slopes, ungulates cause the formation of terracettes (Rahm, 1962; Young, 1972). In New Zealand, Gibbs (1962) reports that deer (*Cervus* sp.) and opossums (*Didelphis* sp.) have induced erosion in steepland soils by breaking the surface mat during grazing and tramplings.

Unique among the faunal contributions to soil formation is the role of Adelie-penguin colonies (*Pygoscelis adeliae*) in Antarctica. Because of intense cold and paucity of liquid water, Antarctica supports a very depauperated terrestrial flora while in contrast, the surrounding ocean harbors a rich marine life. Adelie-penguin colonies perform the important role of transferring organic matter in the form of guano from the rich ocean to the poor terrestrial ecosystem. Areas occupied by penguin colonies display the greatest quantity of organic matter on the soils of continental Antarctica.

Soils developed on penguin guano were named ornithogenic soils by Syroechkovsky (1959) and Avian soils by Campbell and Claridge (1969). Ornithogenic soil consists of a layer of guano resting sharply on unconsolidated mineral material. The effect of the avifauna is not restricted to guano accumulation, but also in building mounds of pebbles at the surface used by the penguins as nests. In the Mirnyy area (East Antarctica), Syroechkovsky (1959) estimated that the population of 1800 penguins per square kilometer removes 556 tons of marine organisms from the ocean during the summer. Ornithogenic or guano-derived soils have been investigated in Antarctica at Cape Royds, Ross Island (Ugolini, 1969, 1972), at Inexpressible Island, Ross Sea (Campbell and Claridge, 1966) and at Signy Island (Allen and Northover, 1967). Analyses of these soils show neutral to alkaline pH, high nitrogen content resulting from the high protein diet of the penguins, a high mainly inorganic phosphorus level and high salinity. Because the population size and the area occupied by penguin colonies varies with time, abandoned portions of the rookeries display degradation of the guano and changes in microrelief. Abandoned sites show a loss of nitrogen with an attendant narrowing of the N/P ratio and the decomposition of the uric acid, present in the penguin excreta, into oxalic acid (Ugolini, 1969). Both N/P ratio and uric/oxalic acid ratios can be used for assessing the relative antiquity of penguin sites (Ugolini, 1969, 1972). Campbell and Claridge (1966) and Ugolini (1972) examined the effect of guano on mineral alteration and concluded that guano had little impact on the mineralogy of the soil. Wilson and Bain (1976), on the other hand, disclosed the presence of an intermediate form of leucophosphite formed by the interaction of penguin guano with layer silicate minerals.

SUMMARY

Organisms play an extremely important role in soil formation and in the cycling of carbon and nitrogen in ecosystems; these three processes are closely related. Carbon fixed in photosynthesis is decomposed by soil microbes at different rates in different ecosystems. The nitrogen cycle is interrelated with the carbon cycle and the rate of nitrogen cycling is closely related to the productivity of ecosystems. Highest productivities generally occur in grasslands, but highest standing biomasses occur in temperate forests. Accumulation of organic matter in soils is a balance between productivity, biomass accumulation and decomposition rate. Organic-matter accumulation and decomposition products have a profound influence on soil formation.

Soil, however, can form also in the absence of biota, but the process proceeds many times faster in its presence. The biota in soil ecosystems consists of: (1) lower plants (fungi, bacteria, algae, lichens and mosses); (2) higher plants; and (3) animals. Only a small proportion ($<5\%$) of the total biomass consists of soil microbes but this percentage perhaps does not reflect their full importance. Bacteria and fungi not only are capable of decomposing organic matter and thus releasing bound nutrients, but also are involved in decomposing rocks and minerals through production of chelating organic acids. Actinomycetes, diatoms, green and blue-green algae have been isolated from rocks and shown capable of solubilizing minerals. The action of lichens and moss rhizoids on rocks includes both physical disintegration and chemical weathering.

Higher plants and their associated soil microfloral and microfaunal populations strongly influence soil formation. This is illustrated by contrasting adjacent temperate forests and prairie soils. Leaching and translocation of iron and clay is greater in the forest where mobile organics depress the pH and chelate and transport the iron from the surface to the B horizon. In the prairie, organic matter is more deeply distributed because grasses produce finer and deeper roots and the soil fauna is more abundant. Although organics capable of complexing iron are present, they are not as mobile as those in forest soils. Thus, two different soil profiles develop.

The impact of the biota on soil formation is manifested in space and time. Spatially, pedogenesis proceeds differently whether the soil is developing beneath the bole of a tree, beneath the canopy, or in the open. This is because precipitation is substantially changed in volume and composition as it is intercepted by the trees. Chronosequences in different environments have demonstrated the temporal relationship between biota and soil properties.

Although the biomass of the soil animals is less than that of the soil microflora, their influence on soil formation can be considerable. This again depends on the ecosystem, with the influence generally being greater in more neutral and warm ecosystems and less in acid and cold ones. Earthworms are extremely important because of their capability of influencing horizon formation by mixing soil and improving soil structure and fertility. Termites and ants have a similar role.

Small rodents and other small vertebrate animals may also rework the soil surfaces, open galleries and change the soil physical and chemical properties. Their influence, however, tends to be more localized than those of earthworms, termites, and ants.

Five factors control soil formation: climate, parent material, topography, time and organisms. This chapter has dealt with organisms and demonstrated the large influence of the biotic factors from bacteria to large ungulates on the soils of the world.

ACKNOWLEDGEMENT

The authors are thankful to Mr. Daniel Mann for his critical review of the manuscript and his editorial suggestions and to the word-processing office for helping us meet the deadline. The comprehensive review by Hole (1981) was published after this chapter was written.

REFERENCES

Abaturov, B.D., 1963. Effect of steppe lemmings (*Lagurus lagurus* Pall.) on soils. Pochvovedeniye, 2: 95—100.

Al-Barrack, S. and Lewis, D.T., 1978. Soils of the grassland—forest ecotone in eastern Nebraska. Soil Sci. Soc. Am. J., 42: 334—338.

Alexander, M.A., 1977. Introduction to Soil Microbiology. Wiley, New York, N.Y., 467 pp.

Allen, S.E. and Northover, M.J., 1967. Soil types and nutrients on Signy Island. Philos. Trans. R. Soc. (London), Ser. B 252: 179—185.

Allen, S.E., Grimshaw, H.M. and Holdgate, M.W., 1967. Factors affecting the availability of plant nutrients on an Antarctic Island. J. Ecol., 55: 381—396.

Arkley, R.J. and Brown, H.C., 1954. The origin of Mima Mound (Hogwallow) microrelief in far western states. Soil. Sci. Soc. Am. Proc., 18: 195—199.

Asahina, Y. and Shibata, S., 1954. Chemistry of Lichen Substances. Maruzen, Tokyo, 240 pp. (English transl.).

Baxter, F.P. and Hole, F.D., 1967. Ant (*Formica cinerea*) pedoturbation in a prairie soil. Soil Sci. Soc. Am. Proc., 31: 425—428.

Bell, M.K., 1974. Decomposition of herbaceous litter. In: C.H. Dickinson and G.J.F. Pugh (Editors), Biology of Plant Litter Decomposition, (1). Academic Press, New York, N.Y., pp. 37—67.

Berthelin, J., 1971. Microbial weathering of a granitic sand. Preliminary note. Sci. Sol., 1: 11—29. In: Soils Fertil., 34: 680.

Berthelin, J. and Dommergues, Y., 1972. Effects of microbial metabolic products on the solubilization of minerals in a granite sand. Revue d'Ecologie et de Biologie du Sol, 9: 397—406. In: Soils Fertil., 36: 1—74.

Beschel, R.H., 1965. Epipetric succession and lichen growth rates in the eastern Nearctic. In: Abstracts INQUA, VII Int. Congress, Boulder, Colo., pp. 25—26.

Bidwell, R.G.S., 1974. Plant Physiology. McMillan, New York, N.Y., 643 pp.

Birkeland, P.W., 1974. Pedology, Weathering, and Geomorphological Research. Oxford Univ. Press, New York, N.Y., 285 pp.

Bockheim, J.G., 1972. Effects of Alpine and Subalpine Vegetation on Soil Development, Mt. Baker, Wash. Ph.D. Thesis. Univ. of Washington, Seattle, Wash., 156 pp.

Borst, G., 1968. The occurrence of crotovinas in some southern California soils. Trans. 9th Int. Congress Soil Sci., Adelaide, 11: 19—27.

Boyer, P., 1955. Preliminary pedological and bacteriological studies of termitarias. C.R. Acad. Sci. Paris., 240: 569—571. In: Bibliography on Termites and Soil Formation (1964—1933). Commonwealth Bureau of Soils, Harpenden, p.4.

Boyle, J.R. and Voigt, G.K., 1973. Biological weathering of silicate minerals: Implications for tree nutrition and soil genesis. Plant Soil, 38: 191—201.

Boyle, J.R., Voigt, G.K. and Sawhney, B.L., 1974. Chemical weathering of biotite by organic acids. Soil Sci., 117: 42—45.

Bretz, J.H., 1913. Glaciation of the Puget Sound Region. Wash. Geol. Surv. Bull., 8: 1—244.

Broersma, K., 1973. Dark Soils of the Victoria Area, British Columbia. M.S. Thesis. Univ. of British Columbia, Vancouver, B.C., 120 pp.

Brown, J., 1966. Soils of the Okpilak River Region, Alaska. U.S. CRREL Res. Rep. 188. Hanover, N.H., 49 pp.

Bryan, W.H. and Teakle, L.J.H., 1949. Pedogenic inertia — a concept in soil science. Nature, 164: 969.

Buntley, G.J. and Papendick, R.I., 1960. Worm-worked soils of eastern South Dakota, their morphology and classification. Soil Sci. Soc. Am. Proc., 24: 128—132.

Buol, S.W., Hole, F.D. and McCracken, R.J., 1973. Soil Genesis and Classification. Iowa State Univ. Press, Ames, Iowa, 360 pp.

Buol, S.W., Hole, F.D. and McCracken, R.J., 1980. Soil Genesis and Classification (2nd ed.). Iowa State Univ. Press, Ames, Iowa, 404 pp.

Cameron, R.E., 1963. Algae of southern Arizona. Part I. Introduction — blue-green algae. Rev. Agrol., 7: 282—318.

Cameron, R.E., 1964. Algae of southern Arizona. Part II. Algal flora (exclusive of blue-green algae). Rev. Agrol, 7: 151—177.

Cameron, R.E. and Fuller, W.H., 1960. Nitrogen fixation by some algae in Arizona soils. Soil Sci. Soc. Am. Proc., 24: 353—356.

Cameron, R.E., King, J. and David, C.N., 1970. Microbiology, ecology, and microclimatology of soil sites in dry valleys of southern Victoria Land, Antarctica. In: M.W. Holdgate (Editor), Antarctic Ecology, Vol. 2. Academic Press, New York, N.Y., pp. 702—716.

Campbell, I.B. and Claridge, G.G.C., 1966. A sequence of soils from a penguin rookery, Inexpressible Island, Antarctica. N.Z. J. Sci., 9: 361—372.

Campbell, I.B. and Claridge, G.G.C., 1969. A classification of frigic soils — the zonal soils of the Antarctic continent. Soil Sci., 107: 75—85.

Clanton, U.S., McKay, D.S. and Ladle, G.H., 1974. Micromorphology of lunar regolith particles. In: G.K. Rutherford (Editor), Soil Microscopy. Proc. 4th Int. Working-meeting on Soil Micromorphology, Dept. Geogr., Queens Univ., Kingston, Ontario, pp. 642—654.

Claridge, G.G.C., 1965. The clay mineralogy and chemistry of some sites from the Ross Dependency, Antarctica. N.Z. J. Geol. Geophys., 8: 186—220.

Cooper, R. and Rudolph, E.D., 1953. The role of lichens in soil formation and plant succession. Ecology, 34: 805—807.

Crocker, R.L., 1952. Soil genesis and the pedogenic factors. Q. Rev. Biol., 27: 139—168.

Crocker, R.L. and Major, J., 1955. Soil development in relation to vegetation and surface age at Glacier Bay, Alaska. J. Ecol., 43: 427—448.

Czerwinski, Z., Jakubczyk, H. and Petal, J., 1971. Influence of ant hills on the meadow soils. Pedobiologia, 11: 277—285.

Dalquest, W.W. and Scheffer, V.B., 1942. The origin of the Mima Mounds of western Washington. J. Geol., 50: 68—84.

Darwin, C., 1896. The Formation of Vegetable Mould through the Action of Worms with Observations on their Habits. Appleton, New York, N.Y., pp. 305—313.

Dawson, H., Hrutfiord, B. and Ugolini, F.C., 1983. Mobility of lichen compounds from *Cladonia mitis* in a soil profile. Soil Sci., 136 (in press).

Delwiche, C.C., 1970. The nitrogen cycle VII. In: F. Dennis and F. Bello (Editors), The Biosphere. Freeman, San Francisco, Calif., pp. 69—80.

Delwiche, C.C. and Likens, G.E., 1977. Biological response to fossil fuel products. In: W. Stumm (Editor), Global Chemical Cycles and their Alterations by Man. Dahlem Konferenzen, Berlin, pp. 73—88.

Dinesman, L.G., 1967. Animal burrows in the study of soil formation in the Holocene. Pochvovedeniye, 4: 76—85.

Dommergues, Y. and Mangenot, F., 1970. Ecologie microbienne du sol. Masson, Paris, 796 pp.

Dregne, H.E., 1976. Soils of the Arid Regions. Elsevier, New York, N.Y., 238 pp.

Duff, R.B. and Webley, D.M., 1959. 2-ketogluconic acid as a natural chelator produced by soil bacteria. Chem. Ind. (London), 1959: 1376—1377.

Edmonds, R.L., 1979. Decomposition and nutrient release in Douglas-fir needle litter in relation to stand development. Can. J. For. Res., 9: 132—140.

Evans, A.C., 1948. Studies on the relationships between earthworms and soil fertility. II. Some effects of earthworms on soil structure. Ann. Appl. Biol., 35: 1—13.

Everett, K.R., 1976. A Survey of the Soils in the Region of the South Shetland Islands and Adjacent Parts of the Antarctic Peninsula. Inst. Polar Studies, Rep. No. 58, 44 pp.

Federer, C.A., Tenpas, G.H., Schmidt, D.R. and Tanner, C.B., 1961. Pasture soil compaction by animal traffic. Agron. J., 53: 53—54.

Flanagan, P.W. and Van Cleve, K., 1977. Microbial biomass, respiration, and nutrient cycling in a black spruce taiga ecosystem. In: U. Lohn and T. Persson (Editors), Soil Organisms as Components of Ecosystems. Swed. Nat. Sci. Res. Council, Bul., 25: 261—273.

Fogel, R. and Cromack Jr., K., 1977. Effects of habitat and substrate quality on Douglas-fir litter decomposition in western Oregon. Can. J. Bot., 55: 1632—1640.

Fogel, R. and Hunt, G., 1979. Fungal and arboreal biomass in a western Oregon Douglas-fir ecosystem: Distribution patterns and turnover. Can. J. For. Res., 9: 245—256.

Friedmann, E.I., 1971. Light and scanning electron microscopy of the endolithic desert algal habitat. Phycologia, 10: 411—428.

Friedmann, E.I., 1978. Melting snow in the dry valleys is a source of water for endolithic microorganisms. Antarct. J., 13: 162—163.

Fry, E.J., 1922. Some types of endolithic limestone lichens. Ann. Bot., 36: 144.

Fry, E.J., 1927. The mechanical action of crustaceous lichens on substrata of shale, schist, gneiss, limestone and obsidian. Ann. Bot., 41: 437—460.

Garrels, R., Mackenzie, F.T. and Hunt, C., 1975. Chemical cycles and the global environmental: Assessing human influences. Kaufann, Los Altos, Calif., 206 pp.

Gersper, P.L. and Holowaychuk, N., 1970a. Effects of stemflow water on the Miami soil under a beech tree: I. Morphological and physical properties. Soil Sci. Am. Proc., 34: 779—786.

Gersper, P.L. and Holowaychuk, N., 1970b. Effects of stemflow on a Miami soil under a beech tree: II. Chemical properties. Soil Sci. Soc. Am. Proc., 34: 786—794.

Gersper, P.L. and Holowaychuck, N., 1971. Some effects of stemflow from canopy trees on chemical properties of soil. Ecology, 52: 691—702.

Gibbs, H.S., 1962. Steepland soils and their problems. Int. Soc. Soil Sci. Joint Meeting Comm. Trans., IV—V: 665—679.

Glazovskaya, M.A., 1950. The effects of microorganisms on processes of weathering primary minerals. Izv. Akad. Nauk SSSR, Ser. Pochv., 6: 79—100 (Transl. from Russian).

Glinka, K.D., 1927. Dokuchaiev's Ideas in the Development of Pedology and Cognate Sciences. USSR Acad. Sci., Russian Pedological Investigations. I. Publishing Office of the Academy, Leningrad, pp. 1—32.

Gosz, J.R., Likens, G.E. and Bormann, F.H. 1973. Nutrient release from decomposing leaf and branch litter in the Hubbard Brook Forest, New Hampshire. Ecol. Monogr., 43: 173—191.

Graustein, W.C., Cromack Jr., K. and Sollins, P., 1977. Calcium oxalate: Occurrence in soils and effect on nutrient and geochemical cycles. Science, 198: 1252—1254.

Greenslade, P.J., 1974. Some relations of the meat ant, *Iridomyrmex purpureus* (Hymenoptera: Formicidae) with soil in south Australia. Soil Biol. Biochem., 6: 7—14.

Gromov, B.V., 1957. The microflora of rock layers and primitive soils of some northern districts of the USSR. (In Russian.) Microbiology, 26: 57—63.

Heal, O.W. and French, D.D., 1974. Decomposition of organic matter in tundra. In: A.J. Holding, O.W. Heal, S.F. Maclean, Jr. and P.W. Flanagan (Editors), Soil Organisms and Decomposition in Tundra. Tundra Biome Steering Committee, Stockholm, pp. 279—310.

Heath, G.W., 1965. The part played by animals in soil formation. In: E.G. Hallsworth and D.V. Crawford (Editors), Experimental Pedology. Butterworth, London, pp. 236—243.

Henderson, M.E. and Duff, R.B., 1963. The release of metallic and silicate ions from minerals, rocks, and soils by fungal activity. J. Soil Sci., 14: 236—246.

Hilgard, E.W., 1884. Report on the physical and agricultural features of the state of California. U.S. Census Office, Tenth Census, 6: 649.

Hole, F.D., 1981. Effects of animals on soils. A comprehensive review. Geoderma, 25: 75—112.

Holland, H.D., 1978. The Chemistry of the Atmosphere and Oceans. Wiley, New York, N.Y., 351 pp.

Hopp, H., 1946. Earthworms fight erosion, too. Soil Conserv., 11: 252—254.

Huck, F.O., Jobson, D.J., Park, S.K., Well, S.D., Arvidson, R., Patterson, W.R. and Benton, W.D., 1977. Spectrophotometric and Color Estimates of the Viking Lander Sites. J. Geophys. Res., 82: 4401—4411.

Hutchinson, G.E., 1970. The Biosphere. In: F. Dennis and F. Bello (Editors), The Biosphere. Freeman, San Francisco, Calif., pp. 3—11.

Iskandar, I.K. and Syers, J.K., 1972. Metal complex formation by lichen compounds. J. Soil Sci., 32: 255—265.

Jackson, T.A. and Keller, W.D., 1970. A comparative study of the role of lichens and "inorganic" processes in the chemical weathering of recent Hawaiian lava flows. Am. J. Sci., 269: 446—466.

Jenny, H., 1941. Factors of Soil Formation: A System of Quantitative Pedology. McGraw-Hill, New York, N.Y., 281 pp.

Jenny, H., 1958. Role of the plant factor in the pedogenic functions. Ecology, 39: 5—16.

Jenny, H., Gessel, S.P. and Bingham, F.T., 1949. Comparative study of decomposition rates of organic matter in temperate and tropical regions. Soil Sci., 68: 419—432.

Joffe, J.S., 1949. Pedology. (2nd ed.) Pedology Publ., New Brunswick, N.J., 662 pp.

Joshi, N.V. and Kelkar, B.V., 1952. The role of earthworms in soil fertility. Indian J. Agric. Sci. 22: 189—196.

Jungerius, P.D., 1969. Soil evidence of postglacial tree line fluctuations in the Cypress Hills area, Alberta, Canada. Arct. Alp. Res., 1: 235—245.

Khodashova, K.S. and Dinesman, L.G., 1961. Role of small marmots in the formation of the complex soil cover in the clayey semi-arid Transvolga. Pochvovedeniye, 1: 68—76.

Kilburn, P.D., 1959. The forest—prairie ecotone in northeastern Illinois. Am. Midland Nat., 62: 206—217.

Kollmannsperger, F., 1952. The importance of earthworms for soil fertility. Decheniana, 105/106: 165—187.

Krasil'nikov, N.A., 1949. The role of microorganisms in the weathering of rocks. Mikrobiologiya, 18: 318—323 (in Russian).

Lamb, I., 1959. Lichens. Sci. Am., 201: 144—156.

Langmeid, K.K., 1964. Some effects of earthworm invasion in virgin Podzols. Can. J. Soil Sci., 44: 34—37.

Lee, K.E. and Wood, T.G., 1971. Termites and Soil. Academic Press, London, 251 pp.

Lodhi, M.A.K., 1977. The influence and comparison of individual forest trees on soil properties and possible inhibition of nitrification due to intact vegetation. Am. J. Bot. 64: 260—264.

Lotspeich, F.B., Secor, J.B., Okazaki, R. and Smith, H.W., 1961. Vegetation as a soil-forming factor on the Quillayute physiographic unit in western Clallam County, Washington. Ecology, 42: 53—68.

Lunt, H.A. and Jacobson, H.G.M., 1944. The chemical composition of earthworm casts. Soil Sci., 58: 367—375.

Lyford, W.L., 1963. Importance of Ants to Brown Podzolic Soil Genesis in New England. Harvard Forum Paper 7. Petersham, Mass., 18 pp.

MacFayden, A., 1963. The contribution of the fauna to the total soil metabolism. In: J. Doeksen and J. Van der Drift (Editors), Soil Organisms. North Holland, Amsterdam, pp. 3—17.

MacLean Jr., S.F., 1974. Primary production, decomposition and the activity of soil invertebrates in tundra ecosystems: on a hypothesis. In: A.J. Holding, O.W. Heal, S.F. MacLean, Jr. and P.W. Flanagan (Editors), Soil Organisms and Decomposition in Tundra. IBP Tundra Biome, Swedish IBP Comm. Wenner-Gren Centor, Stockholm, pp. 197—206.

McComb, A.L. and Riecken, F.F., 1961. Effect of vegetation on soils in the forest—prairie region. In: D.L. Bailey (Editor), Recent Advances in Botany. University of Toronto Press, Montreal, Ont., pp. 1627—1631.

McCraw, J.D., 1960. Soils of the Ross Dependency, Antarctica. N.Z. Soc. Soil Sci. Proc., 4: 30—35.

Mikola, P., 1960. Comparative experiment on decomposition rates of forest litter in southern and northern Finland. Oikus, 11: 161—166.

Milfred, C.J., Olson, G.W. and Hole, F.D., 1967. Soil resources and forest ecology of Menominee County, Wisconsin. Natl. Hist. Surv., Univ. Extension Bull. 85, Soil Ser. 60. Madison, Wisc.

Mishutin, E.N., 1966. The geographic factor, soil types and their microbial populations. In: E.N. Mishutin (Editor), Microflora of Soils in the Northern and Central USSR. Acad. Sci. USSR, Inst. Of Microbiology. Jerusalem, Israel Program for Scientific Translations, 1972 (Transl. from Russian), pp. 1—28.

Mortland, M.M., Lawton, K. and Uehara, G., 1956. Alteration of biotite to vermiculite by plant growth. Soil Sci., 82: 477—481.

Mulder, E.G. and Van Veen, W.L., 1968. Effect of microorganisms on the transformation of mineral fractions in soil. 9th Int. Congress Soil Sci., Adelaide, IV: 651—661.

Neustruev, S.S., 1927. Genesis of Soils. USSR Acad. Sci. Russian Pedological Investigations, 3. Publishing Office of the Academy, Leningrad, pp. 1—98.

Nielsen, G.A. and Hole, F.D., 1964. Earthworms and the development of coprogenous A1 horizons in forest soil of Wisconsin. Soil Sci. Soc. Am. Proc., 28: 426—430.

Nikiforoff, C.C., 1959. Reappraisal of the soil. Science, 129: 186—196.

Nye, P.H., 1955. Some soil-forming processes in the humid tropics. IV. The action of the soil fauna. J. Soil Sci., 6: 73—83.

Odum, H.T., 1970. An emerging view of the ecological system at El Verde: Summary pp. I-191—I-289, Ch. 10. In: H.T. Odum and R.F. Pigeon (Editors), A Tropical Rain Forest. A Study of Irradiation and Ecology at El Verde, Puerto Rico. Div. Tech. Info., U.S. Atomic Energy Commission, Oak Ridge, Tenn.

Olson, J.S., 1963. Energy storage and the balance of producers and decomposers in ecological systems. Ecology, 44: 322—331.

Parfenova, Y.I., 1966. Transformation of biotite into opal in the soils of northern Karelia. Zap. Vses. Mineral. Ova., 2: 585—586 (in Russian).

Parfenova, Y.I. and Yarilova, E.A., 1962. Mineralogical investigations in soil science. Israel Program for Scientific Transl. (transl. from Russian).

Pauli, F.W., 1968. Some recent development in biogeochemical research. Geol. Assoc. Can., Proc., 19: 45—49.

Perel, T.S., Karpachevskii, L.O. and Yegorova, S.V., 1966. Experiments for studying the effect of earthworms on the litter horizon and humus horizon of forest soils. Pedobiologia, 6: 269—276.

Petal, J., Jakubczyk, H. and Wojcik, Z., 1970. Influence des fourmis sur les modifications des sols et des plantes dans les milieux de prairie. In: J. Phillipson (Editor), Symposium on Methods of Study in Soil Ecology. 1967, Paris, Proc. UNESCO/BP, pp. 235—240.

Polynov, B.B., 1945. First stages of soil formation on massive rock crystals. Pochvovedeniye, 7: 325—339 (in Russian).

Polynov, B.B., 1953. The geological role of organisms. Vopr. Geogr., 33: 45—64 (in Russian).

Ponomareva, S.I., 1953. The effect of the activity of earthworms on the creation of a stable structure in a sod-podzolized soil. Tr. Pochv. Inst. Dukachaeva, 41: 304—378 (in Russian).

Press, F. and Siever, R., 1978. Earth (2nd ed.). Freeman, San Francisco, Calif., 613 pp.

Price, L.W., 1971. Geomorphic effect of the Arctic ground squirrel in an alpine environment. Geogr. Ann., 53A: 100—106.

Rahm, D.A., 1962. The terracette problem. Northwest Sci., 36: 65—80.

Ramborger, T.D., 1980. The Influence of Two Tree Species on the Prairie Soils of Pierce County, Wash. M.S. Thesis. Univ. of Washington, Seattle, Wash., 111 pp.

Richards, B.N., 1974. Introduction to the Soil Ecosystem. Longman, New York, N.Y., 266 pp.

Rodin, L.E., Brazilevich, N.I. and Rozor, N.N., 1975. Productivity of the world's main ecosystems. In: D.C. Reichle, J.F. Franklin and D.W. Goodall (Editors), Productivity of World Ecosystems. Natl. Acad. Sci., Washington, D.C., pp. 13—26.

Ruhe, R.V., 1969. Soil, paleosols, and environment. In: W. Dort and J.K. Jones (Editors), Pleistocene and Recent Environments of the Central Great Plains. Univ. Press of Kansas, Lawrence, Kansas, pp. 37—52.

Ryan, P.J., 1979. The Nature of Soils Under Blackbutt and Flooded Gum Forest Communities near Coffs Harbour, N.S.W. M. Nat. Res. Thesis, Univ. New England, Armidale, N.S.W., 210 pp.

Salem, M. and Hole, F.D., 1968. Ant (*Formica exsectoides*) pedoturbation in a forest soil. Soil Sci. Soc. Am. Proc., 32: 563—567.

Schatz, A., 1963. Soil microorganisms and soil chelation. The pedogenic action of lichens and lichen acids. Agric. Food Chem., 2: 112—118.

Schatz, V., Schatz, A., Trelawny, G.S. and Barth, K., 1956. Significance of pedogenic (soil forming) agents. Proc. Penn. Acad. Sci., 30: 62—69.

Schlesinger, W.H., 1977. Carbon balance in terrestrial detritus. Annu. Rev. Ecol. Syst., 8: 51—81.

Schütz, W. and Felber, E., 1956. What microorganisms participate in the formation of soil aggregates in the gut of earthworms? Z. Acker Pflanzenbau, 101: 471—476.

Shields, L.M., Mitchell, C. and Drouet, F., 1957. Alga- and lichen-established surface crusts as soil nitrogen sources. Am. J. Bot., 44: 489—498.

Silverman, M.P. and Munoz, E., 1970. Fungal attacks on rock: Solubilization and altered infared spectra. Science, 169: 985—987.

Singer, M. and Ugolini, F.C., 1974. Genetic history of two well-drained subalpine soils formed on complex parent materials. Can. J. Soil Sci., 54: 475—489.

Söderlund, R. and Svensson, B.H., 1976. The global nitrogen cycle. In: B.H. Svensson and R. Söderlund (Editors), Nitrogen, Phosphorous and Sulphur Global Cycles. SCOPE Report 7. Ecol. Bull., 22: 23—73.

Soderstrom, B.E., 1979. Seasonal fluctuations of active fungal biomass in horizons of a podzolized pine forest soil in central Sweden. Soil Biol. Biochem., 11: 149—154.

Soil Survey Staff, 1960. Soil classification: A comprehensive system. 7th Approx. Soil Conserv. Serv., USDA. U.S. Govt. Printing Office, Washington, D.C., 754 pp.

Sorenson, C.J., 1977. Reconstructed Holocene bioclimates. Ann. Assoc. Am. Geogr., 67: 214—222.

Sorenson, C.J., Knox, J.C., Larsen, J.A., and Bryscn, R.A., 1971. Paleosols and the forest border in Keewatin, N.W.T. Quat. Res., 1: 468—473.

Spedding, C.R.W., 1971. Grassland Ecology. Oxford Univ. Press, London, 221 pp.

Spyridakis, D.E., Chester, G. and Wilde, S.A., 1967. Kaolinitization of biotite as a result of coniferous and deciduous seedling growth. Soil Sci. Soc. Am. Proc., 31: 203—210.

Staffeld, E.E. and Vogt, K., 1974. Measurements of carbon and nitrogen changes in soil. US/IBP Desert Biome Res. Mem. 74—38. Ecology Center, Utah State Univ., Logan, Utah, 15 pp.

Steinbrenner, E.C., 1951. Effect of grazing on floristic composition and soil properties of farm woodlands in southern Wisconsin. J. Forest., 49: 906—910.

Stewart, G.A., 1959. Some aspects in soil ecology. In: A. Keast, R.L. Crocker and C.S. Christian (Editors), Biogeography and Ecology in Australia. Junk, The Hague, pp. 301—314.

Stuiver, M., 1978. Atmospheric carbon dioxide and carbon reservoir changes. Science, 199: 253—258.

Summers, A.O. and Silver, S., 1978. Microbial transformations of metal. Ann. Rev. Microbiol., 32: 637—672.

Swift, M.J., Heal, O.W. and Anderson, J.M., 1979. Decomposition in Terrestrial Ecosystems. University of California Press, Berkeley, Calif., 372 pp.

Swindale, L.D., 1955. Mineralogy and Genesis of some Rhyolite-derived Soils of New Zealand. Ph.D. Thesis, Univ. Wisconsin, Madison, Wisc., 203 pp.

Syers, J.K., 1964. A Study of Soil Formation on Carboniferous Limestone with Particular Reference to Lichens as Pedogenic Agents. Ph.D. Thesis, Univ. Durham, Durham, 210 pp.

Syers, J.K. and Iskandar, I.K., 1973. Pedogenic significance of lichens. In: V. Ahmadjian and M. Hale (Editors), The Lichens. Academic Press, New York, N.Y., pp. 225—248.

Syroechkovsky, E.E., 1959. Role of animals in the formation of primary soils in the conditions of circumpolar region of the earth (the Antarctic as an example). Zool. J. (Zool. Zh.), 38: 1770—1775 (in Russian).

Targul'yan, V.O., 1959. The first stages of weathering and soil formation on igneous rocks in the Tundra and Taiga zones. Pochvovedeniye, II: 1287—1296.

Tedrow, J., 1978. Soils of the Polar Landscapes. Rutgers Univ. Press, New Brunswick, N.J., 638 pp.

Tedrow, J. and Ugolini, F.C., 1966. Antarctic soils. Antarct. Res. Ser., 8: 161—177.

Thiel, G., 1927. The relative effectiveness of bacteria as agents of chemical denudation. J. Geol., 35: 647—652.

Ugolini, F.C., 1968. Soil development and alder invasion in a recently deglaciated area of Glacier Bay, Alaska. In: J.M. Trappe, J.F. Franklin, R.F. Tarrant and G.M. Hansen

(Editors), Biology of Alder. Proc. 40th NW Sci. Assoc., Pullman, Wash., 1967. PNW Forest Range Exp. Stat. USFS, pp. 115—140.

Ugolini, F.C., 1969. A sequence of soils from a penguin rookery, Cape Royds, Antarctica. In: Program and Abstracts. Western Soc. Soil Sci., Pullman, Wash., p.2 (abstract).

Ugolini, F.C., 1972. Ornithogenic soils of Antarctica. Antarctic terrestrial biology. Antarct. Res. Ser., 20: 181—193.

Ugolini, F.C., 1977. The protoranker soils and the evolution of an ecosystem at Kar Plateau, Antarctica. In: G.A. Llano (Editor), Adaptations within Antarctic Ecosystems. Proc. 3rd SCAR Symp. Antarct. Biol. Smithsonian Inst., Washington, D.C., pp. 1091—1110.

Ugolini, F.C. and Anderson, D.M., 1973. Ionic migration and weathering in frozen Antarctic soils. Soil Sci., 115: 461—470.

Ugolini, F.C. and Jackson, M.L., 1982. Weathering and mineral synthesis in Antarctic soils. In: C. Craddock (Editor), Antarctic Geoscience. Int. Union Geol. Sci., Ser. B, 4: 1101—1108.

Ugolini, F.C. and Mann, D., 1979. Biopedological origin of peatlands in southeast Alaska. Nature, 281: 366—368.

Ugolini, F.C. and Schlichte, A.K., 1973. The effect of the Holocene environmental changes on selected Western Washington soils. Soil Sci., 116: 218—227.

Ugolini, F.C. and Tedrow, J.C.F., 1963. Soils of the Brooks Range, Alaska: 3. Rendzina of the Arctic. Soil Sci., 96: 121—127.

Ugolini, F.C., Minden, R., Dawson, H. and Zachara, J., 1977. An example of soil processes in the *Abies amabilis* zone of central Cascades, Washington. Soil Sci., 124: 291—302.

Ugolini, F.C., Reanier, R.E., Rau, G.E. and Hedges, J.I., 1981. Pedological, isotopic and geochemical investigations of the soils at the boreal forest and alpine tundra transition in Northern Alaska. Soil. Sci., 131: 359—374.

Van de Westeringh, W., 1971. Deterioration of soil structure in worm free orchard soils. Pedobiologia, 12: 6—15.

Viereck, L.A., 1970. Forest succession and soil development adjacent to the Chena River in interior Alaska. Arct. Alpine Res., 2: 1—26.

Wall, G.J., Wilding, L.P. and Miller, R.H., 1974. Biological transformation of clay-sized sediments in simulated aquatic environments. Proc. 17th Great Lakes Res. Conf. 1974. Int. Assoc. Great Lakes Res., pp. 207—211.

Watson, J.P., 1960. Some observations on soil horizons and insect activities in granite soil. Proc. 1st Fed. Sci. Congress, Rhodesia and Nyasaland, pp. 271—276.

Watson, J.P., 1974. Termites in relation to soil formation, ground water, and geochemical prospecting. Soils Fert., 37: 111—114.

Webley, D.M. and Duff, R.B., 1965. The incidence, in soils and other habitats, of microorganisms producing 2-ketogluconic acid. Plant Soil., 22: 307—313.

Webley, D.M., Henderson, M.E. and Taylor, I., 1963. The microbiology of rocks and weathered stones. J. Soil Sci., 14: 102—111.

White, D.P., 1941. Prairie soil as a medium for tree growth. Ecology, 22: 398—407.

White, E.M. and Riecken, F.F., 1955. Brunizem-gray brown podzolic soil biosequence. Soil Sci. Soc. Am. Proc., 19: 504—509.

Wiken, E.B., Broersma, K., Lavkulich, L.K. and Farstad, L., 1976. Biosynthetic alteration in a British Columbia soil by ants (*Formica fusca Linné*). Soil Sci. Soc. Am. J., 40: 422—426.

Will, G.M., 1959. Nutrient return in litter and rainfall under some exotic conifer stands in New Zealand. N.Z. J. Agric. Res., 2: 719—734.

Williams, M.A., 1968. Termites and soil development near Brock's Creek, Northern Territory. Aust. J. Sci., 31: 153—154.

Wilson, M.J. and Bain, D.C., 1976. Occurrence of leucophosphite in a soil from Elephant Island, British Antarctic Territory. Am. Mineral., 61: 1027—1028.

Wittich, W., 1963. The importance of an effective earthworm population in coniferous forest for decomposition of litter, formation of humus, and general soil dynamics. Schriftenr. Forstl. Fak. Univ. Göttingen, 30: 3—60.

Yaalon, D.H., 1971. Soil forming processes in time and space. In: D.H. Yaalon (Editor), Paleopedology: Origin, Nature and Dating of Paleosols. Int. Soc. Soil Sci., Israel Univ. Press, Jerusalem, pp. 29—39.

Yaalon, D.H., 1975. Conceptual models in pedogenesis: Can soil forming functions be solved? Geoderma, 14: 189—205.

Yarilova, E.A., 1947. The role of lithophilous lichens in the weathering of massive crystalline rocks. Pochvovedeniye, 3: 533—548 (in Russian).

Young, A., 1972. Slopes. Longman, New York, N.Y., 288 pp.

Zinke, P.J., 1956. Magnitude and Variation of Certain Soil Properties Associated with Three Forest Trees in California. Ph.D. Thesis, Univ. of California, Berkeley, Calif., 54 pp.

Zinke, P.J., 1962. The pattern of individual forest trees on soil properties. Ecology, 43: 130—133.

Zinke, P.J. and Crocker, R.L., 1962. The influence of giant sequoia on soil properties. For. Sci., 8: 2—11.

CLIMATE, TIME AND SOIL DEVELOPMENT

D.H. YAALON

INTRODUCTION — AN OVERVIEW

The realization that soil profiles are a record of soil genesis and history was possibly the most significant discovery in pedology. In this chapter, we shall examine the effect of climate on soil-profile characteristics and how these changes take place with time. Many responses of soil properties to climatic inputs have been described in the literature by simply establishing a sequence of climatic parameters with specific soil properties, assuming other factors ineffective. Univariant solutions of such sequences attempt to quantify soil—climate relationships (Yaalon, 1975).

The climatic input acting over a period of time produces changes in soil which may attain a steady state or continue to change imperceptibly. Difficulties in dating the interval over which the processes and changes have taken place make time a much more elusive factor to evaluate. However, impressive advances in deriving the rate of change of various soil features have been obtained (Bockheim, 1980).

In general, soils acquire their properties over long periods of time measured in hundreds and thousands of years. As the ever-present lag in adjustment decreases, the rate of adjustment and readjustment also diminishes. In other situations, inputs may exceed outputs, or vice versa, over a sufficiently long span of time to leave an impact on the soil.

The *rate of soil formation* is a product of all the component individual reactions taking place in a soil. It is established from chronofunctions of suitably dated surfaces, keeping all other variables, as far as possible, constant. Dating soils and pedomorphic surfaces (Dan and Yaalon, 1968) continues to present a challenge to pedologists. Soil dating is often important in various applied studies, e.g. in soil loss tolerance considerations or tectonic stability evaluations.

Soils affected by an environment different from today's or formed in a landscape of the past, whether they are now buried or non-buried (relict), are called *paleosols* and will form the last part of this chapter. The elucidation of the probable past environment in which paleosols were formed is based mainly on the recognition of slowly adjusting and persistent features of soil (Yaalon, 1971a).

CLIMATE IN SOIL DEVELOPMENT

Climate was recognized by both Dokuchaiev and Hilgard as one of several factors that determines the nature of soil. The two most frequently considered climatic attributes are rainfall and temperature, but several other climatic attributes also leave a strong impact on soil features. For example, the orientation of pedomorphic surfaces (aspect) and the intensity of the wind passing such surfaces control many soil features.

Climatic parameters used in describing an environment are quantities which represent averages for a certain, often considerable, length of time. Soil-moisture regimes suitably integrate and summarize such seasonal changes in soil-moisture reserves or the amount of water available for leaching and weathering and are thus useful descriptors of the soil-forming environment.

The soil-moisture regime and water balance

Water balance. Water in soils is not only the major agent of rock weathering and mineral transformation and necessary to sustain plant growth, but has major functions within the soil profile (pedon) in redistributing, adding, or removing soil materials. Its availability and flux within the pedon determines the rate of most soil-forming processes. How moisture moves and redistributes itself in the soil is thus of paramount relevance to soil formation and is discussed in Chapter 9.

The rigorous analysis of moisture fluxes based on Darcy's law is gradually being expanded to natural soil systems with a heterogeneous and non-uniform pore-size distribution, both with depth and laterally, and to unsteady or variable inputs of solutes. In consideration of the climatic factor in soil genesis, the overall effect of solute fluxes is evaluated and best characterized as the moisture regime of the system. This will thus be treated in more detail in the following.

By *soil-moisture regime*, we generally mean the integration of the periodic and seasonal gains (increments), losses (expenditures), retention and movement of moisture in the soil profile. Quantitatively, the regime is described by the *water balance* of the soil, which integrates changes in soil water storage during specific time intervals and estimates the amount of water available for leaching and evapotranspiration.

Such a water balance, which can be calculated from climatic data but is preferably derived from actual soil measurements, can succinctly describe many of the climatic attributes important to soil formation and plant growth. An example of such a calculation for the Mediterranean region (Table 8.1) shows that while there may be a large deficit of moisture during summer, there is considerable moisture available for leaching soils during the winter.

TABLE 8.1

Example of average monthly water-balance computation for Jerusalem Hills, Israel (in mm)

	J	F	M	A	M	J	J	A	S	O	N	D	Year
*ETP**	63	69	102	132	180	216	216	192	159	132	111	75	1647
P	153	143	68	23	3	0	0	0	0	9	62	89	550
ΔST	66	0	−34	−46	0	0	0	0	0	0	0	14	
ST	80	80	46	0	0	0	0	0	0	0	0	14	
ETA	63	69	102	69	3	0	0	0	0	9	62	75	452
D	0	0	0	63	177	216	216	192	159	123	49	0	1195
L	24	74	0	0	0	0	0	0	0	0	0	0	98

* *ETP*, potential evapotranspiration; *P*, precipitation; ΔST, soil-moisture utilization or recharge; *ST*, soil-moisture storage; *ETA*, actual evapotranspiration; *D*, water deficit; *L*, water available for leaching or run off. Experience shows that best values for *ETP* are obtained from standard open-pan evaporation measurements (U.S. Weather Bureau class A pan), sutiably reduced by a coefficient, 0.7, to account for exposure and screening. The water-balance calculations in each monthly column must satisfy the equations $P = ETA \pm \Delta ST + L$ and $ETP = ETA + D$.

Field measurements of seasonal variations in soil moisture provide the most comprehensive picture of the moisture regime. A basic grouping of moisture regimes is shown in Fig. 8.1. More detailed schemes and actual clas-sifications have been proposed by Russian and East European workers and there is now a growing tendency to use soil-moisture regime data to define soil taxa. The Soil Survey Staff (1975) has defined seven different soil moisture regimes: aquic, peraquic, udic, perudic, ustic, xeric, aridic and torric. Udic and perudic are essentially percolative regimes; ustic, aridic and xeric are subpercolative; aquic is amphipercolative; and peraquic is epiperco-lative. The USDA grouping is to a large extent based on the duration of the dry period rather than on the amount of moisture available for leaching or depth of wetting.

Moisture available for leaching (*L*) is that part of the rainfall (*P*) which is in excess of that lost by evapotranspiration (*ETA*) and that which satisfies the water holding capacity of the soil (*ST*). Hence (in mm):

$$L = P - ETA \pm \Delta ST$$

The shorter the time intervals used in the water-balance scheme, the more realistic the estimates for leaching becomes. In practice, monthly calcula-tions provide a satisfactory basis for evaluation of a soil-moisture regime. Besides monthly rainfall data (*P*), only potential evapotranspiration (*ETP*) and water storage capacity (*ST*) are necessary for such calculations.

Potential evapotranspiration, which is defined as the loss of water through evaporation and transpiration that would occur on a normally vegetated sur-face if an ample supply of water were always available, can be obtained by a number of methods. These include open-tank evaporation or estimations

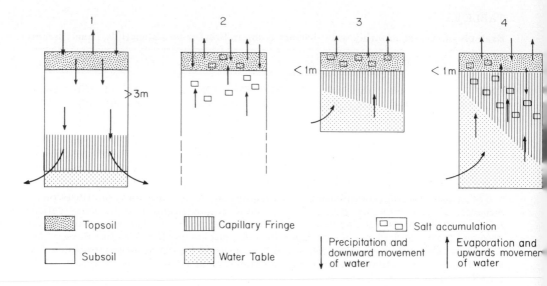

Fig. 8.1. Moisture regimes — percolative, subpercolative, epipercolative, and amphipercolative (after Yaalon, 1963).

Type of moisture regime	1 Normal percolative	2 Subpercolative	3 Epipercolative	4 Amphipercolative
Precipitation/ evaporation ratio	P≥E most of the year	E>P except for very short periods	E>P most of the year	Variable with season
Topography	Flat or sloping low land	Mostly flat	Flat bottomland	Flat bottomland
Permeability of subsoil	Good to moderate	None; dry subsoil	Poor	Poor to fair
Water table	Low	None; dry subsoil	Constantly high	Fluctuating with season
Moisture movement	Outflow of excess moisture	Evaporation of suspended water	Evaporation and ascending movement of imported water	Alternating down movement of imported water
Origin of salts	Weathered and air-borne sea salts leach through the soil profile	Imported by precipitation and released by weathering	Imported by inflowing water	Imported by inflowing water and precipitation
Mode of accumulation	Absorption of Na during possible leaching	At depth of wetting	At surface if water table at <1 m in subsoil if deeper	In subsoil at balance between evaporation and leaching

based on air temperature using suitable calculation and reduction factors. Actual evapotranspiration is obtained by considering the amounts of water stored in the soil.

Where no data are available on the water-holding capacity of the soil, it is commonly assumed to be 100 mm for an average soil. Actual values can vary with grainsize, clay mineralogy and organic-matter content from 50 mm or less on shallow and coarse-textured soils to over 150 mm on deep loamy soils. Actual estimates rather than mean regional values should be used whenever possible. The total amount of water passing any particular depth can also be calculated from this kind of data (Arkley, 1963) and is especially valuable if dissolution and depth of leaching is involved.

Udic—ustic boundary. The minimum amount of moisture needed for solum leaching is of great interest in pedogenesis and hydrology. In Soil Taxonomy (Soil Survey Staff, 1975), it represents roughly the boundary between udic and ustic moisture regimes; the latter commonly contributes to incomplete leaching of calcium carbonates from soil which results in the formation of calcic horizons. In the midcontinent of the United States, approximately 500 to 600 mm precipitation is necessary to adequately leach soil sola (Birkeland, 1974). In hydrology, it represents the boundary between regions with and without regional groundwater recharge. Seasonal rainfall distribution and temperature greatly affect the boundary. We shall exemplify it in

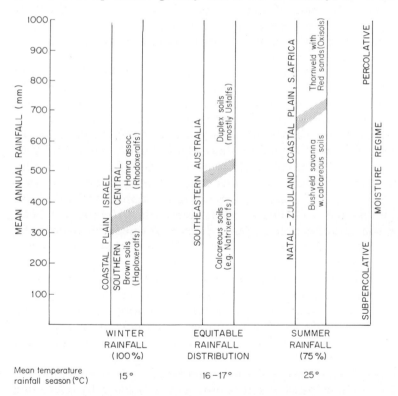

Fig. 8.2. Mean annual precipitation needed for leaching in three regions with different rainfall distribution and temperature. (Based on numerous soil survey maps and groundwater-recharge reports.)

three different regions with a winter, summer, and equitable rainfall distribution, Fig. 8.2.

In the Mediterranean region of Israel which experiences a considerable moisture deficit in the hot summer, a winter rainfall of over 350 mm is needed to produce some leaching and groundwater recharge. In southeastern Australia with its equitable rainfall all months of the year, about 500 mm is needed to produce some leaching. In the summer rainfall region of Natal, in South Africa, rainfall distribution produces a small winter moisture deficit and increases the amount necessary to produce some leaching to about 750 mm. In all three of these regions which have a large interannual rainfall variability, a distinct and fairly rapid rainfall gradient from the leaching to the non-leaching regimes is observed. The boundary is well reflected in the soil-distribution pattern.

Climofunctions. The annual moisture flux leaching the entire depth of the soil profile influences the type of diagnostic horizons that develop. Leaching may vary from 100 to 400 mm of water in percolative regimes of the cool and temperate zones characterized by soils with argillic, spodic or cambic horizons to several times these amounts in equatorial (superpercolative) regimes characterized by oxic horizons.

Intense leaching is accompanied by a shift in clay mineralogy from the dominance of smectites and vermiculites to that of kaolinite, Fig. 8.3 (Jackson, 1965; Barshad, 1966). Quantitative univariant soil-precipitation functions have also been derived for a number of other soil features, mainly organic matter and calcium carbonate (Jenny, 1941, 1979; Yaalon, 1975). Most climofunctions use mean annual rainfall as an index of climate and thus fail to take into account the monthly distribution as given in more meaningful water-balance data. However, the trends thus obtained generally provide supporting evidence for many qualitative trends and regional patterns of soil distribution being related to climate. Such trends have frequently been utilized in older soil classification systems or even formed the main parameter for their groupings. Reliance on distinct climate related trends is also evident in Soil Taxonomy (Soil Survey Staff, 1975).

It needs to be stressed that climofunctions, even the quantitative ones based on water balance, can not provide an explanation of the mechanisms or processes which have produced soil features. Climofunctions, like all other functions, only indicate the driving forces which govern or direct the processes. Actual mechanisms can only be inferred and should be elucidated independently.

Whereas soils with percolative and superpercolative moisture regimes are open systems with leaching losses of soil components (E) generally exceeding input (I) from weathering or other sources ($E > I$), the subpercolative regimes are essentially closed systems with internal redistribution only or with inputs exceeding losses ($E < I$). The redistribution of calcium carbonate

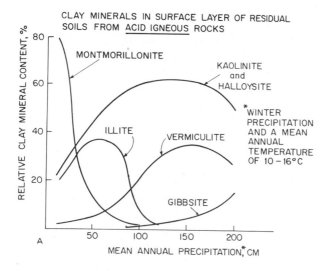

CLAY MINERALS IN SURFACE LAYER OF RESIDUAL
SOILS FROM ACID IGNEOUS ROCKS

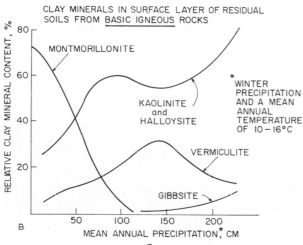

CLAY MINERALS IN SURFACE LAYER OF RESIDUAL
SOILS FROM BASIC IGNEOUS ROCKS

Fig. 8.3. Clay-mineral formation and distribution as function of precipitation (after Barshad, 1966).

and the formation of calcic horizons is one of the most prominent processes which characterize closed systems.

The relationship between depth of $CaCO_3$ accumulation and rainfall is best described by an exponential function between depth to the top of the calcic horizon and mean annual rainfall (Fig. 8.4). Due to the large variability in rainfall in deserts, there is some redistribution of $CaCO_3$ even in the most arid environments. The depth to free carbonates increases

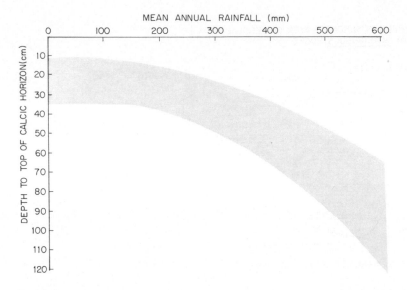

Fig. 8.4. Depth to the calcic horizon as a function of mean annual precipitation. (Based on profile data from Israel.) The general form of the statistically significant function (n = 83) is log $Z = a + bP$. A polynomial function (quadratic) gave an equally good fit (Yaalon, unpubl.).

exponentially with increasing rainfall until percolative leaching exceeds evapotranspiration and sufficient moisture is available for complete removal of $CaCO_3$.

In areas where airborne salts or dust constitute input, salts may accumulate in soils as salic, gypsic, or calcic horizons. Salts will reach a maximum accumulation in the root zone at the average depth of wetting. Due to varying solubilities, chloride, sulphate and carbonate accumulations will occur one above the other. However, occasional wet years or infrequent intensive rainfall of short duration may prevent excessive salinization and leach the salts below the root zone (Arkley, 1981).

In regions with inadequate climatic data, the effective rainfall can be estimated from the position of the maximum salt concentration (Yaalon, 1965):

$$Z = \frac{Pef \cdot Rm}{Wa}$$

where:

Z = depth to the peak concentration (cm);

Pef = effective precipitation (cm), i.e. precipitation not including days with rainfall less than evapotranspiration, or similar expression representing infiltration;

Rm = relative migration coefficient, 1.0 for chloride but <1 for other anions; and

Wa = fractional volume for available moisture, 0.1—0.5, depending on texture.

In areas where $ETA > P$, seasonal or permanent groundwater may supply water equivalent to the evapotranspiration (ETA) deficie. In such epipercolative moisture regimes, salts are likely to accumulate on the surface or a salic or gypsic horizon may be present above a calcic horizon. A moisture regime with alternatively moderate leaching and only a seasonally high groundwater table is called amphipercolative and is characterized by an irregular distribution of imported salts.

Other climatic parameters relevant to soil genesis

Temperature. Temperature or actually solar radiation, exerts a less evident influence on soil properties than precipitation. By far the largest portion of the incoming radiation is used for evapotranspiration. Thus the effect of temperature on pedogenesis, is mainly indirect; temperature controls the quantity of moisture available for soil-forming processes. By affecting the type of vegetation present at each site, temperature significantly affects the quantity and nature of organic residues added to the soil. The energy expended on heating soil, weathering processes and material transport is only a small fraction of the total energy reaching the soil surface. Yet even this relatively small quantity is crucial. It can safely be inferred that the rate of many soil processes is limited by the supply of incoming radiation (Yaalon, 1960; Volobuev, 1964).

Of particular interest in evaluating the effect of temperature on soil processes is its effect on the viscosity of soil moisture. Infiltration rates and hence soil-moisture fluxes are known to increase significantly with increased temperature (Shanan and Tadmor, 1979). Cumulative effects should be pedogenetically significant but an accurate evaluation of this effect in pedogenesis is still lacking. For several chronosequences in high latitudes, Bockheim (1980) obtained a significant positive correlation with mean annual temperature for such properties as depth of oxidation, solum thickness and B-horizon clay content; all of which could be attributed to better moisture infiltration.

The effect of soil temperature on chemical soil-forming processes is not well established. In general, the rate of chemical reactions increases exponentially with temperature, approximately doubling for each $10°C$ rise. Soil Taxonomy (Soil Survey Staff, 1975) recognizes four soil temperature classes — frigid, mesic, thermic and hyperthermic — based on the mean annual soil temperatures at 50 cm depth with two subclasses for the range of seasonal temperature differences.

The main impact of the different soil-temperature regimes is exerted through its effect on the biotic cycles and organic-matter content and quality. The apparent shift from the dominance of podzolization (chelation of iron compounds), prevailing in mesic regimes, to desilication and laterization, in thermic and hyperthermic regimes, is more than anything else due to the different nature or quality of organic matter and its decomposition products in combination with suitable parent material and moisture regimes.

Many differences in weathering rates attributed to temperature are more apparent than real. The concentration range of silica in soil solution and drainage waters (10–40 ppm SiO_2) is not significantly different in warm tropical than in temperate regions (Douglas, 1969) and does not attain the solubility of amorphous silica in either of them. Hence the rate of desilication in various climates is mainly a function of the amount of water available for leaching, as discussed above.

Both Ca^{2+} and HCO_3^- concentrations in groundwaters increase systematically with decreasing latitudes (Harmon et al., 1975; Smith and Atkinson, 1976). Decalcification rates, especially of limestone terrains, appear thus to be a function of soil temperature as more intensive biological activity increases Pco_2 of the system.

Wind. Wind is an important agent effecting the transport and distribution of suspended material (dust and aerosols) over large distances. Aerosols of marine salts are distributed from the coast inland: their concentration decreasing exponentially with distance from the sea coast (Yaalon and Lomas, 1970). In many coastal areas, the continuous and relatively high supply of sodium in rain water renders clay minerals more mobile and more easily eluviated even under relatively acid conditions resulting in rapid formation of argillic horizons (Muhs, 1982). In xeric and aridic moisture regimes, the airborne salts accumulate in the profile at the depth of moisture penetration (Eisenberg et al., 1982) and over a long period of time result in the salinization of Reg soils of stable desert surfaces (Yaalon, 1963; Dan and Yaalon, 1982).

The effect of wind-transported dust, mainly from desert sources or other unvegetated and unstable surfaces, is becoming increasingly recognized as an important modifying agent in soil development. Yaalon and Ganor (1973) distinguish between soils in which the addition becomes incorporated in the soil without altering the direction of soil formation, those in which the soil-forming process has been significantly affected, and those which "grow" upwards by additions of complete layers. Many Terra Rossa soils (Haploxeralfs) associated with hard limestone in the Mediterranean region belong to the first group whereas the second group can be exemplified by the Hamra sandy clay loams (Palexeralfs) of the Israeli coastal plain (Dan et al., 1968). While silt-size loess is the most common material transported and deposited by wind, a clayey loess, locally called parna, seems to be especially important in Australia where it has been redistributed over vast areas (Butler, 1974).

Slope orientation. Slope orientation (aspect) greatly affects the micro-climatic conditions of a slope. Due to variations in incoming radiation, precipitation amounts, rates of dust deposition and other factors the differences in aspect may result in marked differences in moisture regimes, vegetation and hence soil features. The effects are evident in all climatic regions, but perhaps most noticeable in the more extreme ones, the arctic and deserts, where moisture supply is critical (Zaidenberg et al., 1982). In temperate zones, e.g. the Harz forests, West Germany, the difference in runoff between north- and south-facing slopes may amount to 100 mm in the growing season, a significant factor for the rate of leaching (Van der Ploeg and Benecke, 1981).

Discontinuity of the input. A significant feature of the climatic factor in soil formation is its cyclic (rhythmic, periodic) nature and discontinuity of input events. Rainfall is distributed over a number of days with unequal precipitation intensity resulting in continuously changing moisture gradients in the soil. The diurnal or seasonal temperature changes are more regular, but the soil is forever either heating or cooling.

For practical purposes, the climatic parameters used in describing an environment are averages for a certain, often considerable length of time. When attributing soil properties to climatic factors, the diurnal, seasonal, or interannual trends (cf. Fig. 8.2) and their coefficients of variability may be more important than the average. Often it is not the mean climatic conditions which are relevant, but the less frequent ones but more extreme events which may control specific features of the soil or soil landscape.

TIME IN SOIL DEVELOPMENT

An appreciation of the time dimension is essential in any inquiry about soils. Energy and material inputs into soils act over a period of time producing continuous change from the time a new surface has been exposed or created by deposition, emergence, or volcanism. In general, soils acquire their properties over a long period of time, measured in hundreds and thousands of years. Soil features or diagnostic characteristics develop and change at variable rates.

Dynamic equilibrium

Many features of soil genesis may be interpreted in terms of the steady-state concept or dynamic equilibrium (Chapter 3). Inputs (I) of material and energy are balanced by outputs (E). Adjustment to change is in constant progress but seldom at a rate which would upset the dynamic equilibrium ($I = E$). That is changes with time are imperceptible but not necessarily non-existent.

When subjected to a drastic change in one of the determining factors, the system will reestablish a new steady state. Soil properties can be suitably grouped into those which approach the steady state relatively rapidly

($<10^3$ yrs) and those which approach it slowly ($>10^3$ yrs; Yaalon, 1971a). The accumulation of organic matter in a mollic epipedon or the formation of slickensides in Vertisols provide examples of the former whereas an argillic or oxic horizon may take a long time to reach the steady state (Fig. 8.5). Frequently the initial rate of change may be rapid, but gradually becomes asymptotic. Thus the factor of time essentially becomes ineffective even though the terminal state may not yet have been reached.

Because of the inevitable fluctuations in the driving force of pedogenesis (radiation, precipitation, gravity, biological pressure), a lag in adjustment is always present. For example, in response to the daily or annual temperature wave, the soil is always either being heated or cooled and there is a constant temperature flux in the soil. In a similar way, other reactions in the soil will be subject to continuous fluxes and readjustment.

Feedback systems

The complex response of soils to the governing driving forces can be treated as a feedback system. Negative or self-regulating feedbacks tend to moderate or dampen the effect of a process or change in the external conditions until a new level is reached. All buffered and many other chemical processes in the soil system tending toward steady state belong in such a category.

Positive or self-enhancing feedback processes amplify a change within the system, generally until a limiting value halts the process or until the system becomes regulated by another set of feedbacks. Many soil-erosion processes fall into this category (Torrent and Nettleton, 1978). Another example is decreasing permeability due to clay accumulation. Each increment of illuviated clay in the B horizon causes additional plugging of pores with the horizon eventually becoming impermeable until gleying processes establish another set of feedbacks.

Self-terminating processes

Self-terminating processes are those in which the balance of input and output is not maintained and which do not tend toward a steady state. Processes with gains greater than losses ($I > E$) or gains less than losses ($I < E$) are both included in this category. An example of losses exceeding gains occurs in the hyperpercolative moisture regime which yields a deep, highly weathered oxic horizon. Conversely the desert environment with a subpercolative moisture regime provides an example where gains exceed losses. Desert soils act as a sink for material released and introduced from the outside. Thus calcic, gypsic and petrocalcic horizons are produced by such self-terminating processes. The rate of change effected by self-terminating processes generally decreases with time.

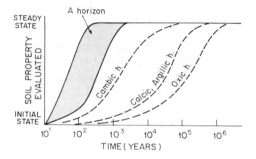

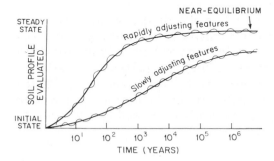

Fig. 8.5. Schematic curves for chronofunctions (after Yaalon, 1971a; and Birkeland, 1974).

Chronofunctions

The time necessary for soil systems to reach steady state may be obtained from plots of the variation of soil features with time (Fig. 8.5). The S-shaped or logistic curve seems best adapted to express chronofunctions.

After overcoming the initial threshold barrier for initiating each process, rates of change are frequently fairly rapid, but gradually decrease with time, becoming asymptotic, indicating little visible change thereafter with time (Fig. 8.5). In general, the position of a soil property on such a curve is established by comparative studies which use a spatial sequence separated in time with all other factors being held constant.

Using quantitative data for 15 soil properties from 32 chronosequences which were available from the literature, Bockheim (1980) calculated a linear regression, with time as log, which best fits most of the data. The properties include pH, base saturation, bulk density, solum thickness, oxidation depth, B-horizon clay and salt content, and properties related to organic-matter content. Bockheim's regression curves essentially represent the second portion of the S-shaped curve, after its inflection point, from the most rapid rate of change toward the gradually decreasing, asymptotic rate of change. Some properties reached a maximum, then decreased with further time. This also applies to soil phosphorus and its distribution among the various silt fractions (Walker and Syers, 1976).

Even though the equations indicate a continuous change, these chrono-sequences do not negate the trend toward a gradually imperceptible rate of change, i.e. the trend toward dynamic equilibrium (steady state). However, the equations do demonstrate the difficulty in quantitatively assessing these functions. A soil profile does not really exhibit a simple numerical age, but a developmental history, the duration of its exposure to soil-forming factors.

A rating and integration of several morphological features into a relative profile-development rating makes use of observed changes in the field, and is thus useful for non-parametric data (Meixner and Singer, 1981).

Because of the inevitable fluctuations in some of the parameters in the past and because of the numerous difficulties in identifying well-dated pedomorphic surfaces, such curves or ratings are at best only approximate and subject to improvement. Nevertheless, they are particularly useful in evaluating the possible resistance of a property to change and in elucidating the environments of ancient soils. Difficulties and limitations in selecting suitable sites for chronosequences have been discussed and pointed out by Stevens and Walker (1970) and Vreeken (1975).

Dating methods

Methods of dating soils or rather the time of the development of certain soil features include all those methods in general use in the earth sciences. Great accuracy in actual dates is neither required nor attainable. Hence stratigraphic criteria and relationships, supported by radiometric, archaeo-logical, or other methods, is the most frequent method used for dating a chronosequence. It should be attempted wherever possible (Vita Finzi, 1973). Only in the case of soil organic matter or pedogenic carbonates can we measure radiometrically actual soil properties. However, such dates more closely reflect turn-over times of humus rather than duration of pedogenesis (cf. Yaalon, 1971b).

Process rates

The rate of change of rock-weathering features decreases with time (Colman, 1981). It becomes constant when an equilibrium thickness of the weathering residue is reached. In empirical expressions of weathering rates, logarithmic functions, $\Delta S / \Delta \log t$, are commonly obtained and only where a dynamic steady state can be assumed can a linear function, $\Delta S / \Delta t$, be used.

Soil scientists have for many years measured rates of soil erosion on ex-perimental plots and equated it to rates of denudation on a watershed or a re-gional basin scale, including local sediment retention. Weathering at the rock—soil interface will replace the soil material removed by erosion. In a steady-state system, rates of erosion and weathering will attain equal values. Numerous measurements of such rates by geomorphologists (e.g. Douglas, 1969) indicate ranges from 10—100 μm yr^{-1} with 20—40 μm yr^{-1} as a model value. In an analogous way, rates of clay formation or $CaCO_3$ build-up in the profile can be calculated. Netterberg (1982) reports a range of 4—20 μm yr^{-1} as being representative for $CaCO_3$ accumulation in calcic horizons.

In general, these rates are in good agreement with the mean rates of many geological processes related to sedimentation in the Quaternary (Kukal, 1970). This lends support to the use of clay or $CaCO_3$ build-up for calculation of the age of a soil where alternative criteria are absent. Rate data are frequently needed as input in simulation studies, for example, in nutrient supply or slope development studies (Kirby, 1977), and will no doubt be needed when a computer simulation of soil genesis is attempted to estimate the time needed for attainment of a certain development stage.

THE CHANGING HISTORY OF PEDOMORPHIC SURFACES

Soil formation is seldom a uniform unidirectional process through time. Minor fluctuations in environmental conditions are a built-in characteristic of the system resulting in constant readjustment. Major adjustments are required in response to major changes in the driving forces of pedogenesis, due to changes in climate, relative sea level, tectonic and volcanic activity, or biological pressure. Periods of landscape stability alternate with periods of landscape instability. All such changes are recorded in the history of soils through geologic time (Yaalon, 1961; Daniels et al., 1971).

Climatic changes were particularly intensive during the Quaternary as a result of the advances and retreats of the polar and mountain glaciers. Temperature changes of up to 15°C in the higher latitudes near the glaciers (less in mid- and lower latitudes) with attendant changes in the wind circulation, precipitation, and moisture regimes accompanied the glaciations. Each time the ice sheets advanced, sea level fell by up to 150 m and the world's arid zones expanded beyond their present margins. Precipitation was lower than today in parts of the tropics, but higher in the subtropics during certain phases of the glacial cycle. The climatic belts of the mid-latitudes and higher were telescoped and pushed southward, but the attendant changes in the tropics and desert regions may not have been in step with the changes in the higher latitudes. Overall, the duration of the glacial and thus drier periods were three to four times longer than the duration of the interglacial periods.

In Europe and North America, the retreating glaciers have left a legacy of highly varied landforms largely covered with thick glacial drift, outwash sand, or periglacial loess. Within a relatively short time after the postglacial warming ($< 10,000$ yrs), a variety of well-differentiated soils (Spodosols, Alfisols, Mollisols) have formed.

In Africa, Australia and South America there are, on the other hand, large tracts of the stable crystalline shields which exhibit surfaces exposed to continuous weathering since the Tertiary. Some of the deeply and intensively weathered surfaces and their soils (Ultisols, Oxisols) may date back at least 2 m.y. (Finkl and Fairbridge, 1979). In many of these soils, some of the features may be acquired by contemporaneous processes, while others are inherited from the past.

Though Entisols and Aridisols are the most prevalent soils in arid and semi-arid landscapes, many of the Aridisols in the large deserts of Africa, Asia, and North America have diagnostic horizons (calcic, gypsic) and features which reflect accumulation and stability over a long period of time going back to the Pleistocene and pre-Pleistocene. Such features often attain a state of minimal change and are characterized by duricrusts.

In mountain landscapes with steep slopes, Inceptisols are common. They are often considered to be young and undeveloped. Though often shallow and weakly differentiated, many Inceptisols are, in fact, in steady state with their steep-slope environment. Such Inceptisols are subject to relatively rapid renewal and will exhibit similar properties as long as the environmental conditions persist.

Vertisols occur in seasonally dry—wet climates on lowland clay plains or basaltic plateaus. They reach steady state rapidly and undergo little perceptible additional change even on surfaces which are extremely old.

Thus the soil pattern in any region or landscape is a complex one. Landscapes consist of soils approaching the steady state and of soils which do not tend toward steady state. Both monogenetic and polygenetic soils frequently occur, the latter preserving some information of the environmental conditions of the past. The impact of the various climatic phases cannot, however, be easily separated in such polygenetic soils. Only where the present environment has not changed the previously acquired features, as for example in Australia where strongly leached Tertiary soils now occur in a desert climate, are such relict features easily recognizable (Mulcahy and Churchward, 1973; Finkl and Fairbridge, 1979).

In many cases, geologic events buried the soils. Burial generally alters soil features, but the preserved features of buried soils bear the best evidence of the environmental conditions of past landscapes. Preserved features have provided one of the major tools for unravelling some of the complex Quaternary climatic fluctuations. Collectively, all the buried and non-buried soils of past landscapes are called *paleosols* and form the subject matter of paleopedology, a subdiscipline of pedology (Yaalon, 1971b).

In the geologic past, the spectrum of soils present may not have necessarily been the same as we know today. Only since land plants spread widely, some 400 m.y. ago (Devonian), can we even expect all the modern kinds of soils. Prior to this, an evolution of the weathering processes took place as the terrestrial environment changed from a reducing one to an oxidizing one producing protosols and primitive soil. With the introduction of life, organic residues were introduced. Decomposition products of these organic materials first resulted in incipient soils and finally, following the spread of flowering land plants, in the horizonation of soils as we know it today (Yaalon, 1961).

SUMMARY

In summary, this chapter shows that a complex system such as a pedon and its features are the results of evolutionary history with variable rates for the numerous processes. Climatic or paleoclimatic interpretation is feasible by carefully considering all the climatic factors and driving forces. It is essential that interpretations are preceded or accompanied by detailed studies of soil morphology. Soils were not always what they are now, nor will they forever remain so. Estimating the rate or time interval over which soil acquired its morphology is an important and corollary part of understanding the distribution of soils in a landscape.

ACKNOWLEDGEMENT

I wish to thank W.B. Bull (Univ. of Arizona) and P.H. Walker (CSIRO, Canberra) for reading the manuscript and offering useful comments.

REFERENCES

Arkley, R.J., 1963. Calculation of carbonate and water movement in soil from climate data. Soil Sci., 96: 239—248.
Arkley, R.J., 1981. The genesis of desert soils in relation to climate and airborne salts. Abstracts Int. Conf on Aridic Soils, ISSS Comm. V—VI and Israel Soc. Soil Sci., pp. 6—7.
Barshad, I., 1966. The effect of a variation in precipitation on the nature of clay mineral formation in soils from basic and acid igneous rocks. Proc. Int. Clay Conference, Jerusalem, 1: 167—173.
Birkeland, P.W., 1974. Pedology, Weathering and Geomorphological Research. Oxford University Press, Oxford, 285 pp.
Bockheim, J.G., 1980. Solution and use of chronofunctions in studying soil development. Geoderma, 24: 71—85.
Butler, B.E., 1974. A contribution towards the better specification of parna and some aeolian clays in Australia. In: A.P. Schick, D.H. Yaalon and A. Yair (Editors), Geomorphic Processes in Arid Environments. Zeitschr. Geomorphol., Suppl., 20: 106—116.
Colman, S.M., 1981. Rock-weathering rates as function of time. Quat. Res., 15: 250—264.
Dan, J. and Yaalon, D.H., 1968. Pedomorphic forms and pedomorphic surfaces. Trans. 9th Int. Congress Soil Science, Adelaide, N.S.W., 4: 577—584.
Dan, J. and Yaalon, D.H., 1982. Automorphic saline soils in Israel. In: D.H. Yaalon (Editor), Aridic Soils and Geomorphic Processes. Catena Suppl., 1: 103—105.
Dan, J., Yaalon, D.H. and Koyumdjisky, H., 1968. Catenary soil relationships in Israel, 1: the Netanya catena on coastal dunes of the Sharon. Geoderma, 2: 95—120.

250

Daniels, R.B., Gamble, E.E. and Cady, J.G., 1971. The relationship between geomorphology and soil morphology and genesis. Adv. Agron., 23: 51—88.

Douglas, I., 1969. The efficiency of humid tropical denudation systems. Inst. Brit. Geogr. Trans., 46: 1—16.

Eisenberg, R., Dan, J. and Koyumdjisky, H., 1982. Relationship between moisture penetration and salinity in soils of the northern Negev (Israel). Geoderma, 28: 313—344.

Finkl Jr., J.W. and Fairbridge, R.W., 1979. Paleogeographic evolution of the rifted cratonic margins of southwestern Australia. Palaeogeogr., Palaeoclimatol., Palaeoecol., 25: 221—252.

Harmon, R.S., White, W.B., Drake, J.J. and Hess, J.W., 1975. Regional hydrochemistry of North American carbonate terrains. Water Resour. Res., 11: 963—967.

Jackson, M.L., 1965. Clay transformation in soil genesis during the Quaternary. Soil Sci., 99: 15—22.

Jenny, H., 1941. Factors of Soil Formation. McGraw-Hill, New York, N.Y., 281 pp.

Jenny, H., 1979. The Soil Resource — Origin and Behaviour. Springer, New York, N.Y., 377 pp.

Kirkby, M.J., 1976. Hydrological slope models — the influence of climate. In: E. Derbyshire (Editor), Geomorphology and Climate. Wiley, London, pp. 247—267.

Kirkby, M.J., 1977. Soil development models as a component of slope processes. Earth Surface Process., 2: 203—230.

Kukal, Z., 1970. Geology of Recent Sediments. Academic Press, London, 490 pp.

Meixner, R.E. and Singer, M.J., 1981. Use of a field morphology rating system to evaluate soil formation and discontinuities. Soil Sci., 131: 114—123.

Muhs, D.R., 1982. A soil chronosequence on Quaternary marine terraces, San Clemente Island, California. Geoderma, 28: 252—283.

Mulcahy, M.J. and Churchward, H.M., 1973. Quaternary environments in Australia. Soil Sci., 116: 156—169.

Netterberg, F., 1982. Optimum moisture regimes of calcrete formation from water balance considerations and radio-carbon dates. Geoderma (in prep.).

Shanan, L. and Tadmor, N.H., 1979. Microcatchment Systems for Arid Zone Development: a Handbook for Design and Construction. Center of Int. Agricultural Cooperation, Israel Ministry of Agriculture, Rehovot, 99 pp.

Smith, D.I. and Atkinson, T.C., 1976. Process, landforms and climate in limestone regions. In: E. Derbyshire (Editor), Geomorphology and Climate. Wiley, London, pp. 367—409.

Soil Survey Staff, 1975. Soil Taxonomy. U.S. Dept. of Agric., Soil Conservation Service, Handbook 436. Washington, D.C., 754 pp.

Stevens, P.R. and Walker, T.W., 1970. The chronosequence concept and soil formation. Q. Rev. Biol., 45: 333—350.

Torrent, J. and Nettleton, W.D., 1978. Feedback processes in soil genesis. Geoderma, 20: 281—287.

Van der Ploeg, R.R. and Benecke, P., 1981. Evaluation of one- and two-dimensional water flow models and field validation of unsaturated flow. In: I.K. Iskandar (Editor), Modelling Waste Water Renovation — Land Treatment. Wiley, London, pp. 92—114.

Vita-Finzi, C., 1973. Recent Earth History. Macmillan, London.

Volobuev, V.R., 1964. Ecology of Soils. Israel Program for Scientific Translations, Jerusalem. (Translated from Russian.)

Vreeken, W.J., 1975. Principal kinds of chronosequences and their significance in soil history. J. Soil Sci., 26: 378—394.

Walker, T.W. and Syers, J.K., 1976. The fate of phosphorus during pedogenesis. Geoderma, 15: 1—19.

Yaalon, D.H., 1960. Some implications of fundamental concepts of pedology in soil classification. Trans. 7th Int. Congress Soil Science, Madison, Wisc., 4: 119—123.

Yaalon, D.H., 1961. Weathering and soil development through geologic time. Bull. Res. Counc. Israel, 11G: 149—150.

Yaalon, D.H., 1963. On the origin and accumulation of salts in groundwater and in soils of Israel. Bull. Res. Counc. Israel, 11G: 105—131.

Yaalon, D.H., 1965. Downward movement and distribution of anions in soil profiles with limited wetting. In: E.G. Hallsworth and D.V. Crawford (Editors), Experimental Pedology. Butterworths, London, pp. 157—164.

Yaalon, D.H., 1971a. Soil forming processes in time and space. In: D.H. Yaalon (Editor), Paleopedology — Origin, Nature and Dating of Paleosols. Int. Soc. Soil Sci. and Israel Universities Press, Jerusalem, pp. 29—39.

Yaalon, D.H., 1971b. Paleopedology — Origin, Nature and Dating of Paleosols. Int. Soc. Soil Sci. and Israel Universities Press, Jerusalem, 350 pp.

Yaalon, D.H., 1975. Conceptual models of pedogenesis: can soil forming functions be solved? Geoderma, 15: 189—205.

Yaalon, D.H. and Ganor, E., 1973. The influence of dust on soils during the Quaternary. Soil Sci., 116: 146—155.

Yaalon, D.H. and Lomas, J., 1970. Some factors controlling the supply and the chemical composition of aerosols in a nearshore and coastal environment. Agric. Meteorol., 7: 443—453.

Zaidenberg, R., Dan, J. and Koyumdjisky, H., 1982. The influence of parent material, relief and exposure on soil formation in the arid region of eastern Samaria. In: D.H. Yaalon (Editor), Aridic Soils and Geomorphic Processes. Catena Suppl., Cremlingen, 1: 117—139.

HYDROLOGY AND SOIL GENESIS OF SOILS WITH AQUIC MOISTURE REGIMES

J. BOUMA

INTRODUCTION

Drainage classes have been widely used in soil survey to characterize the wetness of soils and the fluctuations of the water table during the year. Classes are defined in terms of the estimated rate of removal of water from the soil (Soil Survey Staff, 1951). According to such estimates, *very poorly drained* soils have a water table at or near the soil surface the greater part of the time and *poorly drained* soils for a considerable part of the time, whereas *somewhat poorly drained* soils are wet for significant periods, but not all of the time. *Moderately well drained* soils are wet for small but significant periods. These classifications are qualitative in nature and are subject to varying interpretations. Nevertheless, such distinctions have proved to be meaningful for humid moderate climates. More recent definitions of soil-moisture regimes used physically well-defined criteria to define the range of moisture contents to be expected during the year (Soil Survey Staff, 1975). According to these definitions a soil horizon is considered to be "dry" if water is held at pressure potentials lower than -15 bar, and "moist" at potentials between -15 bar and zero (saturation). A soil horizon is considered to be saturated with water when water stands in an unlined borehole close enough to the top surface of the horizon in question, so that the capillary fringe reaches the top of the horizon. The capillary fringe describes a zone in which the soil is still saturated despite negative pressure potentials which do not yet exceed the air-entry value. *Aquic moisture regimes*, as recently defined (Soil Survey Staff, 1975), are characterized by saturation with water for periods long enough to cause reducing conditions in the entire soil or in lower horizons.

Distinctions of drainage classes and different soil-moisture regimes, as discussed, are based on field experience and on measurements made in selected study areas. Direct physical measurements, though possible, are complicated and costly, certainly for unsaturated moisture conditions. Moreover, monitoring should cover periods of several years to allow the evaluation of the effect of a wide range of natural weather conditions. These technical and operational problems can perhaps partly explain the widespread use of soil morphological features, such as mottling and gleying as indicators for the long-range soil-moisture regime. These features can be easily observed in many soils and are a reflection of the accumulated effects of the soil-moisture regime and associated intermittent reduction and oxidation processes over long periods of time. However, the desired proper interpretation of such morphological features requires a thorough understanding of chemical processes which determine soil genesis in poorly drained soils *and* of relevant physical characteristics and boundary conditions which govern water movement under both saturated and unsaturated conditions. Emphasis in chemical studies for these soils has often been on the effect of reduction and oxidation processes with a focus on iron and manganese compounds since these result in visible morphological features, which have been widely used for predicting soil-moisture regimes. However, other chemical and mineralogical changes, which do not necessarily result in visible features, are also induced by periodic soil saturation, thereby affecting soil properties and soil limitations for different uses. Determining the latter is important when soil-survey data are used for interpretive purposes. The soil-moisture regime, as such, governs physical soil conditions and thereby soil limitations for a wide variety of agricultural and non-agricultural soil uses.

Knowledge about measured or estimated *natural* soil-moisture regimes can be inadequate when not only soil limitations have to be determined for a given use, but also their potential and the means to achieve it. This aspect becomes increasingly relevant for soil-survey interpretations (McCormack, 1974). For example, realizing the use potential of a poorly drained soil by applying reclamation techniques involves drastic changes in natural soil-moisture regimes and associated chemical conditions. The study of such measures is generally considered to be beyond the scope of soil genesis, morphology and classification (soil survey), and will therefore not be discussed further in this chapter. However, valuable contributions can and should be made by soil survey when predicting, evaluating and extrapolating results of reclamation measures, which have, after all, the aim to realize whatever use potential a soil may have (Bouma, 1973, 1977).

Considering these aspects, the aim of this chapter, which is focused on soils with an aquic moisture regime, (poorly drained soils) is to: (1) discuss soil genesis and resulting soil properties of soils with an aquic moisture regime in terms of physical and associated chemical processes; and (2) evaluate the significance of some selected soil morphological features in terms of their ability to predict the soil-moisture regime. Topics to be discussed were selected to be supplementary to existing reviews. For example, an international conference on Pseudogley and Gley has brought together many data on the types of soil to be discussed in this chapter (Schlichting and Schwertmann, 1973).

THE PHYSICAL CHARACTERIZATION OF THE SOIL-MOISTURE REGIME

Introduction

Soil saturation with water may result from a variety of flow regimes. Soils with aquic moisture regimes are often found in valleys surrounded by hills. In such areas, water infiltrates into the soils of the hills and comes to the surface in the valley. The corresponding streamlines are schematically shown in Fig. 9.1. This pattern assumes adequate opportunity for infiltration and downward percolation in the upland soils, allowing only minor runoff. Soils should have no slowly permeable subsoil horizons which could induce lateral flow and surface seepage downslope. Flow systems in watersheds have been extensively studied by hydrologists, emphasizing runoff, infiltration, flow patterns in the groundwater, prediction of flood peaks, minimum low flows to be expected, etc. (Amerman, 1973).

The streamlines in Fig. 9.1 indicate the presence of a water table in the wet valley soils which is fed from below and which may rise to a larger extent than could be explained by a very local water balance considering runoff, runon, precipitation and evapotranspiration. The same is true for the drawdown of the water table in soils of higher elevations. This aspect is being emphasized in the West German soil classification system where "Pseudogleys" and "Gleys" are distinguished not only on the basis of morphometric wetness criteria, as such, but also on the basis of landscape position (Schlich-

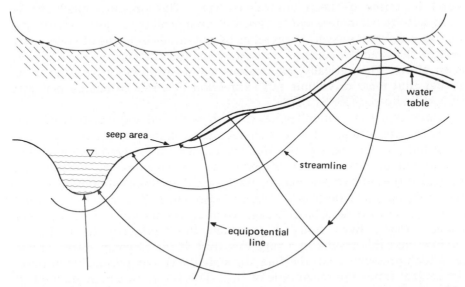

Fig. 9.1. Cross section of a hypothetical hydrological system in a landscape with equipotential lines and streamlines for a relatively dry period (after Amerman, 1973).

ting, 1973). The groundwater aquifer may form one continuous body of water with a fluctuating upper surface, where the water is at atmospheric pressure. This upper surface is called the water table. On the other hand, perched water tables may form on top of slowly permeable horizons which cover more permeable, unsaturated horizons with a water table at greater depth. Depth to water table during the year is part of the legend of soil maps in The Netherlands (Van Heesen, 1970).

Emphasis in the following sections will be on the moisture regime within the solum where pedogenesis has been active and where plants grow (Soil Survey Staff, 1975).

Water movement through soil: a brief review

Water movement through porous media is governed by the basic law of Darcy which states that the flux of water is proportional to the gradient of the hydraulic potential, as follows:

$$q = -K \cdot \frac{\mathrm{d}H}{\mathrm{d}z} = -K \cdot \frac{\mathrm{d}(h + z)}{\mathrm{d}z} \tag{1}$$

where q = flux of water (m^3 m^{-2} s^{-1} = m s^{-1}); K = hydraulic conductivity (m s^{-1}) (K_{sat} is K for saturated soil), and $\mathrm{d}H/\mathrm{d}z$ is gradient of the hydraulic potential (m m^{-1}). The hydraulic potential may be expressed as a hydraulic head (H) in terms of energy per unit weight (m) and is composed of the pressure potential and the gravitational potential, which may also both be expressed in terms of head equivalents (m). The pressure head (h) is measured with tensiometers and the gravitational head (z) is determined by a distance to a reference level. Expression of potentials in terms of energy per unit weight is attractive because it results in simple dimensions for K and q, as shown above. Theoretically, expressions should preferably be in terms of energy per unit mass or volume but expression in terms of energy per unit weight is still allowed (ISSS, 1976).

The Darcy equation, which applies to both saturated and unsaturated soil, illustrates the importance of K as a characteristic *constant*, at any particular water content, which defines the flux at unit hydraulic gradient. K allows the calculation of a wide range of fluxes at a given moisture content as a function of different hydraulic gradients imposed by physical boundary conditions. For example, a permeable horizon with a high K_{sat} may be saturated for a long time with (stagnant) water when it occurs on top of a slowly permeable horizon. Even though K_{sat} is high, the gradient of the hydraulic head is low, and this results in a very low flux. If the stagnant water on top creates a high-pressure head, the flux through the slowly permeable horizon may be several times the magnitude of K_{sat}. This is due to a high gradient of the hydraulic head, particularly when the slowly permeable horizon is thin.

The hydraulic conductivity K drops strongly as the moisture content of

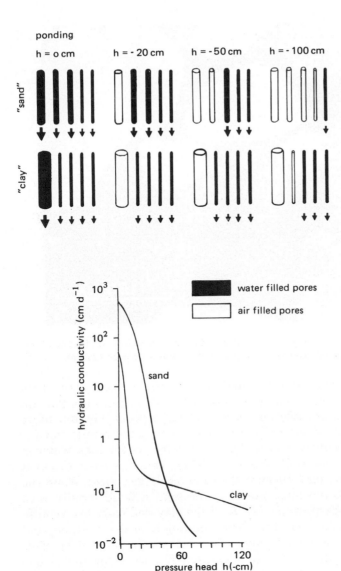

Fig. 9.2. Schematic capillary pore models which demonstrate different hydraulic conductivity (K) values of saturated and unsaturated "sand" (upper diagram) and "clay" (lower diagram). Measured K curves for a coarse sand (C horizon Plainfield loamy sand) and clay (B_g horizon of a dutch Fluvaquent) are included.

the soil decreases. Both K_{sat} and the drop of K are a function of the pore-size distribution and are therefore characteristically different among soils. This phenomenon is illustrated in Fig. 9.2, where a series of capillary tubes

Fig. 9.3. Thin section image of coarse sand particles in the C horizon of the Plainfield loamy sand. The porosity consists entirely of simple packing voids between grains.

represents a relatively coarse porous sand and a fine porous clay. Thin section images of corresponding real soil materials are shown in Figs. 9.3 and 9.4. Two basic properties are relevant here: (1) large pores conduct more water, at a given gradient of the hydraulic head, than small pores; and (2) water in small pores is retained with a higher capillary energy than water in large pores (e.g. Baver et al., 1972; Bouma, 1977). The K_{sat} of the sand is higher than the K_{sat} of the clay because the sand has larger pores. When the soil becomes unsaturated, the large pores in the sand will fill rapidly with air, and this results in a sharp drop of K. K of the clay decreases less rapidly and may become even higher than the corresponding K of the sand, beyond a certain negative pressure head (which is -50 cm in Fig. 9.2). This phenomenon is further illustrated with measured K curves for the coarse sandy C horizon of the Plainfield loamy sand and a clay horizon of a dutch alluvial soil (Fig. 9.2). Desaturation of soil may, in general, be due to application rates of water which are lower than K_{sat} or to surface crusting, which does not allow flow into the larger soil pores.

Unsteady flow systems, where hydraulic gradients and moisture contents vary with time, can also be described by the Darcy equation if an equation of continuity is added. Detailed derivations and an analysis of these equations is beyond the scope of this text, the more so since many references are available (e.g. Hillel, 1971; Baver et al., 1972; Klute, 1973; ISSS, 1976; Bouma, 1977).

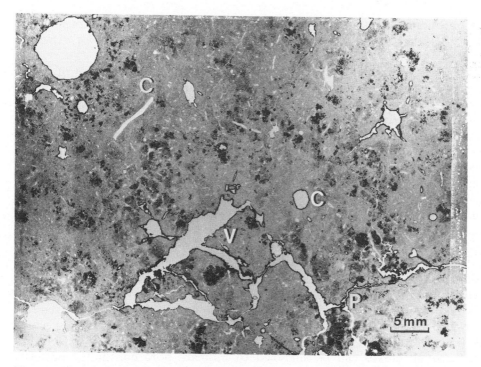

Fig. 9.4. Thin section image of the B_g horizon of a dutch alluvial clay soil (Typic Fluvaquent). The porosity is composed of very fine simple packing voids between the clay particles in the (gray) aggregates and larger structural pores, such as vughs (V), channels (C) and planar voids (P). Pore continuity in the soil sample was characterized by using blue dye, as shown here by dark-colored walls of voids (Bouma et al., 1979).

The Darcy equation should theoretically only be applied under isothermal conditions to idealized, homogeneous and isotropic porous media that do not swell (Klute, 1973). For example, K_{sat} in swelling soils is undefined as it decreases upon continuing saturation and associated swelling (Bouma and Wösten, 1979). Flow theory for swelling soils, which is quite complex, is being developed (e.g. Klute, 1973; Smiles, 1976; Sposito, 1976).

Darcy flow theory focuses on transport of liquid in terms of fluxes. In this context, it is not important whether transport occurs through only a few or through many pores within a given volume of soil. However, movement through only a few (large) pores implies short travel times and, for example, little opportunity for cation adsorption in the soil. Knowing flow *patterns* is therefore important for interpreting adsorption and leaching phenomena which are essential for pedogenesis and for many practical aspects of soil behavior.

The flux term of the Darcy equation represents the rate of movement of a water surface. The "real" velocity of water inside the soil pores is on the average higher due to the presence of the solid phase. An "average" flow velocity (v) inside the soil pores can be estimated as follows: $v = q/\theta$, where θ is the volumetric moisture content ($m^3\ m^{-3}$).

The average flow velocity (v) does not allow reliable estimates of travel times in natural, heterogeneous soils which have continuous planar voids ("cracks"), channels ("root and wormholes") and other structural pores which are larger than the packing pores between the individual soil particles. Flow phenomena are then governed by soil-structure characteristics (Bouma, 1981). For example, preferential flow of water along relatively large soil pores ("macropores") has been either observed or deduced from measurements in several studies. Use of dyes allows direct visual observations as to where the water has moved (Aubertin, 1971; Kissel et al., 1973; Anderson and Bouma, 1973; Bouma et al., 1977). The conductivity at saturation is determined by only a few continuous pores (which contribute little to the total porosity) whereas slow flow through the remaining fine pores hardly contributes to the overall volume of water that can be conducted by the soil (Bouma and Anderson, 1973). The number and the sizes of stained pores, as measured in thin sections (Fig. 9.4), can be used to calculate K_{sat} of clay soils (Bouma et al., 1979). Measuring chloride or tritium contents in the soil after infiltration of such solutions can indicate how deep, and where water has moved (Blake et al., 1973; Quisenberry and Phillips, 1976). Chloride breakthrough curves can be analyzed to indicate pore continuity patterns and to show that a significant portion of the soil volume is by-passed as water flows through macropores around peds (Elrick and French, 1966; Kissel et al., 1973; Cassel et al., 1974, 1975; Anderson and Bouma, 1977a, b; Bouma and Dekker, 1978).

A distinction can be made between rates of water movement within different pores of a soil which has one particular moisture content, and rapid downward movement of free water along continuous, air-filled voids in unsaturated soil. The latter phenomenon has been called "short-circuiting" (Bouma et al., 1978), while the former phenomenon can generally be described by dispersion theory.

The considerations of this section are of more than academic interest. Soils with aquic moisture regimes are saturated for a significant period of time during the year, but the water table is generally lower in the growing season. This implies frequent vertical and lateral movement of water in saturated and unsaturated soil. Soil genesis is strongly affected by such patterns of water movement.

Use of breakthrough curves to characterize flow patterns in soils

Many recent publications testify to the fact that breakthrough curves are increasingly used as a tool in soil research. The following discussion is therefore only a general introduction, intended for pedologists (see also Bouma, 1977).

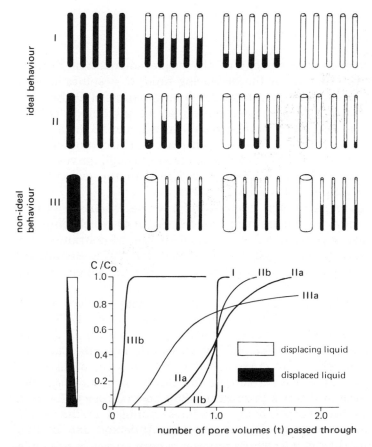

Fig. 9.5. Schematic capillary pore models and breakthrough curves, as examples of different types of hydrodynamic dispersion showing "ideal" and "non-ideal" behavior (see text).

Breakthrough curves are determined in soil columns by replacing untraced liquid (usually water) with a solution containing known concentrations of a tracer. The tracer may or may not be adsorbed by the soil. Chlorides are often used as a tracer which is not adsorbed. The column effluent is monitored in terms of volume and tracer concentration as a function of the accumulated volume of liquid which leaves the column. The latter is commonly expressed as a fraction (t) of the entire volume of (untraced) water which was initially present (Fig. 9.5).

Breakthrough curves can often be mathematically described in terms of an apparent dispersion coefficient (D), but only if the curve expresses "ideal" behavior. Then, the following equation applies (e.g. Brenner, 1962; Rose and Passioura, 1971; Cassel et al., 1974):

$$\frac{\delta C}{\delta T} + v \cdot \frac{\delta C}{\delta X} = D \cdot \frac{\delta^2 C}{\delta X^2} \qquad (2)$$

where: T = time from commencement of the displacement; X = distance from the point of introduction of the displacing fluid; C = solute concentration. Use of tables and graphs facilitates the determination of D (Brenner, 1962). When D is known, breakthrough curves can be predicted. This, in turn, allows predictions of the time to first breakthrough and to the moment when all initially present liquid has been displaced. Unfortunately, the mathematical analysis is more complicated when breakthrough curves do not show "ideal" behavior, and this is the rule rather than the exception in natural soils (Van Genuchten and Wierenga, 1976).

Different types of breakthrough curves will now be discussed using a capillary-tube flow model for illustrative purposes (Fig. 9.5) which simplifies the complex soil-porosity patterns to an "equivalent" set of continuous not interconnected capillary pores (Lindstrom and Boersma, 1971; Bouma and Wösten, 1979). The discussion will be limited to tracers which are not adsorbed by the soil.

Lack of dispersion ("piston type flow") implies instant displacement of the initially present water at $t = 1$ (Fig. 9.5, pore type I, curve I). The displacing liquid moves down as a front. Two different degrees of "ideal" dispersive behavior are shown in Fig. 9.5 by curves IIa and IIb. Curve IIa shows the average breakthrough curve of five 50 cm long undisturbed silty clay loam soil columns with a subangular blocky structure, sampled in B2t horizons of three soil series (average D: 260 cm² per day). Curve IIb shows a similar curve for five prismatic structures, sampled in the corresponding B3 horizons (average D: 2 cm² per day; Anderson and Bouma, 1977a, b). Pore model II (Fig. 9.5) which represents both curves in principle, shows the effect of a range of pore sizes. The initially present liquid is first displaced from the largest pores where flow rates are highest. At the moment of displacement in these pores, initially present water is still present in the finer pores. Effluent from the soil consists therefore of a mixture of both and reaches the concentration of the tracer in the influent only after total displacement of the initially present water from the fine pores. Obviously, the moment of initial breakthrough and the rate of increase of the tracer concentration in column effluent is a function of the pore-size distribution of the soil. In turn, effective pore size distributions can be calculated from breakthrough curves (Klinkenberg, 1957; Bouma and Wösten, 1979). Total displacement of the initially present liquid may be difficult in soils with some continuous large pores and fine porous peds (Fig. 9.5, pore model III). Initial breakthrough will be rapid, whereas total displacement (as evidenced by identical concentrations of the tracer in in- and effluent) may occur only after a very long time due to the relatively small displacement rate in the fine pores (Fig. 9.5, curve IIIa which shows "tailing"). In the extreme, the measured concentration in the effluent may be very close to that in the influent well before all initially present water has been displaced. This implies occurrence of "immobile" water (Gaudet et al., 1976), which may constitute as much as 99% of the soil water in prismatic clay soils with large continuous pores (Fig. 9.5, curve IIIb; from Bouma et al., 1976).

Intermittent flows into pedal soil horizons are often associated with quicker breakthrough than breakthrough occurring during continuous ponding. This is due to rapid movement into and through larger voids, which fill rapidly with air after drainage. Rapid flow of free water through un-saturated soil has been called: "short-circuiting" (Bouma et al., 1978). On the contrary, flow through surface crusts eliminates flow through the large pores and, as a consequence, strongly reduces the initial moment of break-through, thereby increasing the travel time of liquid through the soil. Reduction of the dosing rate has the same effect for intermittent flows. Data in Table 9.1 which were derived from the column experiments by Anderson and Bouma (1977a, b), illustrate these differences. All 55 cm long columns had soil with a silty clay loam texture. However, subangular blocky struc-tures reacted significantly different from prismatic structures. This obser-vation illustrates the potential for using soil structure descriptions for pre-dicting aspects of soil physical behavior.

An extreme case of "short-circuiting" occurs when water is added to dry, cracked clay soil. Vertical infiltration into the soil surface between the cracks will be followed by movement into the air-filled cracks, at least when they are open at the top. Lateral capillary forces will "pull" the water into the dry soil matrix. The resulting distribution of water in the soil, and associated pedogenesis, is a complex function of a number of factors which

TABLE 9.1

Times of initial breakthrough of chlorides as derived from column experiments using silty clay-loam soil with two types of macrostructure. Data were derived for four differ-ent flow regimes (from Anderson and Bouma, 1977a,b). Columns were 55 cm long

Flow regime	Subangular blocky structure		Prismatic structure	
	Flux (cm/day)	Initial breakthrough of chlorides (hr)	Flux (cm/day)	Initial breakthrough of chlorides (hr)
Shallow-ponding saturated flow	9	18	1.6	504
Drained and shallow-ponding	9	1	1.6	360
Once-a-day dose	1	72	1.0	240
Infiltration through surface crust	1	206	0.2	1180

are interrelated: (1) rain intensity and duration; (2) soil surface characteristics, which affect vertical infiltration patterns; (3) the pressure head in the soil and the K-curve govern vertical infiltration rates at the surface and the lateral rate into which soil, once flow into the cracks occurs; (4) flow patterns of water along the vertical ped faces, where cutans may act as barriers to flow; and (5) number and vertical continuity of the cracks, which determine the potential depth of penetration of free water (Bouma and Dekker, 1978; Bouma et al., 1978). A numerical simulation model has been developed to describe and predict flow patterns during infiltration into cracked soil (Hoogmoed and Bouma, 1980).

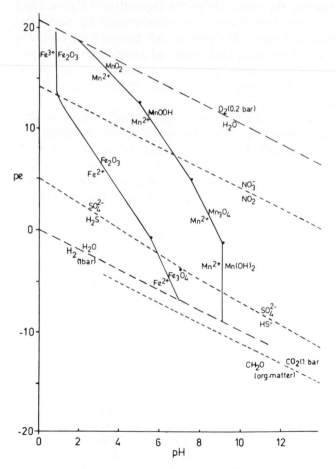

Fig. 9.6. Stability diagram of Mn and Fe(III) oxide species (after Van Breemen and Brinkman, 1976).

CHEMICAL TRANSFORMATIONS IN SOILS WITH AQUIC MOISTURE REGIMES

Introduction

Chemical and mineralogical transformations in soils with aquic moisture regimes are better known than the associated soil-moisture regimes. Recent articles by Van Schuylenborgh (1973), Van Breemen and Brinkman (1976) and Brinkman (1977, 1979) provide comprehensive summaries. Several relevant case studies can be found in Schlichting and Schwertmann (1973).

Reduction and oxidation processes

Soil reduction may be induced by water saturation, but only if organic-matter contents and soil temperature allow microbial activity. For a given redox couple, the position of the equilibrium depends on the locally prevailing value of pe, which is the negative logarithm of the electron activity, compared to pe^0 of the redox couple. The latter value expresses the relative electron activity when reacting species, other than the electrons, are at unit activity (Van Breemen and Brinkman, 1976). In summary: $pe = -\log (e^-)$.

For iron: $pe = pe^0 + \log (Fe^{3+}/Fe^{2+})$ (3)

Reduction processes are often expressed in terms of the redox potential E_h (volt), as follows: $E_h = 0.059$ pe (at 25°C). In soils the prevailing pe values may vary over a wide range, bounded on the "high" side by the simultaneous presence of water and free O_2 under well-aerated conditions and on the "low" side by free water plus free H_2 in saturated soils rich in readily decomposable organic matter. Both protons and electrons are transferred in all redox reactions in soils. Stability diagrams for redox processes can therefore conveniently be presented in terms of pe versus pH diagram (Fig. 9.6). The two dashed lines in this diagram show the stability limits of water at 0.2 bar oxygen and 2 bar hydrogen pressure, respectively. Conditions for equal activities in solution of the pairs nitrate—nitrite and sulfate—sulfide are given by dotted lines. The solid lines represent the boundaries for 0.001 molar Mn^{2+} and 0.001 molar total dissolved iron ($Fe^{2+} + Fe^{3+}$) in equilibrium with different manganese and iron minerals. The bottom (dotted) line gives the pe—pH conditions where CH_2O (organic matter) is at equilibrium with CO_2 at 1 bar pressure. The diagram indicates that "organic matter" is the most reduced of all substances considered. Oxidation of organic matter may occur if an electron acceptor is available. Under soil conditions this may be O_2, NO_3, Mn, Fe and S. Reduction of these compounds by organic matter is thermodynamically possible under soil conditions, but most of the reactions are extremely slow. However, many non-photosynthetic micro-organisms catalytically decompose the unstable products of photosynthesis through these energy-yielding redox reactions, and can use this energy both to synthesize new cells and to maintain existing ones (Ottow, 1973). Therefore, reduction may take place if the following conditions are met simultaneously: presence of organic matter, absence of an oxygen supply, and presence of anaerobic micro-organisms in an environment suitable for their growth. The requirement that an oxygen supply is absent may be fulfilled if the soil becomes saturated with water due to the very low diffusion rate of gases in water. Saturated soil becomes depleted of oxygen, because this is rapidly consumed by aerobic organisms and cannot be replenished quickly enough to prevent its virtual disappearance. The sequence of events to be expected upon flooding of an originally aerobic soil may be derived from Fig. 9.6. Reduction of remaining oxygen will take place first, followed by nitrate, then manganese in neutral soils (or manganese, then nitrate in acid soils). Later, ferrous iron may appear and still later one may expect formation of sulfide and even hydrogen. This theoretical sequence is indeed found in nature. In most soils the redox potential E_h drops from values around 0.5 to 0.7 V under aerobic conditions to values of 0.2 to -0.2 V after a period ranging between one week to several months. If the content of easily reducible Mn oxides is high or if conditions for microbial growth are unfavorable (low organic-matter content, extremely low pH), E_h may remain positive for six months or longer (Van Breemen and Brinkman, 1976). Oxidation processes follow the reverse sequence (Fig. 9.6). For example, ferrous iron is oxidized before reduced manganese compounds.

Weathering under seasonally reduced conditions

In acid soils, dissolved ferrous iron replaces part of the exchangeable cations during the waterlogged stage. This can be inferred from the increase in dissolved Ca^{2+}, Mg^{2+}, K^+ and Na^+ normally following soil reduction. Part of the exchangeable aluminum is displaced as well as ions or polynuclear complexes (Brinkman, 1977, 1979). The displaced cations come into the soil solution and are free to leach out in a manner which is, of course, dependent on hydrological conditions. Leaching may not occur when the prevailing hydraulic head gradient and/or K_{sat} do not allow movement. This may result in a relatively high concentration of salts in the soil solution. When allowed by hydraulic conditions, movement may occur laterally over slowly permeable subsoil horizons or vertically downwards. The soil solution being leached would contain aluminum species, ferrous iron and other cations. As this solution reaches an aerated horizon elsewhere with a higher redox potential, ferric hydroxide would form by oxidation of the ferrous iron (and CO_2). Aluminum ions would displace other exchangeable cations and polynuclear complexes. Al species would tend to form interlayers in the clay minerals (formation of soil chlorite) with a consequent decrease in CEC, even though clay dissolution does not occur (Brinkman, 1977, 1979). Conditions upon aeration of the reduced horizon itself are different. The exchangeable ferrous iron upon oxidation produces ferric hydroxide plus exchangeable hydrogen, which could be neutralized by soluble bicarbonates, if available, forming CO_2. But if bicarbonates have been leached, this process does not take place and the hydrogen will induce dissolution of part of the clay structure (the octahedral layers). In addition, the remaining tetrahedral silica layers are also weakened by dissolution of substituted Al. Silica may be leached out or may accumulate in amorphous form. In horizons that dry out, amorphous silica may become insoluble by dehydration. Dissolution of the clay fraction, as discussed, results in a decrease of structural stability as found in some eluvial horizons of soils with aquic moisture regimes.

In summary, within horizons subject to seasonal reduction and leaching, both clay dissolution and interlayering may take place in alternate seasons, upon oxidation and reduction, respectively, whereas clays in horizons traversed by the leaching products are interlayered but not dissolved. The process of clay decomposition and aluminum interlayering in a seasonally leaching environment has been called "ferrolysis" (Brinkman, 1970, 1977, 1979).

Ferrolysis may explain the formation of many acid hydromorphic soils, with low structural stability and low cation-exchange capacity of the clay fraction. The presence of $CaCO_3$ inhibits ferrolysis in two ways: its dissolution supplies alkalinity in the soil solution, while the high equilibrium pH keeps the Fe^{2+} activity at very low levels. A similar process to ferrolysis takes place in most tidal flats with a luxuriant vegetation. Reduction of dissolved sulphate from seawater in the surface horizons produces FeS and later FeS_2 (pyrite). Part of the dissolved alkalinity (HCO_3^- formed during sulphate reduction) is removed and may be carried to the sea by tidal action. If the sediments are low in $CaCO_3$, they will seriously acidify after drainage. The so-called acid sulphate soils ("catclays") formed this way, are characterized by yellow mottles of jarosite [$KFe_3 (SO_4)_2 (OH)_6$], pH values below 4 and the presence of soluble Al. A basic analysis of these processes was given by Van Breemen (1976).

Leaching and weathering may occur evenly throughout the soil mass, but may also be concentrated along preferential flow patterns, such as the larger pores as discussed earlier. Occurrence of dispersion implies the possibility for rapid movement along larger continuous pores and slow displacement of soil solution inside the peds. As a consequence, chemical and mineralogical transformations and resulting morphological features will tend to be best developed along such larger pores. Examples are the occurrence of tonguing of the eluvial albic horizon in the illuvial argillic horizon and interfingering of albic materials (Soil Survey Staff, 1975). On the contrary, apparent lack of vertical flow channels in the argillic horizon may result in an abrupt textural change with the albic horizon, as found in Planosols (Dudal, 1973; Soil Survey Staff, 1975).

SOIL-MORPHOLOGICAL FEATURES AS INDICATORS FOR THE MOISTURE REGIME

Introduction

Soil-mottling phenomena are widely used as indicators for the soil-moisture regime. The term "mottling" means "marked with spots of different color". These can be brownish concentrations of iron and manganese compounds within a "bleached" ("gleyed") matrix, or bleached spots within a matrix which is composed of interconnected brownish concentrations of iron and manganese. In either case, "mottling" can be described in terms of "having chromas of two or less" and this has the physical implication that the horizon is saturated for some time during the year. Horizons that have chromas of two or less throughout may be "gleyed", but this color condition has no physical implications in the classification scheme (Soil Survey Staff, 1975). These definitions have the advantage of being specific, and they can be used successfully under many conditions.

However, a number of problems exist:

(1) Mottling may not reflect a current, but a relict moisture regime. The latter can be associated with a former climate or may be associated with undrained soil that was changed by tile-drainage.

(2) Mottling may *not* form as a result of saturation due to lack of energy sources or to, for example, the color of the original sediment (Bouma, 1973). Presence of mottling does indicate wet conditions, but lack of it does not necessarily imply lack of saturation.

(3) The definition provided does not identify the length of the period of saturation. Whether this is a matter of hours, days or weeks has, of course, major practical implications.

(4) The strictly morphometric approach avoids ambiguity and this is very important. However, this does not leave room for more qualitative dis-

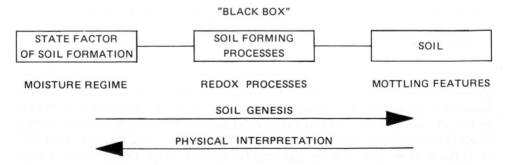

Fig. 9.7. Schematic diagram showing relationships between state factors of soil formation, soil-forming processes, soil morphology and physical interpretation of observed phenomena.

tinctions as found in other classification systems, which define "gley", "pseudogley" and "stagno-gley" soils (Schlichting and Schwertmann, 1973). In these soils, the occurrence of mottling is associated with quite different moisture regimes which are significant from the viewpoint of soil genesis.

(5) The simple definition in terms of "having chromas of two or less" allows application by different field soil scientists, without the risk that major differences in interpretation will result. This is a significant operational advantage. However, more detailed descriptions of soil-mottling features are possible by using elaborate descriptive schemes (Brewer, 1964). This approach could possibly result in a morphological characterization that would allow a more detailed physical interpretation. The considerations raised above will be discussed later by analyzing two case studies.

But first it is useful to review the principles on which the physical interpretation of soil-morphological features are based. Interpretations of mottling features, as discussed, are illustrated in a conceptual scheme proposed by Schelling (1970), which relates "state factors of soil formation" to "soil-forming processes" and finally, the end product, the soil as we see it (Fig. 9.7). Studies on *soil genesis* (arrow to the right in Fig. 9.7) are focused on defining chemical, biological, and, to a lesser extent, physical processes which resulted in the observed mottling features. The relevant "state factor" would be the moisture regime, and redox phenomena would be the relevant "soil-forming processes". This, in principle, allows the *interpretation* of the mottling features in terms of the soil-moisture regime (arrow to the left in Fig. 9.7). However, it is important to know whether the primary focus of attention was on genesis or an interpretation, because this will tend to result in different types of research. Specifically, studies on soil genesis traditionally emphasize chemistry and mineralogy, whereas interpretive work is more focused on soil physics.

Finally, the scheme in Fig. 9.7 emphasizes that mottling features and the moisture regime are *not* directly related, as expressed in the classification, but that they are coupled by means of complex, interacting soil-forming processes.

Some selected case studies

Introduction

A few detailed case studies which are directly related to the previous discussion will be presented here rather than a broad review of published data. The case studies refer to two soils near Madison, Wisc., U.S.A. The well-drained Batavia silt loam (Mollic Hapludalf) had an aquic moisture regime in subsurface horizons, while the poorly drained Ossian silt loam (Typic Haplaquoll) had this regime in the entire solum. Detailed profile descriptions follow:

Batavia silt loam (deep)
Classification: Mollic Hapludalf.
Vegetation: White Oak (*Quercus alba*), Bur Oak (*Q. macrocarpa*) and prairie
  grasses (e.g. *Andropogon gerandi* and *A. scoparius*).

Horizon	Depth (cm)	Description
Ap(Ap)	0—41	Very dark grayish-brown (10YR 3.5/2) silt loam; moderate thin platy structure; friable; many fine, common medium, and few coarse roots; abrupt smooth boundary.
B1(BA)	41—69	Yellowish-brown (10YR 5/4) silt loam; moderate thin platy structure; friable; many fine roots; clear wavy boundary.
B21t(Bt1)	69—89	Light yellowish-brown (10YR 6/4) ped interiors; silty clay loam; moderate medium subangular blocky structure; friable; many fine roots; continuous thin yellowish-brown (10YR 5/4) ped and channel argillans; common fine distinct manganese and iron nodules; clear wavy boundary.
B22t(Bt2)	89—134	Pale brown (10YR 6/3) ped interiors; silty clay loam; moderate coarse prismatic parting to moderate coarse subangular blocky and moderate coarse platy structure; firm; common fine roots; continuous thin dark brown (10YR 4/3) ped and channel argillans; common distinct ped mangans and few fine distinct manganese nodules; common faint ped ferrans, few faint channel neoferrans and common fine distinct iron nodules; gradual wavy boundary.
B31tg(Btg1)	134—160	Light brownish-gray (10YR 6/2) ped interiors; silty clay loam; moderate very coarse prismatic parting to moderate coarse subangular blocky and moderate coarse platy structure; firm; few fine roots; discontinuous thin grayish-brown (10YR 5/2) ped and channel argillans; many distinct planar ferrans; few faint channel neoferrans; few faint channel neoalbans; clear wavy boundary.

B32g(BCg)	160—180	Light brownish-gray (10YR 6/2) silty clay loam; weak very coarse prismatic structure; sticky; mainy distinct planar ferrans; few coarse distinct iron nodules; few faint channel neoferrans and few faint channel neoalbans; gradual wavy boundary.
IICg(2Cg)	180—210	Light brownish-gray (10YR 6/2) silty clay loam; massive; sticky; common distinct planar ferrans, very few distinct channel neoferrans and few coarse distinct iron nodules; few faint channel neoalbans; abrupt irregular boundary marked by a thin (2—4 cm) continuous planar accumulation of iron.
IIIC(3C)	210+	Brownish-yellow (10YR 6/6); sand; single-grained structure; loose.

Ossian silt loam
Classification: Typic Haplaquoll.
Vegetation: Bluejoint grass (*Calamagrostis canadensis*) and prairie grass (*Andropogon gerardi*).

Horizon	Depth (cm)	Description
01(0e)	3—0	Partly decomposed grass litter.
A11(A1)	0—14	Dark grayish-brown (10YR 3/2) silt loam; moderate medium granular structure; friable; many fine, few medium roots; common distinct ped ferrans and channel neoferrans; abrupt wavy boundary.
A12(A2)	14—43	Very dark grayish-brown (10YR 3/2) silt loam; moderate medium platy structure; friable; common fine roots; common distinct ped ferrans and channel neoferrans; abrupt smooth boundary.
B1g(Bg)	43—63	Gray (10YR 5/1) silt loam; weak thin platy structure; friable; common fine roots; common distinct ped ferrans and channel neoferrans; common very fine distinct manganese nodules with distinct thin ferrans on nodular surfaces; clear wavy boundary.
B21t(Bt)	63—81	Gray (10YR 5/1) ped interiors, silty clay loam; moderate fine subangular blocky

		structure; friable; few fine roots; many prominent dark reddish-brown (5YR 3/4) ped organoferrans; common distinct channel neoalbans and many fine distinct manganese nodules with faint thin ferrans on nodular surfaces; clear wavy boundary.
B22tg(Btg)	81—101	Gray (10YR 5/1) ped interiors; silty clay loam; weak fine subangular blocky structure; firm; few fine roots; many distinct dark reddish-brown (5YR 3/4) ped organoferrans; common distinct channel neoalbans; common fine distinct manganese nodules with distinct thin ferrans on nodular surfaces; gradual wavy boundary.
B23g(B'g)	101—116	Gray (5Y 5/1) ped interiors; silty clay loam; moderate fine subangular blocky structure; firm; few fine roots; many thin distinct dark yellowish-brown (10YR 3/4) ped organoferrans; common distinct channel neoalbans; few fine distinct iron nodules; gradual wavy boundary.
B31g(BCg)	116—149	Gray (5Y 5/1) silty clay loam; moderate medium prismatic parting to moderate fine subangular blocky structure; firm; very few fine roots; few prominent channel quasiferrans; common medium prominent iron nodules; common distinct ped neoalbans.
IIB32g(2BCg)	149—184	Gray to light gray (5Y 6/1) loamy sand; massive with few large vertical ped faces extending downwards from the B31g; very friable; very few fine roots; common prominent channel quasiferrans; common medium prominent iron nodules; common fine distinct ped neoalbans along vertical ped faces; gradual wavy boundary.
IICg(2Cg)	184+	Light gray (10YR 7/2) sand; single-grained; loose.

The nomenclature of Brewer (1964) was used to describe morphological features. Detailed results of these studies were reported by Vepraskas et al. (1974), Veneman et al. (1976) and Vepraskas and Bouma (1976). Three relevant aspects will be discussed in this chapter: (1) the occurrence of short saturation in a soil horizon with chromas less than two; (2) the duration of saturation in horizons with chromas less than two; and (3) the different flow

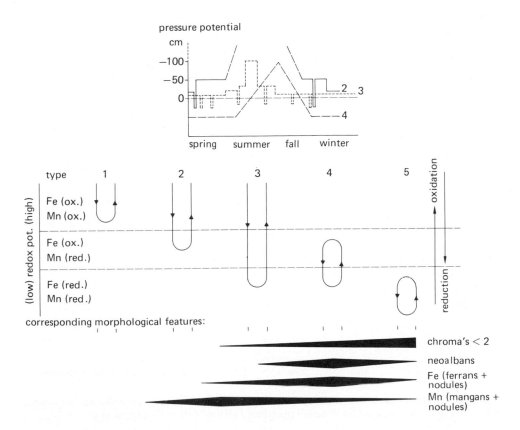

Fig. 9.8. Schematic representation of soil-moisture regimes and associated mottling features, as discussed in text.

patterns associated with the occurrence of "perched" and "ground" water tables. A schematic diagram relating mottling features to the type of soil-moisture regimes being discussed, is presented in Fig. 9.8.

Moisture regimes measured with tensiometry during the growing season in major horizons of both soils, (which had a grass vegetation) are shown in Fig. 9.9. Weather conditions were normal in the monitoring period. The amount of precipitation is shown in Fig. 9.9. The observed mottling features are considered representative for the actual moisture regime of the two soils.

Occurrence of short saturation periods in high-chroma soil horizons

An example is the B22t horizon of the Batavia silt loam. The measured pressure heads (Fig. 9.9) were positive (the horizon was saturated) for only short periods of time, which generally did not exceed a few days. Saturation usually followed periods with many showers (Fig. 9.9). Mottles with chromas of two or less did *not* occur in this horizon and the measured

274

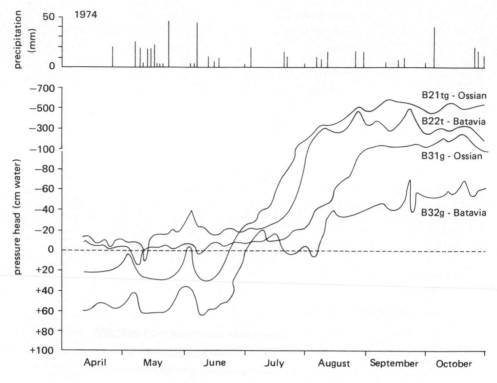

Fig. 9.9. Different moisture regimes in four horizons of Batavia and Ossian silt loams, which can be characterized by detailed mottling features (after Veneman et al., 1976).

saturation, and the associated reducing environment, would therefore *not* have been predicted using current criteria (Soil Survey Staff, 1975). The description of the horizon indicates the presence of ped mangans and Mn nodules and, less prominently, some concentrations of Fe. Processes of reduction in this horizon, associated with short-duration, were apparently just strong enough to reduce the Mn but not significant amounts of Fe. Little iron movement occurred therefore and the soil matrix retained a high chroma. The mobilized Mn moved towards and was oxidized on ped surfaces, where relatively large planar voids were filled with air in generally unsaturated soil. This type of mottling (dominated by high chromas in peds, occurrence of ped mangans and few iron mottles) is thus associated with very short periods of saturation. This type of mottle was reproduced in model experiments using artificial, brown, sandy clay-loam cores through which a nutrient solution could freely evaporate at a pressure head which was maintained at −7 cm water (Vepraskas and Bouma, 1976).

Duration of saturation in low-chroma soil horizons

A separation can be made between horizons that are saturated for either short or long periods.

An example of the first category is the B32g horizon of the Batavia silt loam. The measured pressure heads (Fig. 9.9) were positive, indicating saturation for periods of only several days at a time (a perched water table), whereas high pressure heads of −15 cm water occurred for several months. The horizon is therefore very wet, but the occurrence of unsaturated soil (negative pressure heads) implies that an unlined augerhole would *not* fill with water. The distinction between the saturated condition, which is limited in duration in this horizon, and the unsaturated, but very wet condition is therefore relevant. Only larger pores, such as worm and root-channels and planar voids between peds, will be filled with air at pressure heads, near −15 cm water. This physical condition results in a particular morphology. The interiors of the peds are saturated for several months and reduction of not only Mn but also Fe does occur. Some of the reduced compounds may be vertically leached from the soil with percolating water, others may oxidize inside peds as nodules or along the larger voids (which are filled with air) as ped and channel neoferrans or ferrans. Redox potentials may be sufficiently high at some distance from an air-filled void to precipitate Fe, which will then occur as a neoferran with a diffuse inner boundary. Occurrence of ferrans on the walls of larger voids indicates water movement along those walls, and therefore somewhat wetter conditions. Removal of Fe from the interiors of peds results in low chromas of the remaining soil material. Mn compounds, oxidizing less easily than Fe may be vertically leached from the horizon. This type of mottling (dominated by chromas of *two* inside peds and iron cutans along larger pores, with few manganese mottles) is thus associated with short periods of saturation and periods of several months in which the horizon is close to saturation. Another example of this type of mottling was discussed by Vepraskas et al. (1974).

An example of the second category are the B21tg and B31g horizons of the Ossian silt loam. The measured moisture regimes (Fig. 9.9) show that the entire horizon was saturated for a period of several months. All pores, including the larger ones, will then be filled with water rather than with air as in the B32g horizon of the Batavia silt loam. This essential difference is reflected in soil morphology. Saturation of the horizon, which occurs in spring after snowmelt, proceeds by water flowing into the larger pores *first* and from there into the more fine-porous and very slowly permeable peds. This flow regime is also characteristic for water saturation in pseudo and stagnogley soils (Schlichting, 1973). Organic matter in the form of decomposed roots is generally present in the larger planar voids and channels and a reducing environment can thus be established following saturation. Water moves into the peds, which are initially unsaturated and contain air.

Iron is oxidized at some distance from the void as a quasiferran, leaving a "gleyed" zone around the pore. This zone can be considered as a "neocutan" (Brewer, 1964) and the name "neoalban" has been proposed (Veneman et al., 1976). The entire horizon is then saturated for several months and processes of reduction are likely to be well developed, inside peds. A part of the reduced iron and manganese compounds may be removed from the profile by leaching and low chromas result. Some of the iron, if not removed, may again be oxidized inside peds upon aeration as nodules, whereas most of the Mn is bound to be removed. But iron and manganese cutans along larger voids, as found in the B horizons of the Batavia pedon, were not observed. Whether or not these cutans do form will also depend on the permeability of the soil. A low hydraulic conductivity and low gradients can reduce leaching, and lateral diffusion of reduced iron (and manganese) compounds too and oxidation along larger voids as neocutans may then occur following aeration (Bouma and Van Schuylenborgh, 1969). The type of mottling in the Ossian silt loam (dominated by low chromas of one inside ped, ped and channel neoalbans and virtual lack of manganese mottles) is thus associated with periods of continuous saturation for several months at a time. The morphology of some surface-water gley soils ("pseudogleys") may be different when the period of saturation in surface horizons is shorter. Then, reducing processes may again occur along larger voids, but they may not be sufficiently strong inside the peds to cause gleying (Van Breemen and Brinkman, 1976). The physical interpretation of such mottling will then be different in that the period of saturation is shorter. However, occurrence of chromas of two or less along larger voids distinguishes this type of mottling from the one, discussed earlier.

Channel neoalbans were formed in model experiments using artificial, brown, sandy clay-loam cores, which were subjected to periodic saturation from below, and drainage, with nutrient solution. Measured redox potentials confirmed the mobility of both Fe and Mn compounds (Vepraskas and Bouma, 1976).

Differences between perched and real water tables

The previous case studies described the occurrence of periodically *perched* water tables in the deeper horizons of the Batavia pedon. A permanent very deep water table at 40 m below the soil surface was found in the underlying brown, unmottled, outwash sand. In contrast, the water table in the Ossian pedon, which was at the soil surface in spring but receded to a level of about 2.5 m below the soil surface in summer and fall, was a "real" water table. These two case studies have shown that relations between soil-moisture regimes and associated morphological features are often complicated and offer more opportunities for interpretation than is suggested by simplified schemes. Both types of water tables are characterized by some period in which the soil is saturated with water, as indicated by a free water surface in an unlined borehole. Unlined boreholes should not be used in clayey, pedal soils for establishing the level of the water table. Preferential movement of water along larger pores into the unlined borehole may result in a water level that is found within unsaturated soil. Use of tensiometers or piezometers is to be preferred for establishing the level of the water table in clayey, pedal soils (Bouma et al., 1980). Saturation may occur due to either infiltration of rain or surface water in soils with perched water tables or to a rise of the groundwater table. Most effective infiltration often occurs after a dry season, or at least after a season in which evapotranspiration exceeded rainfall. Swelling soils are then often dry and cracked and infiltration rates can be very high, at least initially before the cracks close. Deep penetration may occur at low rainfall intensities (Bouma and Dekker, 1978; Bouma et al., 1978).

A perched water table can only exist for some time if physical conditions, which caused it to be formed initially, remain in effect. Two important conditions are: (1) A low K_{sat} of a subsurface soil horizon or layer, which covers unsaturated, more permeable soil (e.g. Argillic horizons or fragipans as described by Soil Survey Staff, 1975). K_{sat} values in swelling soils often decrease upon continued swelling. Definition of a *single* K_{sat} value, or determination of K_{sat} in initially dry soil may lead to erroneous results which are too high. (2) A lithological discontinuity that may cause stagnation of water in a heavier textured horizon, overlying unsaturated more permeable deposits. This condition is common and an illustration will therefore be given for a specific example which assumes the presence of 100 cm of silty clay loam on top of sand in which a deep water table is found at least 160 cm below the soil surface to allow steady pressure heads at the different fluxes in the sand adjacent to the silt cap. Calculations of steady downward fluxes were made by a graphical integration technique, using eq. 1 and K curves and moisture-retention data (e.g. Bouma, 1973, 1977). Pressure heads in the silt cap would remain constant with depth for each of the fluxes (gravity flow: hydraulic head gradient 1 cm cm^{-1}), if the sand would not occur and if the groundwater would be very deep.

The diagrams in Fig. 9.10 show that the sand has a dominant effect on the hydraulic conditions in the lower part of the silt loam. *But this effect is clearly a function of the flow rate.* At the high flow rates of 10 cm per day (curve *1* in Fig. 9.10B) and 5 cm per day (curve *2*), the lower part of the silty clay loam becomes *drier* than it would have been without the sand. On the contrary, it becomes *wetter* at the lower flow rates of 1 cm per day and 1 mm per day (curve *4*). The effect at the latter flow rate is very pronounced. The pressure head in the silty clay loam at a flow rate of 1 mm per day (hydraulic gradient: 1 cm cm^{-1}) is -100 cm water (see K curve in Fig. 9.10A). But this value is only reached in the very upper 10 cm. The deeper layers are wetter than they would have been without the sand. Moisture contents (Fig. 9.10C) were derived from the calculated pressure heads

278

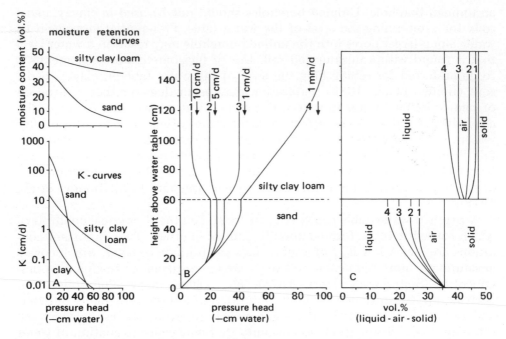

Fig. 9.10. Theoretical moisture conditions calculated for four steady downward fluxes in a hypothetical soil profile consisting of two horizons.

(Fig. 9.10B) by using moisture-retention data (Fig. 9.10A). The low vertical fluxes most resemble natural conditions, and the underlying sand will therefore primarily impede drainage of the heavier textured soil.

Discussions so far dealt with perched water tables. Rise of water tables may be due to either surface infiltration or to a rise from below by water originating from adjacent areas. Both conditions will often involve preferential movement of water along larger, vertical voids, if present, initially bypassing peds. This process is followed by lateral movement into the peds, thereby sometimes producing characteristic morphological features.

ACKNOWLEDGEMENT

Helpful suggestions by R. Brinkman (Agric. Univ. Wageningen), C.W. Boast (Univ. of Illinois) and A. Breeuwsma (Soil Survey Inst., Wageningen) are gratefully acknowledged.

REFERENCES

Amerman, C.R., 1973. Hydrology and soil science. In: R.R. Bruce, K.W. Flach and H.M. Taylor (Editors), Field Soil Water Regime. SSSA, Spec. Publ., 5: 167—178.

Anderson, J.L. and Bouma, J., 1973. Relationships between hydraulic conductivity and morphometric data of an argillic horizon. Soil Sci. Soc. Am. Proc., 37: 408—413.

Anderson, J.L. and Bouma, J., 1977a. Water movement through pedal soils. I. Saturated Flow. Soil Sci. Soc. Am. J., 41: 413—418.

Anderson, J.L. and Bouma, J., 1977b. Water movement through pedal soils. II. Unsaturated Flow. Soil Sci. Soc. Am. J., 41: 419—423.

Aubertin, G.M., 1971. Nature and extent of macropores on forest soils and their influence on subsurface water movement. USDA, Forest Serv. Res. Pap. NE-192. Forest Serv. USDA, 33 pp.

Baver, L.D., Gardner, W.H. and Gardner, W.R., 1972. Soil Physics. Wiley, New York, N.Y., 491 pp.

Blake, G., Schlichting, E. and Zimmermann, U., 1973. Water recharge in a soil with shrinkage cracks. Soil Sci. Soc. Am. Proc., 37: 669—672.

Bouma, J., 1973. Use of physical methods to expand soil survey interpretations of soil drainage conditions. Soil Sci. Am. Proc., 37: 413—421.

Bouma, J., 1977. Soil Survey and the study of water movement in unsaturated soil. Soil Surv. Pap., 13. Soil Survey Institute, Wageningen, 107 pp.

Bouma, J., 1981. Soil morphology and preferential flow along macropores. Agric. Water Manag., 3: 235—250.

Bouma, J. and Anderson, J.L., 1973. Relationships between soil structure characteristics and hydraulic conductivity. In: R.R. Bruce, K.W. Flach and H.M. Taylor (Editors), Field Soil Water Regime. SSSA, Spec. Publ., 5: 77—105.

Bouma, J. and Dekker, L.W., 1978. A case study on infiltration into dry clay soil. I. Morphological observations. Geoderma, 20: 27—40.

Bouma, J. and Van Schuylenborgh, J., 1969. On soil genesis in temperate humid climate: VII. The formation of glossaqualf in a silt loam terrace deposit. Neth. J. Agric. Sci., 17: 261—271.

Bouma, J. and Wösten, J.H.M., 1979. Flow patterns during extended saturated flow in two undisturbed swelling clay soils with different macrostructures. Soil Sci. Soc. Am. J., 43: 16—22.

Bouma, J., Dekker, L.W. and Verlinden, H.L., 1976. The vertical hydraulic conductivity at saturation of some dutch "knik" clay soils. Agric. Water Manag., 1: 67—69.

Bouma, J., Jongerius, A., Boersma, O., Jager, A. and Schoonderbeek, D., 1977. The function of different types of macropores during saturated flow through four swelling soil horizons. Soil Sci. Soc. Am. J., 41: 945—950.

Bouma, J., Dekker, L.W. and Wosten, J.H.M., 1978. A case study on infiltration into dry clay soil. II. Physical measurements. Geoderma, 20: 41—51.

Bouma, J., Jongerius, A. and Schoonderbeek, D., 1979. Calculation of hydraulic conductivity of some saturated clay soils using micromorphometric data. Soil Sci. Soc. Am. J., 43: 261—265.

Bouma, J., Dekker, L.W. and Haans, J.C.F.M., 1980. Measurement of depth to water table in a heavy clay soil. Soil Sci., 130: 264—270.

Brenner, H., 1962. The diffusion model of longitudinal mixing in beds of finite length. Numerical Values. Chem. Eng. Sci., 17: 229—243.

Brewer, R., 1964. Fabric and Mineral Analysis of Soils. Wiley, New York, N.Y., 470 pp.

Brinkman, R., 1970. Ferrolysis, a hydromorphic soil forming process. Geoderma, 3: 199—206.

Brinkman, R., 1977. Surface-water gley soils in Bangladesh: genesis. Geoderma, 17: 111—144.

Brinkman, R., 1979. Ferrolysis, a Soil-forming Process in Hydromorphic Conditions. Agric. Res. Rep. 887. Pudoc, Wageningen, 106 pp.

Cassel, D.K., Krueger, T.H., Schroer, F.W. and Norum, E.B., 1974. Solute movement through disturbed and undisturbed soil cores. Soil Sci. Soc. Am. Proc., 37: 36—38.

Cassel, D.K., Van Genuchten, M.Th. and Wierenga, P.J., 1975. Predicting anion movement in disturbed and undisturbed soils. Soil Sci. Soc. Am. Proc., 39: 1015—1020.

Dudal, R., 1973. Planosols. In: E. Schlichting and U. Schwertmann (Editors), Pseudogley and Gley. Proc. ISSS Symp., pp. 275—287.

Elrick, D.E. and French, L.K., 1966. Miscible displacement patterns on disturbed and undisturbed soil cores. Soil Sci. Soc. Am. Proc., 30: 153—156.

Gaudet, J.P., Jegat, H. and Vachaud, G., 1976. Simulation of miscible displacement in unsaturated proous media using the concept of mobile and stagnant fluid. In: M. Kutilek and J. Sutor (Editors), Proceedings Symposium: "Water in Heavy Soils". ICID and ISSS, Bratislava, pp. 120—131.

Hillel, D.I., 1971. Soil and Water: Physical Principles and Processes. Academic Press, New York, N.Y., 288 pp.

Hoogmoed, W.B. and Bouma, J., 1980. A simulation model for predicting infiltration into cracked clay soil. Soil Sci. Soc. Am. J., 44: 458—461.

International Society of Soil Sciences (ISSS), 1976. Soil physics terminology. Bull. 49: 26—36.

Kissel, D.E., Ritchie, J.T. and Burnett, E., 1973. Chloride movement in undisturbed clay soil. Soil Sci. Soc. Am. Proc., 37: 21—24.

Klinkenberg, L.J., 1957. Pore size distribution of porous media and displacement experiments with miscible liquids. Pet. Trans. AIME, 210: 366—369.

Klute, A., 1973. Soil water flow theory and its application in field situations. In: R.R. Bruce, K.W. Flach and H.M. Taylor (Editors), Field Soil Water Regime. SSSA, Spec. Publ., 5: 9—31.

Lindstrom, F.T. and Boersma, L., 1971. A theory on the mass transport of previously distributed chemicals in a water saturated sorbing porous medium. Soil Sci., 111: 192—199.

McCormack, D.E., 1974. Soil potentials: A positive approach to urban planning. J. Soil Water Conserv., 29: 258—262.

Ottow, J.C.G., 1973. Bacterial mechanisms for iron reduction and gley formation. In: E. Schlichting and U. Schwertmann (Editors), Pseudogley and Gley. Proc. ISSS Symp., pp. 29—37.

Quisenberry, V.L. and Phillips, R.E., 1976. Percolation of surface applied water in the field. Soil Sci. Soc. Am. J., 40: 484—490.

Rose, D.A. and Passioura, J.B., 1971. The analysis of experiments on hydrodynamic dispersion. Soil Sci., 111: 252—257.

Schelling, J., 1970. Soil genesis, soil classification and soil survey. Geoderma, 4: 165—195.

Schlichting, E., 1973. Pseudogleye and Gleye-Geneses und Nützung hydromorpher Boden. In: E. Schlichting and U. Schwertmann (Editors), Pseudogley and Gley. Proc. ISSS Symp., pp. 1—7.

Schlichting, E. and Schwertmann, U., 1973. Pseudogley and Gley. Proc. ISSS Symp. Chemie Verlag, Weinheim, 771 pp.

Smiles, D.E., 1976. Theory of liquid flow in saturated swelling materials: Some problem areas. In: M. Kutilek and J. Sutor (Editors), Proceedings Symposium: "Water in Heavy Soils" ICID and ISSS, Bratislava, pp. 32—42.

Soil Survey Staff, 1951. Soil Survey Manual. USDA Handbook 18, Washington, D.C., 503 pp.

Soil Survey Staff, 1975. Soil Taxonomy. A Basic System for Soil Classification for Making and Interpreting Soil Surveys. Agric. Handbook, 436, 754 pp.

Sposito, G., 1976. On the theory of infiltration in swelling soils. In: M. Kutilek and J.

Sutor (Editors), Proceedings Symposium: "Water in Heavy Soils" ICID and ISSS, Bratislava, pp. 107—119.

Van Breemen, N., 1976. Genesis and Solution Chemistry of Acid Sulfate Soils in Thailand. Agric. Res. Rep., No. 848. Pudoc, Wageningen, 263 pp.

Van Breemen, N. and Brinkman, R., 1976. Chemical equilibria and soil formation. In: G.H. Bolt and M.G.M. Bruggenwert (Editors), Soil Chemistry. A. Basic Elements. Elsevier, Amsterdam, pp. 141—170.

Van Genuchten, M. Th. and Wieringa, P.J., 1976. Mass transfer in sorbing porous media. I. Analytical solutions. Soil Sci. Soc. Am. J. 40: 473—480.

Van Heesen, H.C., 1970. Presentation of seasonal fluctuation of the water table on soil maps. Geoderma, 4: 257—279.

Van Schuylenborgh, J., 1973. Sesquioxide formation and transformation. In: E. Schlichting and U. Schwertmann (Editors), Pseudogley and Gley. Proc. ISSS Symp., pp. 32—42.

Veneman, P.L.M., Vepraskas, M.J. and Bouma, J., 1976. The physical significance of soil mottling in a Wisconsin toposequence. Geoderma, 15: 103—118.

Vepraskas, M.J., Baker, F.G. and Bouma, J., 1974. Soil mottling and drainage in a mollic hapludalf as related to suitability for septic tank construction. Soil Sci. Soc. Am. Proc., 38: 497—501.

Vepraskas, M.L. and Bouma, J., 1976. Model studies on mottle formation simulating field conditions. Geoderma, 15: 217—230.

SUBJECT INDEX

294

AUTHOR INDEX

298